MASTERING AUTODESK FUSION

27 STEP-BY-STEP 3D MODELING PROJECTS FOR
3D PRINTING, PROTOTYPING, AND MAKING

2ND EDITION | 2024 - 2025

Authors: Jake O Sugden & Joshua Manley
Published by CADclass

2nd Edition | 2024 - 2025

ISBN-13: 979-8-9881894-5-9 (Paperback)

ISBN-13: 979-8-9881894-6-6 (Hardcover)

Publisher: CADclass.org

Written By: Jake O Sugden & Joshua Manley

Weatherly, Isaac. "Electric Guitar." Pexels, 3 Feb. 2019, (www.pexels.com/photo/photo-of-guitar-near-river-2156327/). Accessed 6 Apr. 2023. "Clear Light Bulb." Pexels, LED Supermarket, 2 Aug. 2017, (www.pexels.com/photo/clear-light-bulb-577528/). Accessed 6 Apr. 2023. Chapter Pages Image was created by fanjianhua on Freepik and is licensed under Creative Commons(www.freepik.com/free-photo/architectural-blueprints_1120487.htm#query=technical%20drawing&position=1&from_view=keyword&track=ais).

For information on distribution, translation, or bulk sales, contact **create@CADclass.org** directly.

PREFACE

In the early 2010's I was a first-year engineering student taking my first Computer Aided Design (CAD) class . On the first day the professor walked in, handed us the syllabus, said, "this is going to be difficult," and walked out. I shot a confused look at my classmates, whose expressions resembled mine. I wondered what I had gotten myself into and if this was what university was really like.

She was right; it was difficult. For the next 16 weeks, I read textbooks, attended office hours, asked questions, and generally felt lost. I googled questions with complex answers I couldn't understand. I tried to find mentors or peers who could help but to no avail. I was on my own.

I struggled through the course, using willpower and a hefty dose of caffeine, but it was not easy. When it was over, all I felt was relief. If it weren't for people insisting on the importance of CAD, I'm sure I would have sworn it off forever.

And now years later, I love making 3D models and use CAD every day. As I type this, my 3D printers are working on autopilot, making 3D models I've designed for my clients, literally making money as I sleep.

The truth is, the course did not work well for me, but the professor was right. CAD is difficult to learn.

However, I now know that learning CAD does not have to be like this. With the right training program and the proper guidance, learning CAD is like learning how to ride a bike. It's fun and rewarding and gets even better as you practice. Making a 3D model helps you visualize what could be.

So, I set out to build the CAD class I wished I had when I first learned. I wanted:

- To build models I found exciting and could make in the real world.
- To feel the real sense of progress from practice exercises that are not too hard but not too easy either but build up from the foundation.
- A community of peers and mentors who understood where I was and when I was struggling and could help when I ran into problems.
- To build my dream projects and feel confident doing them.

This is that CADclass!

Does any of this sound familiar to you?

- You've spent months or years imagining what you could do if only you knew how to make a 3D model and share your ideas with the world.
- You've endlessly searched for free tutorials on YouTube, LinkedIn, and Google, watched them and tried to follow along but didn't get what you needed and still don't feel like you truly "get it."
- You tend to get excited to start learning, progress through a few tutorials and make some progress, but then give up a few weeks later.

- You have questions but aren't sure how to ask them due to your limited knowledge.
- You watch a tutorial, get stuck, and Google solutions but cannot find a suitable answer to your question.
- You feel demoralized and conclude that learning CAD may be too difficult.

I have good news. The problem is not you, your intelligence, or your learning ability. The problem is the system, or rather the lack of one, you are trying to follow. If you have the proper structure and relevant content at the correct time, and you are surrounded by the right community and mentors, learning feels enjoyable and happens naturally.

Is it impossible to learn online for free? Absolutely not. It's simply going to take you a great deal of extra time and quite a bit of frustration to do it. You will have to develop your syllabus, tutorials, learning plan, and troubleshooting help when things get tough. If you persevere, you will get it, but the path will be anything but straightforward and will likely take much more time than you anticipated.

What we're offering to you is a well-thought-out plan engineered with your success in mind. You'll have access to a community of fellow CAD modelers working through the same projects simultaneously.

WELCOME TO CADCLASS

We are very excited to have you join an exclusive club of engineers, makers, artists, hobbyists, and entrepreneurs. Throughout this course, you will learn everything you need to know to go from beginner to being able to make your dream projects.

You will have a chance to connect with peers, the authors, and share what you build along the way. This course is the best investment you can make for your future self. We believe it takes 3 things to be successful with CAD modeling:

1 - Good instruction that starts with the basics and builds up from there.
2 - Access to a community of people working on the same thing.
3 - Practice, practice, and more practice.

Learning CAD is a useful skill allowing you to communicate your 3D ideas to people and machines. Sharing your ideas increases your chances of getting hired, making a sale, or solving a problem.

Until recently, it was prohibitively expensive to learn CAD, and only a few specialists with access to the software learned it. Now many programs have free trials or inexpensive subscriptions, making it possible for anyone to learn. Still, not many people do. Why?

Learning CAD is hard. Not because learning the program is hard but because the resources available are a mix of boring, outdated, unclear, tailored to the wrong skill level, and simply unhelpful. This course covers 27 projects spanning 12 different topic areas. Each is engineered to introduce a few new ideas and gradually become more complex and challenging. These projects will combine the tangible art of making with the digital confidence of CAD.

WHAT YOU'LL NEED TO GET STARTED

Internet + Laptop or Computer (most iPads, tablets, and Chromebooks will not work). Autodesk Fusion is a cloud-based software and requires an internet connection to function fully. Ensure you also check the latest computer specifications on the Fusion website for information about whether your machine will work. 3D design software tends to be processor intensive.

A mouse with a clickable scroll wheel and two buttons. Some programmable mice may not work. You can use a simple and inexpensive mouse to navigate around our projects.

Autodesk Fusion CAD software (Make sure you sign up for the free Hobbyist or Education version)

Join the Discord community: **Discord.gg/5hbt6xDPqf**

This is where you will Discuss projects and progress with your fellow students. Please do join and Discuss! If you need help with this, email **create@CADclass.org**, and we'll set you up.

And here are some things that are nice to have but not necessary:

- An inexpensive second monitor can be a game changer. If you can afford a second monitor, buy it.
- Calipers - These are great for making and modeling Dimensionally accurate practical objects.

WHAT IS AUTODESK FUSION?

Autodesk Fusion (formerly known as Fusion 360) is the Swiss army knife of design and manufacturing tools. As the name implies, it is a fusion of several different types of software.

With Autodesk Fusion, you can design parts, make blueprints, create photo-realistic images, animate assemblies, render objects, simulate CNC manufacturing, create Exploded Diagrams, and more.

You can build various practical CAD skills by combining a visually helpful toolset with complex and powerful workspaces.

ERRATA

Since the publication of the 1st Edition and the growth of our vibrant community, we have incorporated thousands of suggestions, comments, ideas, and software updates into this version. As Autodesk Fusion is a dynamic program, it continually receives updates with new tools, designs, and functionalities. At CADclass, we are committed to staying current and explaining the latest tools Fusion has to offer. This Edition not only includes a wealth of improved and more enjoyable models to create and build but also places a greater emphasis on professional CAD techniques to enhance your efficiency and expedite your projects.

ACKNOWLEDGMENTS

We want to acknowledge those who helped us establish a love for building and design, the worldwide communities of helpful and enthusiastic makers, and those friendships built on sawdust, sweat, and pints.

A special thanks to our Beta Testers, Discord Moderators, and CADclass Graduates who helped polish, advise, and edit, and who affirmed our belief that the best way forward in CAD education is alongside a friendly community of like-minded tinkerers and manufacturers. Their months of help and assistance improved this book, our courses, and the future of CADclass.

Finally, a big thank you to our contributor, Ed Charlwood, whose invaluable insights and creativity have been instrumental in shaping this book's content and ensuring its quality and fun factor stay high.

ABOUT THE AUTHORS

Jake O Sugden is a mechanical engineer and lifelong maker passionate about engineering and design. He taught many making Disciplines at one of the nation's premier makerspaces, testing many of the concepts found in this book over the last six years with thousands of students. He is co-owner of CADclass, an additive manufacturing company focused on product development and education. He's an Autodesk Fusion expert who works with the program daily.

Professor Joshua Manley is an entrepreneur and educator with a passion for making. He is a published scientist who ran a science tutoring business in New York City, teaching Math, Chemistry, Biology, Physics, and SAT/ACT prep. He then led the education department of one of the nation's largest and most successful makerspaces. He's taught thousands of students, educators, and administrators worldwide. His TED-Ed talk about bicycle physics has millions of views.

DEDICATED TO

This book is dedicated to our families and loved ones. Thanks to you, we kept our heads high and our minds clear as we wrote this book and continue to build our business. Without Kasey and Ilana's unwavering confidence, Wayne, Jane and Holly's unending support, Libby's unquestioned positivity, and the many words of encouragement from those closest to us, we would not have succeeded.

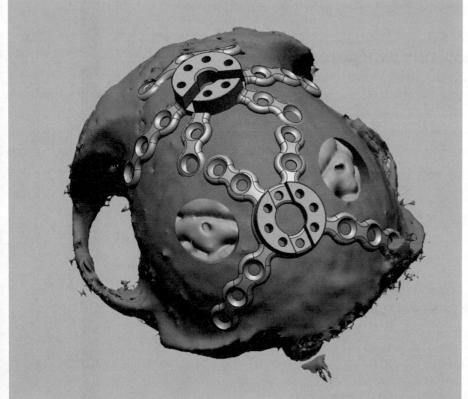

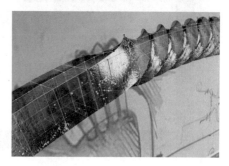

TABLE OF CONTENTS

PREFACE III

ACKNOWLEDGMENTS VI

CHAPTER 1 FUNDAMENTALS 12
INTRODUCTION OF CAD MODELING WITH AUTODESK FUSION
THE BASICS...14
CLASSIC DONUT 22
SATURN V ROCKET...30
FINGER SURFBOARD 40
TENSEGRITY TOWER..48
CARABINER 56

CHAPTER 2 MECHANICAL DESIGN 66
THE BASICS OF DESIGN USING MANUFACTURING PRINCIPLES
PLAY BRICK 68
GEOCACHE HIDE 76

CHAPTER 3 PARAMETRIC DESIGN 86
HOW TO CUSTOMIZE YOUR DESIGNS WITH DIMENSIONS AND PARAMETERS
METRIC BOLT 88
PROTOTYPE DRONE 96

CHAPTER 4 ASSEMBLIES...110
HOW TO BUILD YOUR PROJECT WITH MULTIPLE PARTS
FIRE PISTON...112
3D PRINTER HOT END 124

CHAPTER 5 JOINTS...142
HOW TO JOIN PARTS FOR REALISTIC MOVEMENT
PIZZA CUTTER 144
TESLA TURBINE 156

CHAPTER 6 MOTION ANIMATION 178
HOW TO MAKE YOUR MODEL MOVE AND COME ALIVE
STRANDBEEST 180
GEAR TRAIN...188
ROBOTIC HAND 196

CHAPTER 7 APPEARANCES......................................208
HOW TO GIVE YOUR 3D MODELS COLOR, TEXTURE, AND DECALS
AMERICAN FOOTBALL...210
SMARTPHONE CASE...218

CHAPTER 8 RENDERING...226
HOW TO MAKE YOUR PARTS LOOK PHOTO-REALISTIC
EDISON BULB...228
A.I. VILLAIN...240

CHAPTER 9 ENGINEERING DRAWINGS 254
HOW TO MAKE YOUR OWN BLUEPRINTS
DRUMSTICKS...256
SPACE PROP EMITTER..262

CHAPTER 10 EXPLODED DIAGRAMS 272
HOW TO EXPLODE YOUR PROJECTS AND REBUILD THEM
JAPANESE PULL SAW..274
MACHINIST HAMMER...286

CHAPTER 11 CAM...298
HOW TO MANUFACTURE PARTS ON A CNC WITH COMPUTER-AIDED
MANUFACTURING
WOODEN LONGBOARD..300
ELECTRIC GUITAR..312

CHAPTER 12 FULL ARC...328
BRING EVERYTHING YOU'VE LEARNED TOGETHER IN A FINAL PROJECT
SPACE PROP HILT...330

TOOL REFERENCES / INDEX...................................354

CHAPTER ANSWERS..356

RESOURCES 357

WHERE TO TURN...

CADCLASS.ORG AUTODESK FUSION COURSE

Everyone learns new tools in different ways; some prefer physical books they can hold, some prefer the handiness of a digital PDF file, and some prefer the visual assistance of video content.

Here at CADclass we want to offer our services in your CAD education in the format that works best for you. Our online Video Course follows along with the projects in this book with additional design and engineering information on each project. The projects in the 1st Chapter are free to watch at CADclass.org.

As a thank you for purchasing this book, here is a discount code: **25CADCLASS** to help you along the way on your CAD education.

CAD eduction works best using multiple different formats simultaneously to enhance learning and cater to various learning styles.

WEEKLY YOUTUBE PODCAST

Need live help with your projects? Then check out the CADclass Podcast streamed live every Wednesday at 9:30 am PST to explain the newest updates in Fusion, highlight our favorite community builds of the week, and philosophize on the nature of being and how 3D Printing fits into it all.

Visit the CADclass Official YouTube channel to get any questions you may have answered live by the authors and hang out with your fellow community members.

With featured guest experts, CADclass graduates, and community makers who share their insights and experiences, offering unique perspectives on CAD design and 3D printing, the CADclass Podcast provides a rich and diverse learning environment that caters to all skill levels and interests.

...WHEN YOU'RE STUMPED

CADCLASS DISCORD SERVER

We all have experiences of asking questions on a forum and receiving unhelpful or overly advanced responses that leave us feeling more confused and frustrated than before.

The CADclass Discord Server aims to eliminate all of those problems by mixing a vibrant and helpful community of fellow makers with individual channels for each project so you can get specific help on a specific project.

Make a Discord account and sign into: **Discord.gg/5hbt6xDPqf** to get access.

Here, you can post questions, images, screen recordings, or your Fusion file to an audience of your program peers and CADclass Graduates.

A.I. HELPERS

Learning CAD from the ground up isn't easy, and in the beginning often feels like you need a helper right next to you. With the new advancements in A.I., learning CAD has become easier and more efficient than ever before.

Fusion's new Autodesk Assistant can answer any specific question by linking to their excellent index of articles for information about tools, UX, or design techniques. This tool can be found in the bottom right corner of the program.

Other A.I. tools like ChatGPT allow you to take pictures of your screen, upload them to your A.I. tool of choice, enter a brief description of your problem, and will give you step by step solutions to your issues and where you might have gone wrong.

CHAPTER 1
FUNDAMENTALS

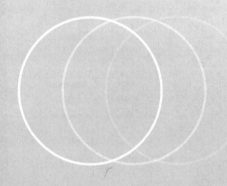

THE BASICS OF DESIGN AND CAD
MODELING WITH AUTODESK FUSION

- THE BASICS
- CLASSIC DONUT
- SATURN V ROCKET
- FINGER SURFBOARD
- TENSEGRITY TOWER
- CARABINER

FUSION
SHORTCUTS

DESIGN WORKSPACE

Appearance	A
As-built Joint	Shift+J
Compute All	CTRL + B CMD + B
Extrude	E
Freeform Selection	2
Hole	H
Joint	J
Measure	I
Model Fillet	F
Design Shortcuts	S
Move	M
Paint Selection	3
Press Pull	Q
Show/Hide	V
Component Color	Shift+N
Window Selection	1

SKETCH WORKSPACE

2-point Rectangle	R
Center Diameter Circle	C
Line	L
Construction	X
Offset	O
Project	P
Sketch Dimension	D
Trim	T

DRAWING WORKSPACE

Balloon	B
Center Mark	C
Dimension	D
Move	M
Projected View	P
Text	T

ANIMATION WORKSPACE

Auto Explode All Level	U
Manual Explode	E
Publish Video	P
Transform Components	M
View	C

CAM WORKSPACE

Duplicate	CTRL + D CMD + D
Generate Toolpath	CTRL + G CMD + G
Scripts and Add-Ins	Shift + S
Show Log	CTRL + L CMD + L

RENDER WORKSPACE

Appearance	A

SYSTEM COMMANDS

Recovery Save	CTRL+Shift+S CMD+Shift+S
Save Version	CTRL+S CMD+S

CANVAS SELECTION

Copy	CTRL + C CMD + C
Cut	CTRL + X CMD + X
Orbit	Shift+Click+Hold Middle Mouse
Pan	Hold Middle Mouse
Paste	CTRL + V CMD + V
Redo	CTRL + Y CMD + Y
Undo	CTRL + Z CMD + Z
Zoom	Roll Middle Mouse

THE BASICS

CHAPTER 1

This chapter covers the user interface features inside of Autodesk Fusion 360 helping you build a foundation for using the software.

It will be helpful to know the major menus by name since we will reference them often.

Those menus include the data panel, browser, timeline, workspaces, navigation bar, and view cube.

DIFFICULTY:
★☆☆☆☆

TIME ESTIMATE:
1 HOUR

KEY LEARNING:
- Menus: what they do
- How to make and edit basic shapes
- How to navigate using your mouse

DISCORD LINK:
Discord.gg/5hbt6xDPqf

INTRODUCTION

Learning how to make simple designs in Autodesk Fusion (formerly Fusion 360) is the quickest way to improve your familiarity with the interface while building a solid foundation using the software. As you work through these projects, your skill set will improve, and you will soon be designing complex models on your own. When inspiration hits, you'll be able to design it and make it.

CAD models are 3D objects made from 2D sketches that can have dimensions, appearances, and physical materials. Single parts, known as components, can be joined together to make an Assembly. You will learn more about Assemblies in a later chapter.

If you're new to Autodesk Fusion, you will want to work through these projects sequentially as each introduces you to a few new concepts, workspaces, and ideas.

Autodesk Fusion is a cloud-based software that is updated and improved monthly. To keep up with the changes, you can find the most up to date version of this book at **CADclass.org**. This PDF version is searchable with the Find tool (Ctrl/Cmd+F) to locate specific keywords or to be able to zoom into photos to see finer detail.

Good luck and happy making!

CAD

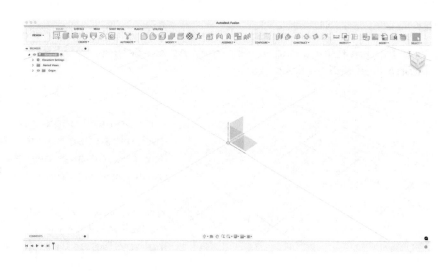

Open the software. You'll see a large white grid with a small white dot in the middle. This dot, known as the Origin, is the critical starting point for most of your designs.

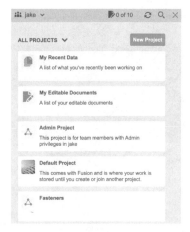

The 3 x 3 grid at the top left is your Data Panel, a powerful tool for organizing your Fusion files. Like your computer, you can create folders and subfolders to organize your projects.

If you are using the paid license, click on your name in the top left corner and notice you can create a team. You and your peers can create teams to work on group projects while seeing each other's progress.

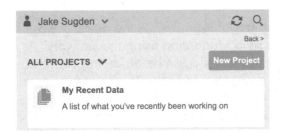

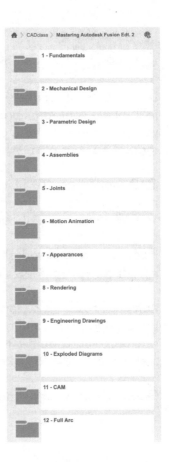

To keep the projects you will make in this course organized, click New Project and name it Mastering Autodesk Fusion Edt. 2.

Click New Folder and name it 1 - Fundamentals, to store the files from Chapter 1. Repeat this process for Chapters 2-12.

Click on the 1 - Fundamentals Folder to open it and see an empty file soon to be filled with your first projects!

Click the X at the top right of the Data Panel to close it.

The Browser is on the top left and is where you will find information such as Units, 3D objects, Construction Planes, and 2D Sketches. As you design new objects, this section will expand with more information and sections like.

Click on the triangle next to the word Document Settings; the Units should be set to Millimeters (mm). If they are not, hover your mouse over the word Units and click on the small pop-up to the right that says Change Active Units.

This will open a pop-up known as a Dialog Box. Click on the pulldown next to Unit Type, set it to mm, check the box that says Set as Default, and click OK.

Click the Eye Icon in the Browser next to the word Origin. Notice the Planes, Axes, and Origins that appear or disappear on your screen.

Eye Icons represent information that can be hidden or shown. Triangles indicate that information can be expanded or rolled up.

If your vertical Axis is green instead of blue, don't worry; this will be fixed later in this chapter.

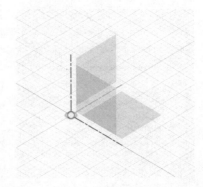

These Planes are the 2D surfaces where you sketch 2D geometry, such as circles, rectangles, and text. Click the Eye Icon again to Hide the Origin.

In general, it is best practice to choose the plane that logically makes your project appear like it does in real life. Designing a coffee mug standing up, not on its side or upside down, makes the most sense.

This skill may be confusing now, but it will improve as you design more projects in this book.

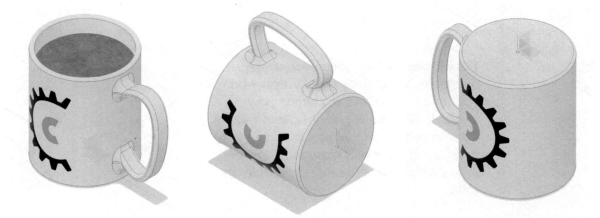

The Timeline is on the bottom left of the screen. It will populate your project's history as your design progresses. Each icon represents different types of Features and Operations.

If you want to edit a feature in your project, you can double-click these icons in the Timeline or right-click it and select Edit Feature.

You can also drag the black vertical line known as the History Marker at the far right to roll back or roll forward changes.

In the top left corner of your screen, you will see a gray box that says Design. This refers to the workspace you are currently working in. Each workspace includes unique tools. If you change the workspace, your tools change. The Design workspace is where you will spend most of your time and is where 2D sketches and 3D models are created.

Click on Design and notice the other workspaces in the dropdown menu, such as Render, Generative Design, Simulation, and Manufacture. Some of these are blocked behind a paywall, denoted by a blue starry circle, and are only accessible if you pay for a license. You will not be using any of the paid workspaces in this book.

The Design Toolbar is along the top of the screen. In this course, you will navigate to the Create, Modify, Assemble, Configure, Construct, Inspect, Insert, and Select menus.

The Configure menu is a new addition to the program and won't be used in this course. It is advanced and most often used in prototyping products that require multiple configurations to test.

The Create menu lists tools for converting a 2D Sketch into a 3D Body, such as extruding a square into a cube.

The Modify menu lists tools to change the 3D Body, such as rounding the sharp corners on a cube.

You will see the Navigation Bar on the bottom middle of the screen. This is where you can move your view, change your layout, hide or show grid lines, and modify the workspace. For the most part, you will avoid using this menu throughout this book because shortcuts are more accessible and faster.

For example, let's edit the grid. Click on Grid and Snaps, Grid Settings, check Fixed, change the Major Grid Spacing to 50 mm, change Minor Subdivisions to 5, and click OK.

This will give you a cleaner workspace and make it easier to design.

Uncheck Reference Numbers to remove the scale values on the axes.

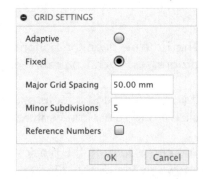

The other primary way to navigate is by using your mouse. It is essential to have a 2-button mouse with a clickable scroll wheel. Some gaming-style programmable mice may not work correctly.

You can operate this software with a trackpad on a laptop, but it is much more challenging and slows down your design momentum. Other types of mice will also work with Autodesk Fusion, but you might need to adjust the settings.

- To zoom in and out, roll the scroll wheel forward and backward.
- To pan, click and hold down on your scroll wheel and move your mouse side to side.
- To orbit, hold down Shift on your keyboard while clicking and holding down the scroll wheel as you move your mouse to orbit in 3-Dimensions.

The View Cube is in the top right corner. This cube has clickable faces, edges, and corners and will help you quickly orient your view. You can orbit by clicking on it and moving your mouse around.

Now, hover your mouse over the View Cube. Notice a small house icon that appears above it. Clicking on the house icon will give you an Isometric view of the project. An Isometric view is a diagonal downward view, which is good for quickly seeing a standard 3-dimensional view. You will click on this house often.

Clicking a face such as TOP will orient your view for a top-down perspective.

Click the edge between the Top and Front faces and notice how your view orients between the two.

Clicking the View Cube and moving your mouse is another way to orbit around the workspace. You will often go back and forth between this and the mouse shortcut.

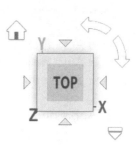

Several settings can improve your CAD experience in Fusion. To modify them, click on the profile icon at the top right and then click Preferences.

This pop-up lists the various areas within the program and should currently show the General options. Navigate to Default modeling orientation and ensure it is set to Z up.

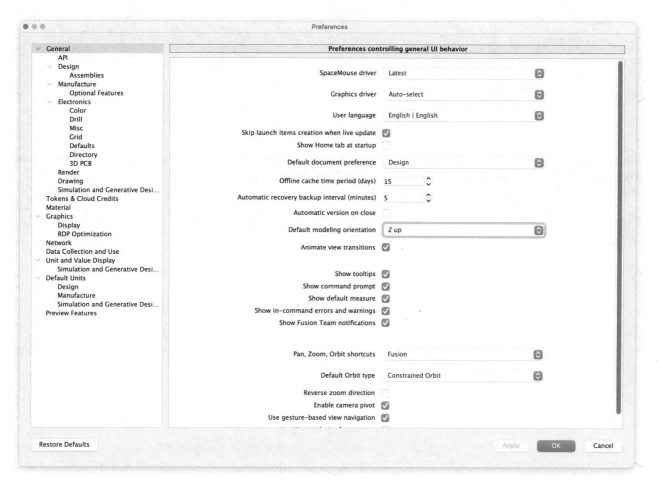

Click on Design in the left column and check the following options:

Check: Auto Project Edges on reference
Check: Auto Project active geometry on sketch planes
Check: Scale entire sketch at first dimension

Click Apply and OK.

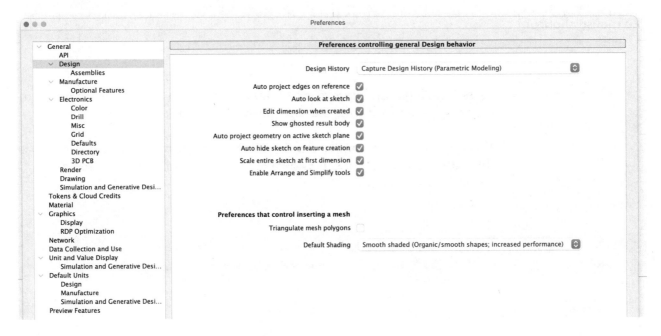

We will discuss many other features and menus throughout this book. For now, we simply want you to know about customization possibilities inside the Preference menu.

Galaxy S21 FE 5G

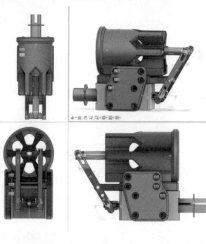

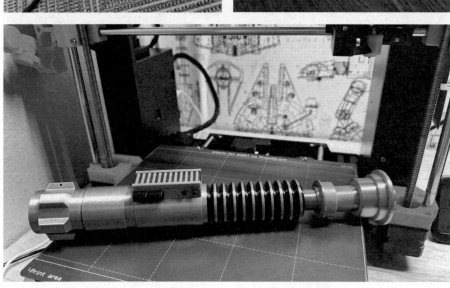

CLASSIC DONUT

CHAPTER 1

Glazed? Jelly Filled? Mathematically accurate Torus-shaped?

How ever you like your donuts, the classic cartoon-ish donut with pink icing is an instantly mouthwatering desert beloved by all nuclear power-plant working fathers of Springfield.

This project is all about how complex-looking 3D models can be made simply and quickly with almost no dimensions!

DIFFICULTY:
★☆☆☆☆

TIME ESTIMATE:
1 HOUR

KEY LEARNING:
- Revolve Tool
- 2D Sketches
- Splines
- Split Body
- Decal Appearances

DISCORD LINK:
Discord.gg/5hbt6xDPqf

Most projects in this course will be made in mm. On rare occasions, like metalworking or woodworking projects, using inches is a more appropriate unit, considering the tools involved in manufacturing the project. All other projects will be made in mm, a more globally accepted unit, especially in the world of 3D printing and laser cutting.

Verify your project is set to mm by clicking on the triangle next to Document Settings.

If the Units are set to inches, hover your cursor over Units: in, click on the Change Active Units pop-up, set the Unit type to mm, and check Set as Default.

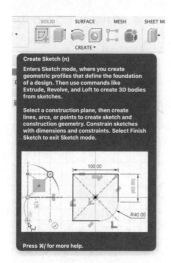

Sketches are the 2D blueprints that become 3D models and include geometries like lines, text, polygons, and curves. In Fusion, most projects start with a 2D sketch.

Start a new Sketch by clicking Create Sketch in the top left corner below the word SOLID. This will prompt you to click on 1 of 3 yellow squares (AKA Planes) that run through the 3 axes (the red X-axis, the green Y-axis, and the blue Z-axis). If you do not see these Planes, you may need to show them by clicking the Eye Icon next to Origin in the Browser.

Click on the yellow square between the red X-axis and the blue Z-axis to select the Front Plane. You can also click Front on the View Cube and select the Plane in view. After selecting it, the View Cube should say FRONT. Verifying this each time you start a new sketch is good practice.

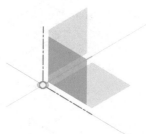

If the vertical axis is green instead of blue, review the Z up setting in Preferences on page 19.

Notice the new tools that populate across the top of your workspace. These tools change each time you start or finish a new Sketch and can confuse beginners.

Notice the Sketch Palette that appears on your workspace's right side. Since you will rarely use it, you can click the (-) symbol to minimize it, and click and drag it to the right side of the screen giving you more room to work. If you don't see it, it may be collapsed by default. In this case, you should see a small (+) next to the words Sketch Palette. If that's the case, you can leave it as is.

Type C for Circle, click to the right of the Origin near the X-axis, move your cursor upwards, and click again to define the circle's size. Notice that the circle's center isn't perfectly aligned with the X-axis; you will correct this in a later step.

Also, notice the circle icon next to your cursor, indicating that the Circle tool is still selected. Since you don't need to make any more circles, press the Esc key to deselect the Circle tool.

Currently, both the location and the size of the circle are unknown or undefined. You are able to click and drag the center of the circle around the Workplane and click and drag the circle's perimeter to change the diameter.

To define sketches, you will first apply constraints and then add dimensions. In general, the fewer dimensions on a sketch, the better. This methodology makes sketches cleaner and easier to edit in the future.

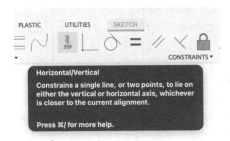

To horizontally align the circle's center with the Origin, navigate to Constraints >> Horizontal/Vertical constraint and select the circle's center and Workplane Origin. It should snap in place on the X-axis.

If it is closer to the X-axis, it will snap to the X-axis. If it's closer to the Y-axis, it will snap to the Y-axis.

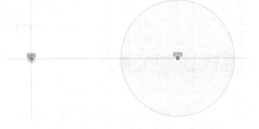

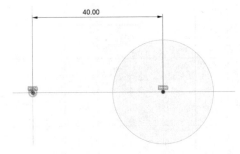

Type D for Dimension, click the Workplane Origin, the circle's center, move your cursor upwards, click again, type 40, and press Enter.

With the Dimension tool still enabled, click the circle's perimeter, move your cursor away, click again, type 40, and press Enter.

Notice how the circle started blue and is now black. When sketches are blue, they have an undefined size, location, or both. Now that your circle has both, your sketch is defined!

Defining 2D sketches is generally best practice in Fusion since undefined sketches can be moved or resized, sometimes without you noticing, leading to future mistakes.

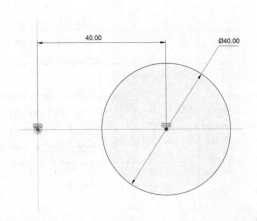

Untitled v1

SELECT ▾   FINISH SKETCH ▾

Now click the green Finish Sketch check mark in the top right corner to return to the 3D Design workspace.

As a rule of thumb, when transitioning from a 2D Sketch to a 3D Workspace, you should be in a 3D view, known as an Isometric view. To get this view, move your cursor to the View Cube and click on the house icon that appears.

To make this a Donut, you will use the Revolve tool, which rotates a 2D profile around an axis to make a rotationally symmetric part.

Navigate to Create >> Revolve. Because there is only 1 profile, the circle will be auto-selected. Click on the blue vertical Z-axis as the Axis of Revolution to make a torus (the mathematical name for a donut) and click OK. You may need to zoom out to see or click it.

Congratulations, you have just made your first 3D object!

In Fusion, this is called a Body. Click on the triangle next to Bodies in the Browser and see Body1. If you were to make multiple 3D objects in this file, they would populate this area as Body2, Body3, Body4, etc.

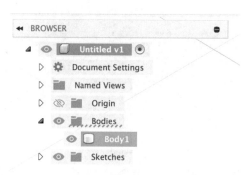

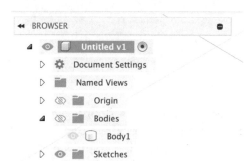

Click on the Eye Icon next to Bodies. Don't worry, your project hasn't been deleted! It has simply been hidden. Click the Eye Icon again to Show the Body.

A common beginner mistake (both authors included) is hiding the model and thinking it has been deleted. It may simply be hidden.

To make the donut look more…like a donut, you can add a donut-colored material to give it the illusion of fried dough.

Press A for the Appearance tool, click on Fusion Appearances, scroll down through the types of material, select Wood, click the download arrow next to Oak, and drag the Oak material icon onto the donut.

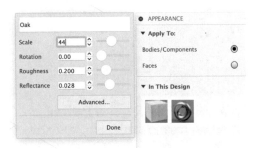

In the "In This Design" window, you can see the Original Steel appearance for the default material and the new Oak appearance. Double-click on the Oak cube appearance and change the Scale to 44%. Click Done and close the Appearance Dialog Box.

To add the classic pink icing to the top of the donut, you need to cut it in half some way.

One method is to use the Split Body tool, but that would leave you with an unrealistic, perfectly sharp edge of icing.

Instead of a horizontal cut, we want a curved cut that's more organic to give the appearance of icing flowing down the donut.

Navigate to Create >> Create Sketch and select the Front Plane, which intersects the blue and red axes.

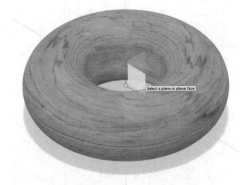

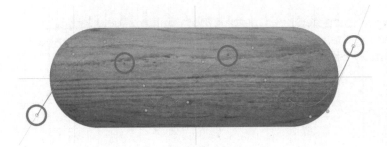

Navigate to Create >> Spline >> Fit Point Spline and click above and below the X-axis 6 times so the spline's first and last points are outside the Donut. Press Enter to finish the Spline tool. Unlike other tools, pressing Esc to deselect the Spline tool will delete the spline itself.

Splines are one of the few tools that aren't dimensionally driven. Instead, they can be better described as organic or artistic shapes.

Trying to define dimensions would be frustrating and time-consuming. Instead, navigate to Constraints >> Fix/Unfix and click the Spline.

This turns it green, signifying that its position and size are now fixed without adding values or relationships.

Click the green Finish Sketch check mark in the top right corner.

Navigate to the Browser and verify that the Eye Icon next to Sketch 2 is selected and the Spline is visible in the 3D workspace.

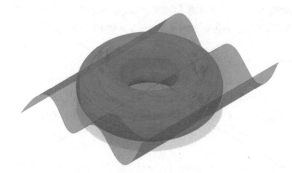

Navigate to Modify >> Split Body, and select the Donut Body. Click "Select" next to Splitting tool, and select the Spline sketch. Click OK.

Verify Sketch 2 is hidden. If it is still visible, click the Eye Icon next to Sketch 2 in the Browser to Hide it.

The Split Body will leave you with an upper and lower half of the Donut that was cut with the wavy line of the Spline.

To take a bite out of the Donut, navigate to Create >> Create Sketch and select the Top Plane, which intersects the green and red axes.

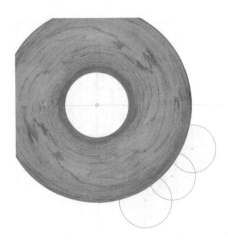

Type C for circle and draw 3 overlapping circles near the outer edge of the donut, where the circle's centers are outside the donut's Body.

Press Esc to deselect the Circle tool.

Hold down Ctrl/Cmd, select each circle's perimeter, and click the Fix/Unfix constraint.

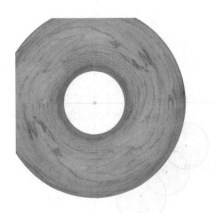

Click the green Finish Sketch check mark in the top right corner.

Move your cursor to the View Cube and click the house icon for a 3D view.

Navigate to Create >> Extrude, and select the 3 circles and 2 overlapping areas. In the Dialog Box, change the Direction to Symmetric so the circles cut up and down simultaneously.

Click and drag the blue arrow up so the profiles cut through the Donut completely. You can also type 20 mm in Distance since the Measurement is set to Half Length and the total height of the donut is 40 mm.

Note that the volume is transparent and red because you are performing a cutting operation. Click OK.

Press A for Appearance and double-click the Steel-Satin cube appearance.

Change the color by clicking somewhere in the color box, moving the (+) symbol to the top left corner, and moving the color slider above it until you find a pink color you like. Click Done.

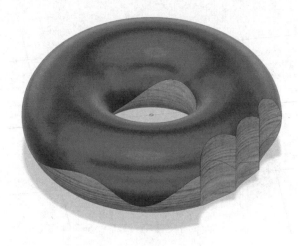

To add the pink color only to the top of the donut, change the "Apply To" from Bodies/Components to Faces, and click and drag the new pink appearance to the donut's top.

Congratulations! You just finished your first CAD project!

Hold down the Shift key and your mouses scroll wheel to Orbit around you model.

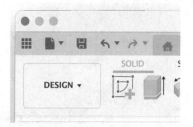

Click the Save icon in the top left corner. Save the name as Classic Donut in the Week 1 - Fundamentals Folder.

DISCUSSION

10 Editable Files

The free version (Hobbyist version) of Autodesk Fusion allows for 10 files to be Editable at a time. To make an 11th file, you must change one file from Editable to Read Only. As soon as you want to work on that file again, you must change it back to Editable. You may make as many files as you want, but only 10 are immediately changeable.

CHALLENGE

Make a Sketch of a vertical line from the Origin, make a series of arcs, lines, and splines on the right side of the line, enclose the profile with a horizontal and vertical line, and revolve the profile about the vertical line.

Add a wooden appearance to the Body and a green felt-like appearance to the bottom face.

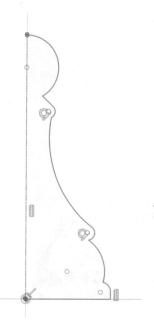

@Vasile
Discord User #498

SATURN V ROCKET

CHAPTER 1

Recreate the Saturn V Rocket that took man to the moon in July 1969!

Use simple tools and appearances to customize your own rocket.

DIFFICULTY:
★★☆☆☆

TIME ESTIMATE:
1.5 HOURS

KEY LEARNING:
- Basics of making finished project
- Cylinder Tool
- Tapering
- Appearances

DISCORD LINK:
Discord.gg/5hbt6xDPqf

INTRODUCTION

In July 1969, NASA sent humans to the moon for the first time, captivating the world and ushering in a new era of space travel. An estimated 400,000 engineers, scientists, and manufacturers worldwide are accredited for helping build the rocket.

To commemorate this milestone, you will model the Saturn V Rocket responsible for the journey at 1/180th of the Original scale. The design can be exported and viewed in augmented reality and saved as an STL for 3D printing. The bottom cavity will fit a model rocket motor if you want to 3D print and launch one!

As the broadcaster of Apollo 8 said in 1968, "And we have liftoff!" If you would like to download the CAD or augmented reality file, navigate to **CADclass.org** and select the **FREE DOWNLOADS** tab.

CAD

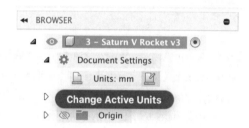

Verify the Units are set to Millimeters (mm) by expanding the Document Settings.

Expand the Create pulldown in the top left and click Create Sketch.

Select the Top Plane (which intersects the red X-axis and the green Y-axis) since you will be building this rocket from the bottom up.

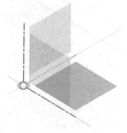

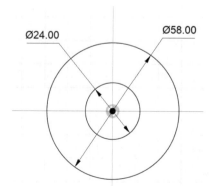

Press C for circle, click the Workspace Origin, move your cursor away, and click again to define the first circle. Repeat this operation to make a second smaller circle.

Press D for Dimension, click on the larger circle, pull your cursor away, click again, type 58, and press enter. This will define 1 circle as having a diameter of 58 mm.

Repeat this operation for the other circle but set it to 24 mm. This inner hole allows you to fit a hobby rocket motor in it.

Click Finish Sketch (green check mark) in the top right corner.

Move your cursor to the View Cube in the top right corner, and click on the house icon to get a 3D view of your Sketch.

Press E for Extrude, click on the ring profile in the Sketch, and set it to a Distance of 365 mm. Click OK.

Press A for Appearance, and type "White Paint" in the search bar. Click and drag 1 of the options onto the Body to change its color. Right-click on the white cube appearance and click Add to Favorites which will add this material to a customizable list found on the right side of the dialog box. This course will often use a white color, a black color, Polished Aluminum, and Polished Brass. Click OK.

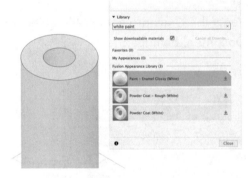

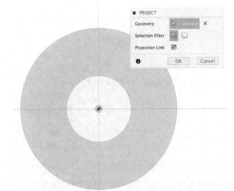

Create a new Sketch on the top of this Body by clicking new Sketch and selecting the top surface. This will give you a top-down view.

Press P for Project, click on the ring profile, and click OK. This should turn the 2 circular edges purple. This allows us to click on the top ring and middle circle on this layer. Click Finish Sketch.

Press E for Extrude. Click on the ring profile and the inner circle and pull the blue arrow upwards 32 mm. You can also type 32 into Distance.

Notice the black and white ring icon above the arrow. This adjusts the extrusion's Taper angle. Set the Taper angle to -16 degrees and click OK.

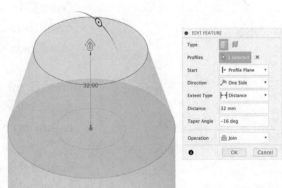

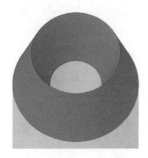

If you didn't Project the top surface, then the Extruding step would only taper the ring profile, not the entire flat top. By Projecting the top surface, you were able to click both the ring profile and the inner circle at the same time.

Type A for the Appearance tool and search for Black Oxide.

Right-click it and add it to your Favorites too. Change the "Apply To" to Faces, and click and drag this appearance to the outer tapered surface.

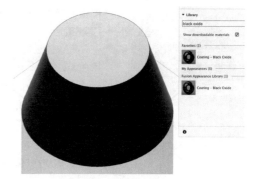

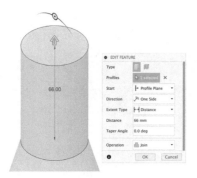

The building blocks of this project will be a series of cylinders and tapered cylinders stacked on top of each other. Both can be made using the Extrusion tool.

The nice thing about the Extrude tool is that you can extrude any flat face without making a new sketch every time.

Press E for Extrude, click on the top of the tapered cylinder, type 66, and click OK.

On the real Saturn V Rocket, this cylinder has a black ring at the top, but if you added the Black Oxide appearance to this surface, the entire cylinder would turn black. Alternatively, if you tried to extrude two cylinders on top of each other, they would merge into one cylinder. The solution is to use the Split Face tool to cut the outer surface into a top and bottom, but still be one part.

Navigate to the Construct menu and select Offset Plane. Select the top flat surface of the cylinder and type -13 mm to create a new Plane that intersects with the cylinder.

Navigate to Modify >> Split Face, select the outer curved surface of the cylinder, click "Select" next to Splitting tool, select the Offset Plane, and click OK.

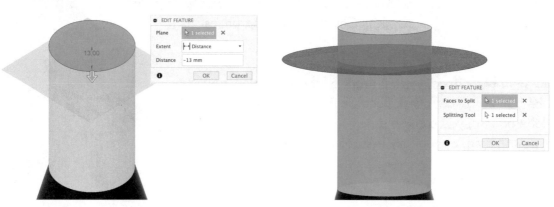

Type A for Appearance, set the "Apply To" to Faces and drag the Black Oxide appearance onto the top curved surface of the cylinder to change its appearance.

Click the Eye Icon next to Construction in the Browser to Hide this Offset Plane.

Press E for Extrude, click the top of this Cylinder and set it to 57 mm tall with a -9 degree Taper. Click OK.

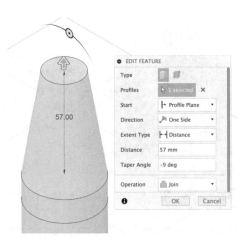

Create these 6 extrusions on top of each other:

- Extrusion 5: 23 mm

- Extrusion 6: 7 mm, -35.7 degree Taper

- Extrusion 7: 15 mm, -6 degree Taper

- Extrusion 8: 3 mm, -30 degree Taper

- Extrusion 9: 27 mm

- Extrusion 10: 5 mm, -25 degree Taper

Type A for Appearance, search for Stainless Steel - Brushed Linear Long, and drag it onto Extrusion 5's Face.

To replicate the cross-hatch frame on the Saturn V Rocket, search for Stainless Steel Mesh - Square Large, drag it onto Extrusion 7, double click on its Appearance in the Dialog Box, and change the Rotation to 45 degrees. Click OK and notice how this decal has gaps known as a Cutout Decal, which will be covered in more depth in Chapter 7: Appearances.

With the main body done, you will work on the 4 thrusters and fins at the bottom of the rocket. Because they are equally spaced around the bottom, you can use a new tool called Circular Pattern, saving time, as you only need to make 1 thruster and 1 fin.

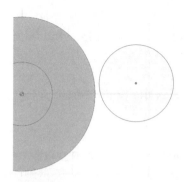

Make a new Sketch on the bottom face of the rocket Body. Press C for circle, click to the right of the Origin away from the rocket, pull your cursor away, and click again. Select the Horizontal/Vertical constraint, and click on the Origin and the circle's center. This will prevent it from moving up and down.

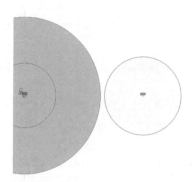

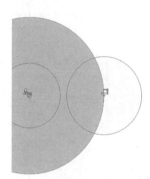

Select the Coincident constraint, click on this circle's center and the rocket's outer circle's circumference.

Finally, press D for Dimension, click the sketched circle, move your cursor away, click again, type 25, press Enter, and click Finish Sketch.

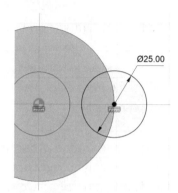

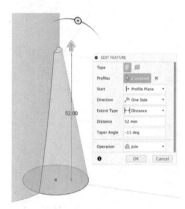

Press E for Extrude, click on the 2 profiles that make up the circle, and orbit your view to the top side of the rocket. Extrude the 2 profiles 52 mm up with a -11 degree Taper.

Because you are making something that interferes with another existing Body, the cone will be red. Change the Operation from Cut to Join at the bottom of the Dialog Box, and click OK.

To round over the top of the cone, type F for Fillet, click the top curved edge (not the top face), type 2.9, and click OK.

Fillet (pronounced Fill-et), is a radius cut onto an edge.

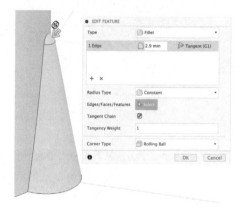

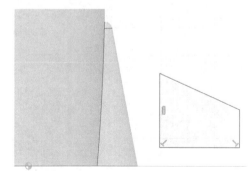

To make the rocket's fin, Create a new Sketch on the Front Plane. Press L for the Line tool and roughly make the shape in the picture.

Press Esc to get rid of the Line tool.

The shape should have blue lines and have a pale light blue filling, meaning it is fully enclosed.

Select the Coincident constraint, click the bottom horizontal line, and the Origin

This tool extends an imaginary line to intersect at a point.

Press D for Dimension and add the dimensions shown. Note that when you click on two points and move your cursor around, you will see that you can define the horizontal, vertical, or diagonal distance between the two.

Depending on the order in which you added dimensions, you may notice that the sketch stretches or shrinks in strange ways. Remember that as long as a line is blue, it can be clicked and dragged to more closely resemble the pictures. Click Finish Sketch.

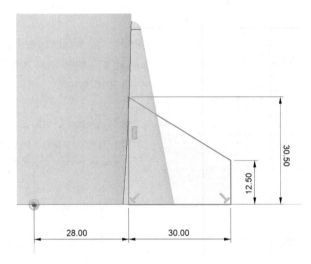

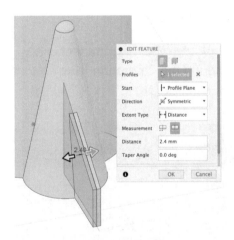

Press E for Extrude and click on the new profile.

Change the Direction to Symmetric, the Measurement from Half Length to Whole Length, set the Distance to 2.4 mm, and click OK.

On the real Saturn V Rocket, the left and right faces of the fins were black and white to help with thermal control.

To get this effect on your fin, you can split the fin in half.

Navigate to Modify >> Split Face, click the angled and vertical faces on the thickness of the fin (highlighted in the picture), click "Select" next to Splitting tool, click the triangle next to Origin in the Browser to expand it, select the XZ Plane (Front Plane), and click OK.

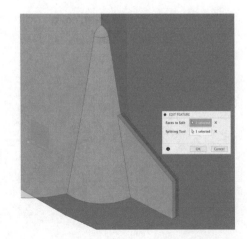

Type A for Appearance, set the "Apply To" to Faces, orbit your view around to the right side of the fin (Shift+click Scroll Wheel), and drag the Black Oxide appearance onto the 3 faces.

Click and drag the Stainless Steel - Brushed Linear Long appearance onto the 2 faces of the cone.

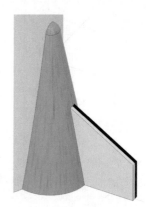

Now you have 1 thruster and 1 fin and will use the Circular Pattern tool to make 3 more.

Navigate to Create >> Pattern >> and select Circular Pattern. Change the Object Type to Features and click on the 4 highlighted Features in the Timeline.

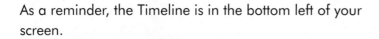

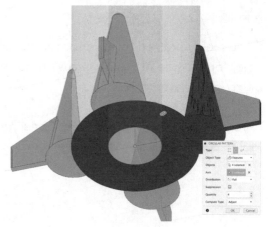

As a reminder, the Timeline is in the bottom left of your screen.

Click on Select next to Axis, select any round surface on the Rocket Body, change the Quantity from 3 to 4, and click OK.

And you are done! This replica is now ready to be exported for Augmented Reality.

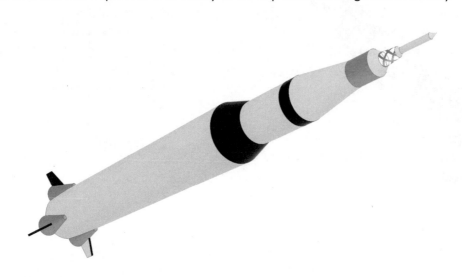

Saturn V Rocket AR model

Navigate to File >> Export >> and change the file type to .USDZ.

Save this file to a cloud account of your choosing (like iCloud Files, an AR viewer app, or Google Drive) so you can open it up on your smartphone.

If you are using iOS, save the file to your Files app, and open it.

Move your camera over a tabletop, and it should appear. You can move your camera to look at details or double-finger pinch to scale it up or down. Magic!

CHALLENGE

If you feel energized by this process, consider using other tools inside of Fusion to customize your rocket and make it look even cooler.

Experiment with the Appearance, Decal, and Emboss tool to customize your own Rocket.

@ Raluca A
Discord User #794

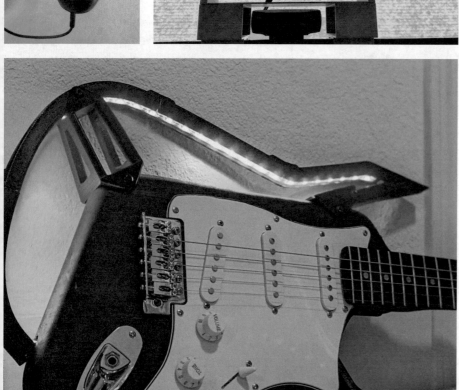

FINGER
SURFBOARD

CHAPTER 1

CAD modeling often feels abstract, making it difficult to relate objects on your screen to objects in the real world. For this reason, we enjoy modeling things we use and then thinking about how the model on our screen relates to the real thing.

In this project you will model a simple surfboard that you can ride out of your car's window, using some surprising techniques to make it easy.

DIFFICULTY:
⭐☆☆☆☆

TIME ESTIMATE:
1.5 HOURS

KEY LEARNING:
- Loft Tool
- Offset Planes
- Canvases
- Intersect Projection
- Tracing with Splines

DISCORD LINK:
Discord.gg/5hbt6xDPqf

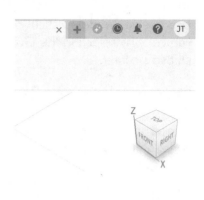

INTRODUCTION

If continuing from a previous project, click + at the top to make a new tab.

In this lesson, you will use the Loft tool to make a Finger Surfboard. The Loft tool connects 2 or more 2D profiles into a hybrid 3D object. For example, you can turn this:

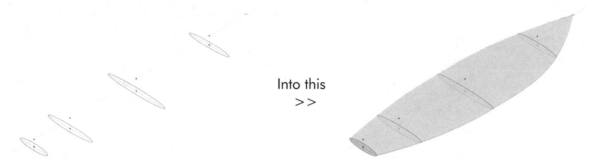

Into this
>>

You will make a series of ellipses at different distances from the Origin and then use the Loft tool to loft between them to make a continuous 3D Body that flows through each 2D Sketch.

CAD

Expand Document Settings in the Browser and verify your Units are set to mm.

You will make a series of ellipses on new Planes. To make a new plane, navigate to Construct >> Offset Plane. Select the Right Plane intersecting the green Y-axis and the blue Z-axis, set the Distance to 24 mm, and click OK.

If your Origin is still visible, click the Eye Icon next to Origin in the Browser to Hide the Original Origin/ Planes.

Start a new Sketch on this new Offset Plane. Notice in the Browser that there is a new section called Construction. This is where all the Construction planes will be available to show or hide.

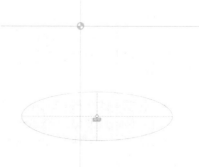

Navigate to Create >> and select Ellipse. Draw an ellipse by clicking somewhere below the Origin near the Y-axis, moving your cursor to the right, clicking again, moving your cursor up, and then clicking one last time.

Use the Horizontal/Vertical constraint to constrain the ellipse vertically by selecting the Origin and the small white circle at the ellipse's center.

Press Esc to deselect the Horizontal/Vertical constraint.

Click and drag the ellipse's center and see how the Vertical constraint restricts it to only vertical movement.

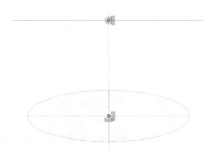

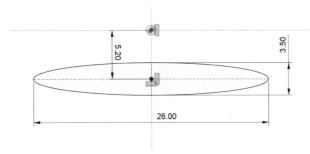

Type D for Dimension, set the ellipse's width (the horizontal orange dashed line) to 26.00 mm, and the ellipse's height (the vertical black dashed line) to 3.50 mm.

Click the Origin, then the ellipse's center, and set this distance to 5.20 mm.

Afterward, the ellipse should be black, which indicates it is now fully defined. If it is still blue, double-check that you've entered all dimensions and constraints. Click Finish Sketch.

Click the triangle next to Sketches to expand it, and click Sketch 1's Eye Icon to Hide it.

Using the same process, you will make 3 more ellipses on 3 more Planes. The numerical values are in the table below.

1. Construct an Offset Plane from the Right Plane
2. Make a new Sketch on this Plane
3. Draw an ellipse below the Origin, Vertically Constrain it, and add the height, width, and center to the Origin dimensions.
4. Finish Sketch, Hide the sketch, and repeat.

Ellipse #	Plane Offset Distance	Ellipse Width	Ellipse Height	Ellipse Center-to-Origin
2	72 mm	38.0 mm	4.0 mm	7.0 mm
3	116 mm	29.6 mm	4.0 mm	6.0 mm
4	140 mm	18.0 mm	4.0 mm	4.2 mm

Note that it is sometimes easier to work on a blank Canvas. You can turn on or off the previous Sketches by navigating to Browser >> Sketches and clicking the Eye Icon to the left of the Sketch you want to Hide/Show.

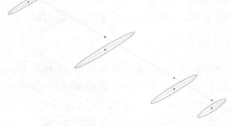

Click each Sketch's Eye Icon to Show all 4. Once you have completed all four Sketches, click the house icon next to the View Cube, and your workspace should look like this:

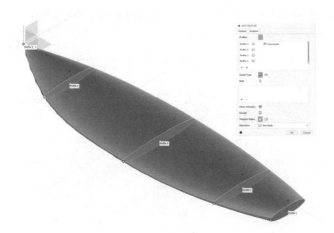

Navigate to Create >> and select Loft. This will allow you to join your ellipses into 1 Body. Click the ellipses in Sketch 4, 3, 2, 1, and then the Workspace Origin in that order.

The surfboard shape will appear as you go. Click OK.

Press A for Appearance and search for Polystyrene (AKA Styrofoam), a Decal Appearance. Click and drag the material to the part.

Double click on the Appearance icon and st the Scale to 25%.

Zoom in closely on the surface and notice the color has changed and that there's a new bubbly foam Decal.

Visit **CADclass.org** and navigate to the **Free Downloads** tab. This will open a Google Drive folder containing this course's necessary files and documents.

This Google Drive is organized by book chapters or weeks of the online course. Inside "1 - Fundamentals", you will find all files pertaining to this project.

Download the Surfboard Canvas.png file to your computer.

Navigate to Insert >> Canvas, Insert from my computer, select the PNG file, select the Front Plane, and click FRONT on the View Cube.

Set the Scale Plane XY (not Scale X or Scale Y) to 8.25 and click Horizontal Flip in the Dialog Box.

Drag the white square to position the Canvas over your model as closely as possible, and click OK.

Now you will make the fin and join it to the surfboard's underside. This step can be tricky since the surface is rounded, unlike the flat planes you have worked on previously.

First, you need to know the shape of the surfboard's underside. You can find that shape using the Intersect tool, which traces around the Body where the Plane Intersects.

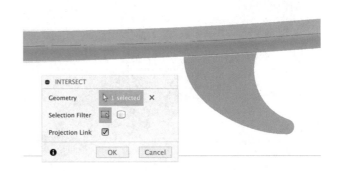

To use the Intersect tool, Create a Sketch on the Front Plane. Navigate to Create >> Project/Include >> and select Intersect. Click the surfboard and click OK. Notice the new purple curves.

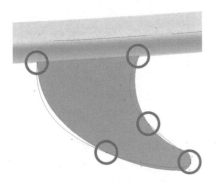

Navigate to Create >> Spline >> Fit Point Spline. Click on the fin's top left corner so it snaps onto the bottom projected purple curve.

Click on 3 more points along the fin's perimeter, click on the top right corner of the fin where it snaps to the projected purple line, and press Enter or click the small gray check mark that appears next to your cursor.

Then press Esc to close the tool.

Each of the Spline's points has green tangent lines connected to them; you can change the angle and the length of these lines to adjust the Spline's curvature at that point.

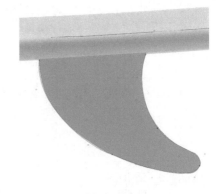

Play around with the location of the Spline's 3 lower points and their green vertex lines until they roughly form the shape of the fin in the picture.

This may take some time and is an iterative approach to tracing over a Canvas. It doesn't have to be perfect, but tracing images with splines to recreate 3D objects from pictures is a valuable skill to develop.

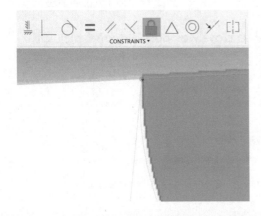

This Spline is not dimensionally driven, meaning it is impractical to define it with dimension.

To fix its position, click on the Fix/Unfix constraint and click on the Spline. It will turn green and cannot be moved. Click Finish Sketch.

Click the Eye Icon next to Canvases in the Browser to Hide it.

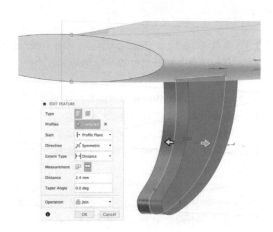

Press E for Extrude and select the fin profile. Change the Direction to Symmetric, the Measurement to Whole Length, the Distance to 2.4 mm, the Operation to Join, and press OK.

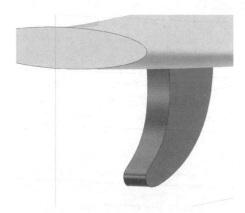

If the fin is gray steel, then you accidentally set the Operation to New Body. To fix this, double-click the most recent feature in the Timeline and change the Operation to Join.

Click OK, and notice that the fin is now the same off-white color as the rest of the surfboard.

Make a new Sketch on the Top Plane, type C for circle, and add a small circle at the surfboard's tail.

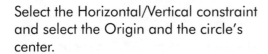

Select the Horizontal/Vertical constraint and select the Origin and the circle's center.

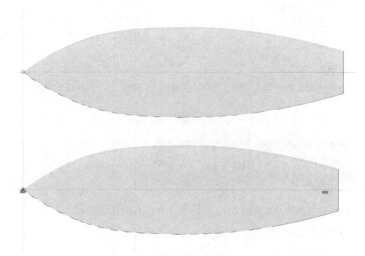

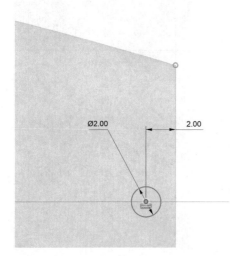

Type D for Dimension, click the circle's center and the Surfboard's right edge, move your cursor away, click again, and set it to 2 mm.

Click the circle's perimeter, move your cursor away, click again, and set it to 2 mm.

Note the circle with an angled line icon in front of the second dimension denoting this value refers to a circle's diameter.

When dimensioning arc in future projects, there will be an "R" before the value denoting the value is a radius dimension.

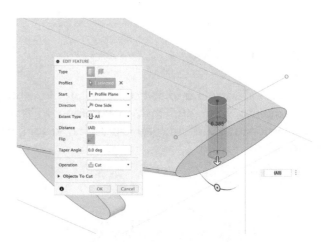

Finish the Sketch and click on the house icon on the View Cube to get an Isometric View.

Type E for Extrude and the circle's profile will automatically be selected. Change the Extent Type to All and click the Flip button so there is transparent red cut through the entire Body. Click OK.

This hole will allow you to pass some string through it to tie it to your finger.

Press F for Fillet, select both the fin's edges and the hole's inner surface, set the radius to 1 mm, and click OK. Note that you don't click the fin's outer faces, just the edges.

If you get an error, it is likely caused by a too-sharp curve in your fin's spline. Reduce the filet's radius to 0.5 mm or lower to fix it.

Notice that the Fillet tool applies a radius to the edges you selected. Because you also selected a curved face, the fillet is applied to any edges that touch the face, i.e., the hole's top and bottom edges.

Save this file to your Data Panel in the 1 - Fundamentals Folder as Finger Surfboard.

3D PRINTING

If you have access to a 3D Printer, navigate to File > Export and save the file as an STL to your Desktop.

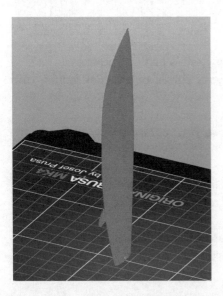

Open your 3D Printer slicer software of choice, import your STL model, and rotate it 90 so it is standing up on its tail.

For this print to be successful, enable support material to hold up the fin while printing, set the wall count to 3 and the infill to 0% to minimize weight, and add a Brim of 10 mm so this tall model doesn't fall over and break mid-print.

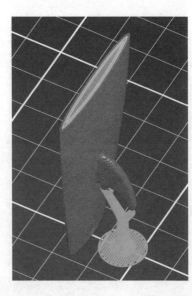

The surfboard's top surface should be grippy to be ridden from a car window. This can be achieved in multiple ways:

One way is to add grip tape or non-slip tape with the Cut Out Template PDF. Another is to enable Fuzzy Skin in your slicer, which vibrates the nozzle during the outer layer to give a textured, grippy surface.

Thread some string through the hole, tie a knot, and tie another end around your ring finger.

Have a friend get up to speed, lower your window, and ride your surfboard in the air!

Save this file to your computer and get 3D Printing!

CHALLENGE

Use the Loft tool and Offset Planes to make a type of glass bottle with a distinct and curvy profile. Make a Canvas on the Front Plane of your glass bottle of choice and use it as a guide to make shapes on Offset Planes parallel to the Top Plane.

@ **Merlwynd**
Discord User #385

@ **Vasile**
Discord User #498

TENSEGRITY
TOWER

CHAPTER 1

Defy gravity with a model to confuse your friends and family!

Tensegrity Towers use the power of tension to levitate parts in mid-air!

With only 1 file you can make this desktop anomaly yours!

DIFFICULTY:

TIME ESTIMATE:
1.5 HOURS

KEY LEARNING:
- Extruding Profiles
- Chamfers
- 2D Mirroring
- Color Components Tool

INTRODUCTION

In this project, you will design a 3D printable Tensegrity Tower that appears to float in mid-air using only the tension of strings. The tower will consist of 2 identical 3D-printed parts, a few bolts, and some fishing line to hold it together.

CAD

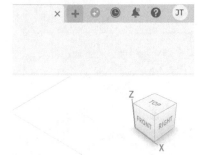

If continuing from a previous project, click + at the top to make a new tab.

Verify you are working in millimeters (mm). Projects you plan on 3D printing work best when starting in millimeters, as most 3D printing slicing software operate in metric.

Create a new Sketch on the Top Plane.

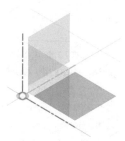

Make a hexagon at the Origin by navigating to the Create menu >> Polygon >> Circumscribed Polygon, clicking the Origin, moving your cursor up and to the right, and clicking again.

Don't worry about the scale or if it is tilted slightly.

Add a Horizontal / Vertical Constraint to the top horizontal line.

Press D for Dimension, click on the leftmost point, the rightmost point, move your cursor above the hexagon, and click to place the dimension.

Type 100 and press Enter. The hexagon should turn black and be defined.

If, when you enter the dimension, the polygon becomes larger than your screen or incredibly tiny, you may not have the correct preferences enabled on page 19.

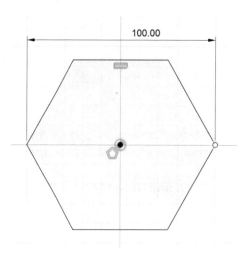

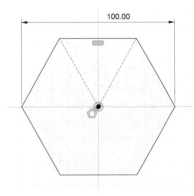

Press L for Line, X for Construction, click the top left point of the hexagon, the Origin, and finally the top right point of the hexagon to make a V-shape of dashed Construction lines.

Press X again to return to standard Sketch geometry, not Construction geometry.

Press L for Line and make a triangle inside the Construction lines.

You may notice that when you make sketches, Fusion will automatically add constraints for you.

For example, in this sketch, because the top line of the sketched triangle was drawn perfectly horizontally, a Horizontal/Vertical constraint was added.

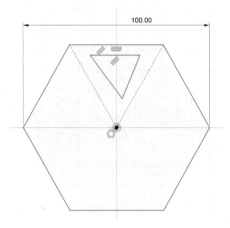

If your sketch added a Parallel constraint between the triangle's top line and the hexagon's top line, then you would achieve the same result. Start identifying these constraints in your sketches to better understand how and when to use them.

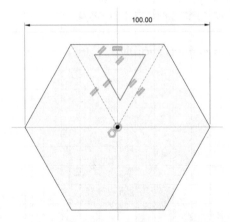

Select the Equal constraint tool and make the triangle's left and right lines equal in length.

Select Parallel constraint and select the left sketched line and the left Construction line to make them parallel with each other. Repeat the operation for the right lines.

If you see an error message in the bottom right corner, then this constraint was automatically added when you sketched the lines and can be ignored.

Press D for Dimension and set the left sketch line and the left Construction line to be 3 mm apart.

Add the same dimension for the right sketch and Construction line.

Set the top horizontal line of the triangle and the top horizontal line of the hexagon to be 6 mm apart.

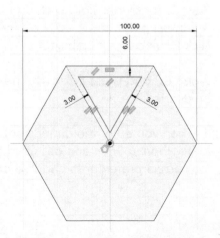

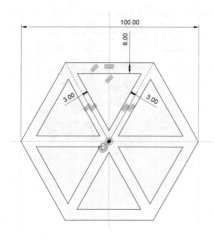

Navigate to Create >> Circular Pattern. Double-click on the triangle's horizontal line to select all connecting lines, click "Select" in the Dialog Box next to Center Point, select the Origin, change the Quantity to 6, and click OK.

This will make 6 copies of the triangle about the Origin that are all evenly spaced.

Press C for Circle, click anywhere on the left Construction line, move your cursor away, and click again.

Using the Coincident constraint tool, select the circle's center and the top triangle's top horizontal line.

Press D for Dimension, click the circle, and set it to 3.5 mm.

This circle will be a 3D printed hole, allowing an M3 bolt or a piece of 2.75mm filament to fit into and secure some fishing line. Note that not all 3D printers are built the same, and tolerances may vary; after printing one part, you may need to reduce or increase the diameter of this hole by 0.2 - 0.4 mm.

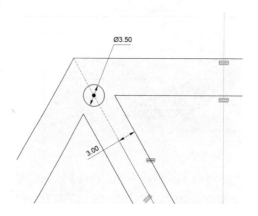

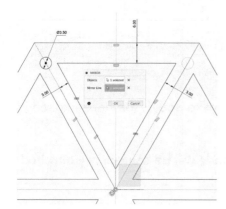

Click on the eye icon next to Origin in the Browser. You should see an orange rectangle (Top Plane), a green vertical line (Y-axis), and a horizontal red line (X-axis).

Navigate to Create >> Mirror, select the 3.5 mm circle, click Select next to Mirror Line, and click the vertical green Y-axis. Click OK.

Repeat this process for the 2 circles to be mirrored about the horizontal red X-axis.

Click the Eye Icon next to Origin in the Browser to turn them off.

Click Finish Sketch.

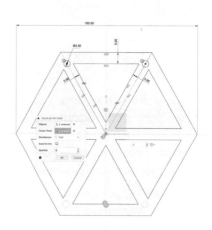

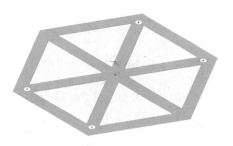

To get an Isometric view of the 3D workspace, hover your mouse over the View Cube, and click the house icon.

Press E for Extrude, select the inner profile, type 6 mm, and click OK.

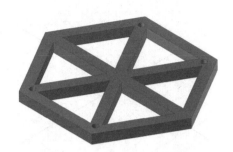

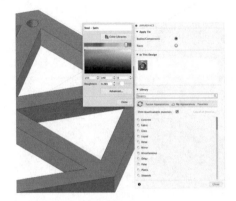

Press A for Appearance and double-click on the Steel-Satin appearance icon.

Move the color slider to change the Body's color. If you have a 3D printer, add a color of the filament you have on hand.

Make a Sketch on the Front Plane. Verify you are on the correct plane if the View Cube reads FRONT.

Press P for Project and select the highlighted face in the picture. Press OK. You should now see 4 purple points on each corner of this face.

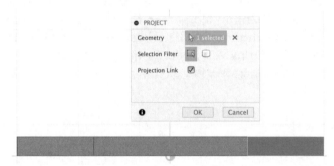

Press L for Line, and move your cursor to Body's top horizontal edge until an X appears.

The X means that any line that is made will be coincidently attached to the Body.

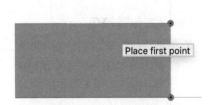

Roughly draw this shape with 5 lines and press the Esc key to deselect the Line tool.

Verify it is an enclosed profile by placing your cursor inside the shape; this profile should turn blue.

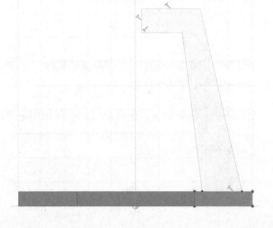

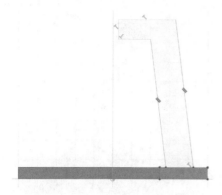

Select the Parallel constraint tool and click both angled lines. The order of your clicks doesn't matter.

Verify the top left lines have T-shaped Perpendicular constraint icons.

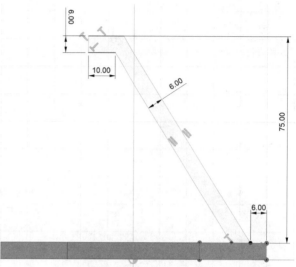

Add the following dimensions to the sketch.

Test the sketch by clicking and dragging the top left point; it should only be able to shift left and right.

Note the blue lines in the sketch meaning it is undefined.

Navigate to Create >> Point, move your cursor to the bottom horizontal line until you see a triangle, and click.

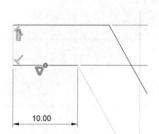

This triangle icon denotes that the Point is at the midpoint of the line.

Click the Horizontal Constraint tool and select this Point and the Origin.

This Sketch should be fully defined. Click Finish Sketch.

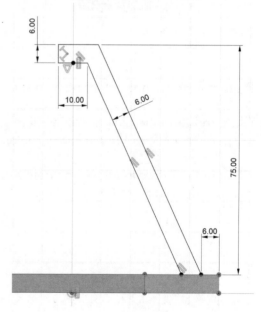

Click the house icon above the View Cube to get an isometric view.

Press E for Extrude and select the profile.

Change the Direction to Symmetric, change the Measurement to Whole Length, and set the Distance to 6 mm.

Press OK to make the Arm of the project.

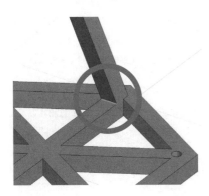

Navigate to Modify >> Chamfer, select the arm's inner corner, set it to 20 mm, and click OK.

This will add material to strengthen the 3D print.

Orbit to the underside of the project by holding down Shift, clicking and holding the scroll wheel, and moving your mouse. Zoom in the under-surface of the Arm.

Press H for Hole and select the face shown.

Click and drag the blue dot at the hole's center to snap to the white dot at the face's center.

Change the Extent to All, set the hole's diameter to 3.5 mm, and Press OK.

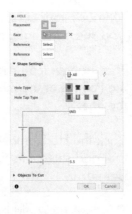

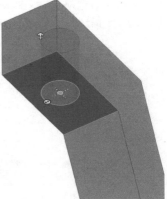

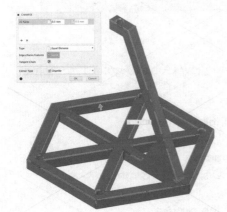

Click the house icon above the View Cube to get an isometric view of the Body.

Highlight the entire project, select Modify >> Chamfer, and change the dimension to 0.5 mm.

These chamfers will make screwing in the bolts easier and make the entire project stronger.

Save this File to the 1 - Fundamentals Folder as Tensegrity Tower.

Right-click Body1 in the Bodies section in the Browser, and click Save as Mesh.

If your favorite slicer software of choice is Cura, check the Send to 3D Print Utility box, select Cura, and click OK. This will open the Cura program and automatically import your model into the workspace.

3D print 2 copies of this parts with solid infill and support material.

Cut 5 pieces of fishing line to pass through the 5 sets of holes and screw in 10x M3x6 bolts through all the holes to secure the fishing line in place.

If the bolts cut the fishing line, add another 0.5mm to the hole diameter and reprint the parts.

Trim the excess fishing line and place objects on top to make the project float in thin air.

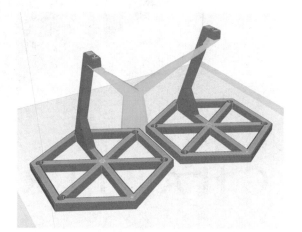

CHALLENGE

Model a simple Domino. This object can be made by extruding a rectangle, making a new Sketch on the front face, cutting in the pips and lines, and adding fillets to the corners.

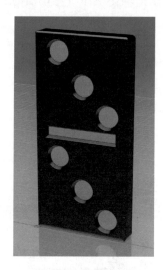

@ IAmKale
Discord User #990

CARABINER

CHAPTER 1

Design a 3D printed Carabiner that's as tough as it is versatile.

With 3D printing, you can refine every curve and detail, ensuring it's not just a tool, but a statement of innovation ready to tackle any challenge.

DIFFICULTY:
★☆☆☆☆

TIME ESTIMATE:
1 HOURS

KEY LEARNING:
- Basics of making functional projects
- Sweeping Tool
- Extrude Cutting

DISCORD LINK:
Discord.gg/5hbt6xDPqf

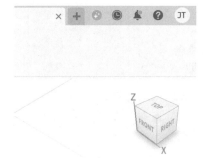

If continuing from a previous project, click + at the top to make a new tab.

This project will primarily use the Sweep tool to make a 3D Body. Sweeping is a design tool that traces a profile along a path, like tracing a circle along a coil to make a spring or a hexagon along an L shape to make an Allen key.

Start by verifying that your Units are set to mm. Projects you plan to 3D print should almost always be designed in mm, so you don't have to deal with strange scaling factors when using other units.

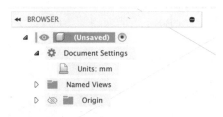

Navigate to Create >> Create Sketch, and select the Top Plane, which intersects the green Y-axis and red axes X-axis.

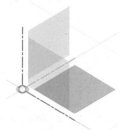

This project requires you to make a carabiner shape using the Line tool and a special trick, so let's practice before you start.

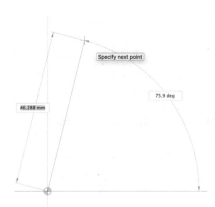

This trick allows you to make a series of lines and arcs connected to each other without switching back and forth between the Line tool and the Arc tool.

Type L, click on the Origin, move your cursor up to make a straight line, click and hold your left mouse button, and move your cursor to the right to make a tangent arc.

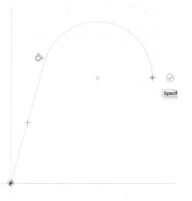

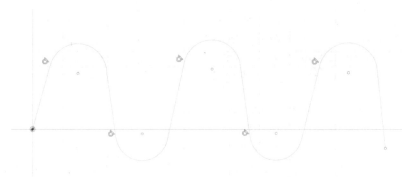

Repeat this trick a few times until you can successfully create this line-to-arc snake.

Once you have done this, press Esc to deselect the Line tool, highlight the entire sketch, and press Delete to clear the workspace.

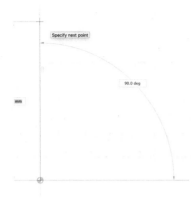

Type L for Line, click on the Origin, and move your cursor up to see the blue vertical constraint preview icon next to the line.

Click and hold your left mouse button, move your cursor over to the left to automatically make a tangent arc, and release your mouse to place the end point of the top arc.

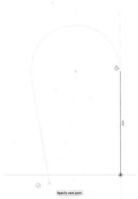

Move your cursor below and to the left of the Origin to make another straight line, click and hold to make another arc, move your cursor to the Origin, and release.

Notice that there are Tangent constraint icons on the top right and bottom left endpoints.

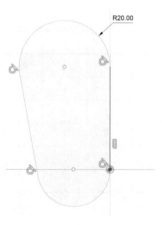

You need to add Tangent constraints to the other 2 endpoints. Navigate to Constraints >> Tangent, click on the top arc, then the left line, then click on the bottom arc, and then the right line.

Verify that there is a Tangent constraint icon on each of the 4 endpoints.

Press D for Dimensions, click the top arc, move your cursor up, click again to place the dimension, type 20, and press Enter.

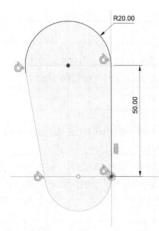

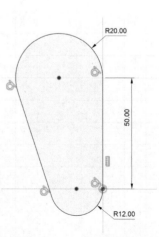

With the dimension tool still highlighted, click on the right line, move your cursor to the right, click again, type 50, and press Enter.

Click the bottom arc, move your cursor down, click again, type 12, and press Enter.

Navigate to your Browser and click on the triangle next to Sketches. You should see a red padlock icon to the left of "Sketch 1" to signify that the sketch is fully defined. If you see a pencil icon, then something in your sketch is undefined.

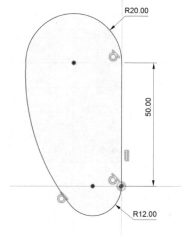

A common problem when making this sketch is that one line can accidentally be drawn as an large diameter arc, which has the appearance of a straight line.

Navigate to Create >> Slot >> Center to Center Slot. Click on the bottom arc's center point, trace your cursor along the bottom arc until it snaps to the midpoint (denoted with a blue triangle), click to define the slot's length, move your cursor to the right, and click again to define the slot's width.

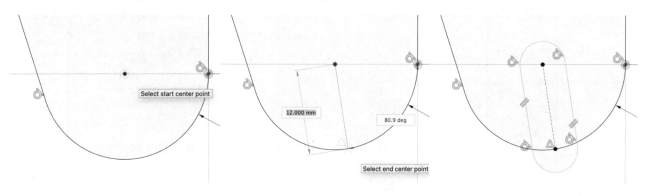

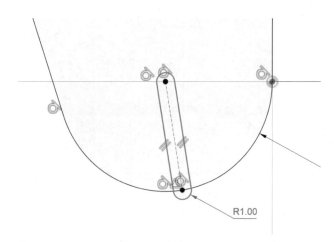

Press D for Dimension, click on the slot's bottom arc, move your cursor away, click again, type 1, and press Enter to set the slot's radius.

1 mm radius also equals a 2 mm Slot width.

This slot will remove some material from the Carabiner's inner surface so it can flex better without breaking, but one slot isn't enough.

Navigate to Create >> Circular Pattern. Click on the slot's 2 lines and 2 arcs. Verify the Dialog Box reads "4 Selected" next to Objects.

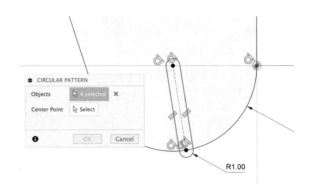

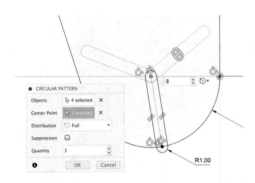

Click "Select" next to Center Point and click on the slot's top center point. This will give you a preview of 3 slots patterned around this point.

In the Dialog Box, change the Quantity to 8 and check Suppression. This will add check marks to each slot, allowing you to hide the slots you don't need.

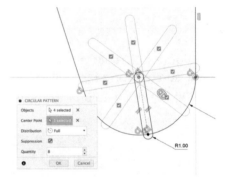

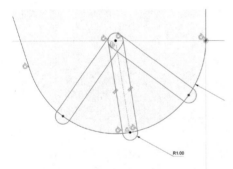

Uncheck the top 5 check-boxes and click OK.

Press Finish Sketch.

Click the house icon on the View Cube to get an isometric view and start a new Sketch on the Front Plane, which intersects the blue Z-axis and the red axes X-axis.

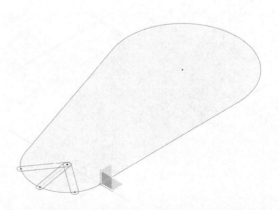

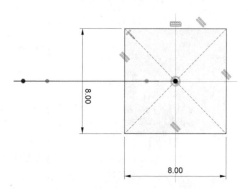

Navigate to Create >> Rectangle >> Center Rectangle. Click on the Origin, move your cursor up and to the right, type 8, the Tab key, 8, and Enter.

Now, you have a profile and a path to use the Sweep tool. Click Finish Sketch.

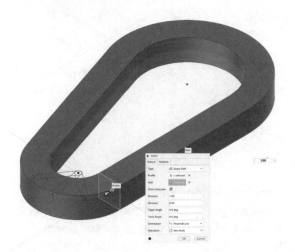

Navigate to Create >> Sweep. Select the square profile made in the previous sketch.

Click "Select" next to Path and click on the Carabiner shape from Sketch 1, not the slots. Click OK.

For this to be a working Carabiner, you need a latch mechanism that allows it to spring open and then snap closed.

Navigate to Create >> Create Sketch and select the Top Plane, not the Carabiner's top face, which intersects with the green and red axes.

Type P for Project, click on the left and right vertical lines of the top surface, and click OK.

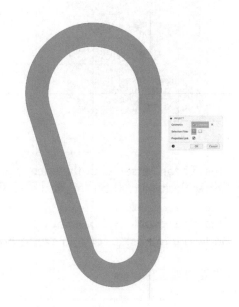

Verify you selected the correct lines by orbiting to an angled view to see 2 purple lines that have been projected from the top surface of the Body onto the Top Plane.

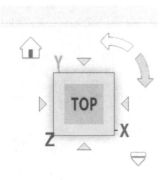

Click TOP on the View Cube to return to a top-down view.

If your View is sideways, hover your cursor over the View Cube and click on the rotation arrows to turn your view 90 degrees.

Press L for Line and click on the top left purple projected point.

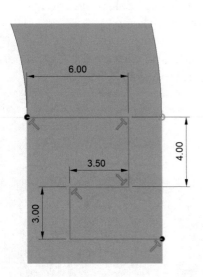

Move your cursor horizontally to the right, type 6, click, move your cursor down vertically, type 4, click, move your cursor to the left horizontally, type 3.5, click, move your cursor down vertically, type 3, click, move your cursor to the right horizontally and click on the right edge.

Press O for Offset, click the lines, change the Offset Position to 0.5 mm, and click OK.

This inner profile will be cut away from the Body in a later step for a latch mechanism.

Click Finish Sketch.

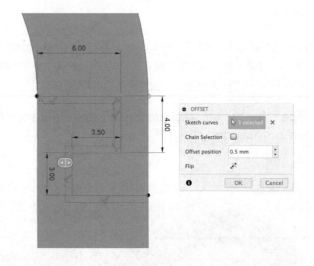

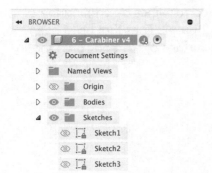

Look at the Sketches in the Browser and notice that all 3 sketches now have a red padlock, meaning they are all defined and ready to proceed to the next step.

Click the Eye Icon on Sketch 3 to turn it off.

Navigate to Modify >> Chamfer and orbit your view to the underside of the Carabiner by holding down the Shift key and your mouse's scroll wheel and moving your mouse.

Select the bottom face, set the chamfer distance to 2 mm, and click OK.

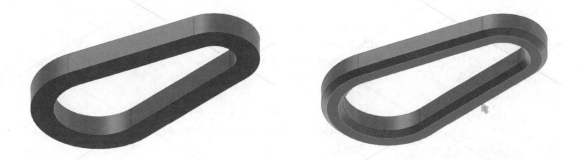

Orbit to a top view of the Carabiner. Navigate to Modify >> Fillet and select the chamfer's top edge and the Carabiner's top face. The Dialog Box should read "1 Face, 4 Edges". Set the dimension to 4 mm and click OK.

When 3D printing, you want a substantially flat surface touching the build plate so the part doesn't break away mid-print, leading to the deliciously named fatal error of 3D Printing: Spaghetti-ing.

Carabiners need to be smooth and rounded. If they had a perfect circular profile all the way around, they would build up pressure and break. Adding chamfers to the bottom and fillets to the top and side walls gives you the best of both worlds.

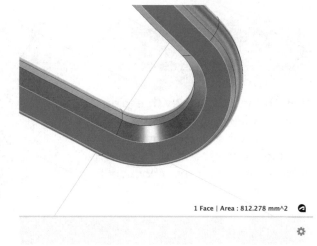

1 Face | Area : 812.278 mm^2

In fact, you can click on the model's flat underside and see that the area has been calculated for you in the bottom right corner to be 812.278 mm ^ 2. This value will decrease slightly as we cut away the latch and spring mechanic next, but it is a good final estimation.

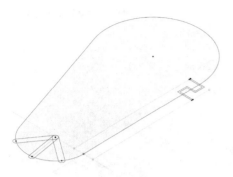

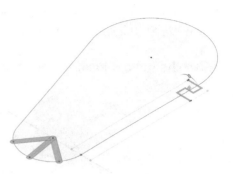

Expand Sketches in the Browser and turn on Sketch 1 and 3. Click the Eye Icon next to Bodies to Hide the Carabiner Body.

Press E for Extrude and click on all the profiles that make up the latch profile and the 3 slots.

In the Dialog Box, set the Direction to Symmetric, click the Eye Icon next to Bodies in the Browser to show the Body, and set the Extent Type to All.

Because the profiles are now extruding into the Carabiner's Body, the Operation is changed to Cut, displayed as a red transparent operation on the model. Click OK.

The reason you hid the Body and then turned it back on was because the sketches were inside it, which would make it hard to select the necessary profiles to extrude. Finally, click the Eye Icon next to Sketches to Hide them.

To smooth over the spring mechanism's sharp edges, navigate to Modify >> Fillet, click the 3 inner surfaces of the spring, set the radius to 0.4 mm, and click OK.

Click the Save icon in the top left corner. Save the name as Carabiner in the 1 - Fundamentals Folder.

CHALLENGE

Make a Mobius Strip by Sweeping a center rectangle at the Origin about a circle that runs through the rectangle's center with a 180-degree Twist Angle. Add 2 mm chamfers to the 2 edges.

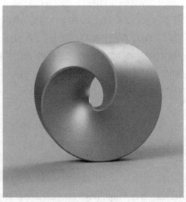

@ GhostPepper
Discord User #540

@ Merlwynd
Discord User #385

CHAPTER 1 QUESTIONS

1. Transitioning from a 2D Sketch to a 3D Body would require a tool from the _____ menu?

    a. Create

    b. Modify

    c. Sketch

    d. Utility

2. A red padlock icon next to your Sketch in the Browser ensures that it is...?

    a. A broken Sketch

    b. Workable but about to be broken

    c. Fully Defined

    d. Over Defined

3. The ring icon in the Extrude tool does what?

    a. Rotates the direction of extrusion

    b. Makes circular extrusions

    c. Changes taper angles

    d. All of the above

4. To pattern 2D geometry about a central point, you would choose the _____ Pattern tool?

    a. Rectangular

    b. Circular

    c. Along a Path

    d. Axial

5. What is the Extrude tool's shortcut?

    a. X

    b. E

    c. Shift+ ^

    d. Shift+E

6. Constraining the center of a circle to the Origin would require a...?

    a. Concentric constraint

    b. Horizontal / Vertical constraint

    c. Cocentric constraint

    d. Coincident constraint

7. How would you edit a dimension?

    a. Double click the dimension value

    b. Right-click the dimension value

    c. Single click the dimension value

    d. You cannot edit dimension values

8. To see the previous steps of the project build, navigate to the...?

    a. Browser

    b. Data Panel

    c. Timeline

    d. Navigation Bar

9. Before making the first sketch, you must first...?

    a. Select a plane

    b. Set a dimension Unit

    c. Draw geometries

    d. Open the dimension tool

10. To change Dimension Units, you would navigate to...?

    a. Data Panel

    b. Workspace Navigator

    c. Browser

    d. Navigation Bar

CHAPTER 2
MECHANICAL DESIGN

THE BASICS OF DESIGN USING
MANUFACTURING PRINCIPLES

- PLAY BRICKS
- GEOCACHE HIDE

MECHANICAL DESIGN

The goal of designing a CAD model is often to create a digital representation of a manufacturable object. A mechanical design approach to CAD modeling considers tools, machines, tolerances, and technicians.

Making objects in the real world presents a few challenges. For example, a 1" pin will fit perfectly into a 1" hole in Autodesk Fusion, but not in the real world. A CAD modeler must add a small gap, known as a tolerance, to allow these parts to interface.

Machines and people also have limitations on how they can produce a part. For example, communicating your project with others requires more foresight and organization. This includes but is not limited to the following:

- Naming Features, Sketches, and Bodies
- Organizing Sketches and Dimensions
- Limiting the number of features in the Timeline

In this chapter, you will learn how to make models using real-world Dimensions, Fillets, Chamfers, and other mechanical design principles as if you or someone you know will make the object in real life.

PLAY
BRICKS

CHAPTER 2

Plastic building toys have inspired engineers and makers for decades. At first glance, they appear simple.

However, there are many subtle design features that make them more complex than meets the eye.

DIFFICULTY:

★★☆☆☆

TIME ESTIMATE:
2 HOURS

KEY LEARNING:

- Rectangular patterns
- Shell a part to turn a solid body into a thin-walled part
- Add draft angles for PIM

DISCORD LINK:
Discord.gg/5hbt6xDPqf

INTRODUCTION

Simple building toys are often the spark that leads people to pursue careers in engineering and manufacturing. Often, plastic building blocks, although simple, contain ingenious plastic engineering secrets that make them infinitely reconfigurable and easy to manufacture. In this build, you will explore the world of plastic manufacturing by learning about draft angles, wall thicknesses, tapers, and more.

CAD

Verify you are working in Millimeters (mm).

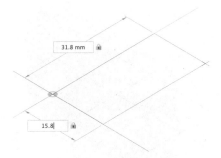

The basic geometry of the PLAY brick is a rectangular box, and luckily, Fusion has a tool to make one quickly and efficiently without needing to sketch a rectangle and then extrude it into a box.

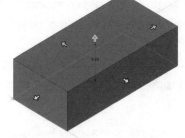

Navigate to Create >> Box, select the Top Plane, click the Origin, move your cursor to the right, type 31.8, press the Tab key, type 15.8, press Enter, type 9.6, and click OK.

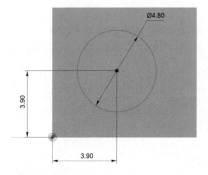

Create a new Sketch on the top surface of the box. Press C for circle and make a small circle in the bottom left corner of the rectangle. Dimension this circle to 4.8 mm in diameter. Position it 3.9 mm above the Origin and 3.9 mm to the right of the Origin. Finish the Sketch.

Reorient the model to get an isometric view and extrude this circle 1.8 mm upwards.

Now, you will add draft angles. A draft angle makes removing plastic parts from the mold easy by giving the edges a taper and reducing friction between the mold and the part.

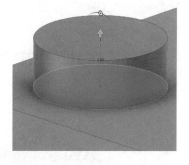

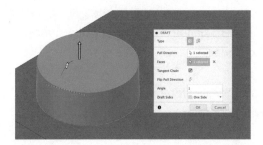

Navigate to Modify >> and click Draft. Select the top face of the cylinder as the Pull Direction, the curved surface as the Face, set the angle to 1 degree, and press OK.

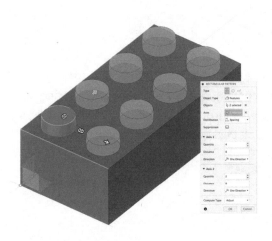

Navigate to Create >> Pattern >> and select the Rectangular Pattern tool.

Change the Object Type to Features. Navigate to the Timeline and select the most recent Extrude and the Draft features. Objects should state 2 selected.

For Axes, select the brick's length and width. Click and drag the blue arrows to see how this tool makes a grid of the features selected. Set the Distribution to Spacing instead of Extent.

Set Axis 1 to a Quantity of 4 and set Distance to 8 mm. Set Axis 2 to a Quantity of 2 and a Distance of 8 mm. This will give you a 4 x 2 grid of evenly spaced cylinders.

Note this may be reversed depending on the order you clicked on the length and width of the brick. If your cylinders are replicated in the wrong direction, add a negative sign (-) to the Distance value.

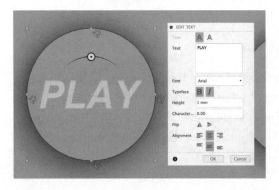

Navigate to Modify >> and select Shell. Select the bottom face, set the Inside Thickness to 1.2 mm, and press OK.

Start a sketch on top of the circle and make a text box around the circle. Type any 4-letter word of your choosing, select **bold** and *italic*, set the height to 1 mm, and select middle and center alignment. Press OK. Apply a Tangent constraint between each line of the rectangular text box and the circle. Add a Horizontal Constraint to the top line.

Extrude the text up 0.1 mm. Note that you don't want to click the entire top circle, just the text.

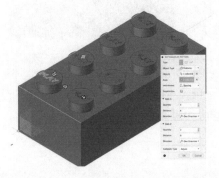

Using the same Rectangular Pattern Settings as above, pattern the Text Extrude feature to the 8 cylinders.

This operation was done in a separate step as the Shell operation can often crash when analyzing complex surfaces found in the text.

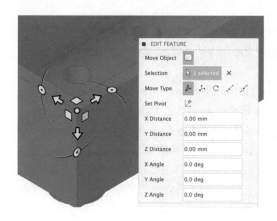

The rest of the design for this project will be made on the bottom face of the PLAY Brick. Because the "lighting" in the software comes down from above, sketching on the underside of a part can be a little hard due to the shadows.

The solution is to rotate the part 180 degrees, finish the design, and finally rotate it back into the correct orientation.

Type M for the Move tool, expand Bodies in the Browser, click on Body 1, change the Y Angle to 180, and click OK.

Start a new Sketch on the current top face of the Body that is highlighted in the picture.

The geometry on this face will be extruded down, but this part could also be designed by sketching on the bottom face of the shelled surface and extruding up.

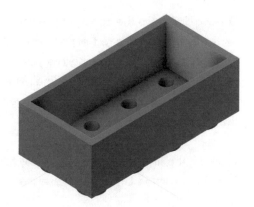

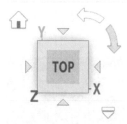

If your sketch is in the vertical orientation instead of the horizontal view as in the pictures, move your cursor to the View Cube and notice the two curved arrows in the top right corner that you can click to rotate the sketch's view 90 degrees.

Draw 3 sets of 2 Concentric circles as shown. Apply an Equal constraint to the 3 outer circles by holding down Ctrl/Cmd, clicking the perimeter of each circle, and then selecting the Equal constraint.

Repeat this process for the 3 smaller circles.

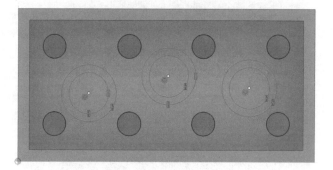

Navigate to Create >> Point, move your cursor along the left vertical line until you see a triangle denoting the midpoint of that line, and click to place a Point.

Hold down Ctrl/Cmd, click on this Point and the 3 circle's centers, and select the Horizontal/Vertical constraint.

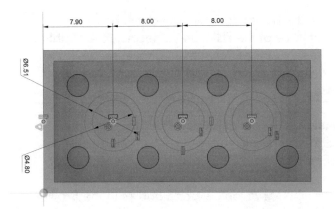

Dimension the outer circles' diameters to 6.51 mm and the inner circles' diameters to 4.8 mm.

Set the distance between the left and middle circles to 8 mm and the distance from the right to the middle circle to 8 mm. Set the distance from the left circle to the left vertical line to 7.9 mm.

Draw a line from the center of the middle circle vertically downwards to the first horizontal line below. You should see a triangle next to your mouse icon, indicating the midpoint of that line. Make another line from the middle circle's center to the left and click on the midpoint.

Click on the lines and press the X key to turn them into Construction Lines. You'll use these 2 new lines as Mirror Lines.

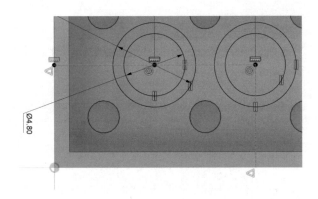

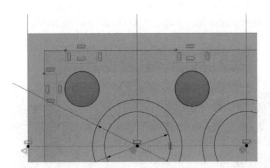

Draw 3 rectangles as shown in the picture. Use the Equal tool to set all lengths and widths equal. Note that this may be tricky due to hidden Constraints in Autodesk Fusion. Dimension these rectangles to be 0.2 x 0.6 mm.

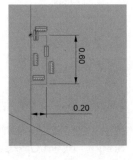

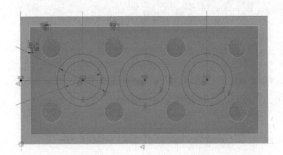

Press P for Project and select the entire inside face, highlighted in blue. Click OK.

This will add a projected purple point at the center of the circles, and you will use these points to line up the 2 rectangles.

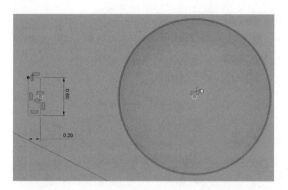

Use the Point tool, and click on the midpoint of each of the 0.6 mm lines of the 3 rectangles. Select the Horizontal/Vertical constraint and click a Point and the circle's center. Do this for the other 2 rectangles. This will align the center of the rectangles with the center of the circles.

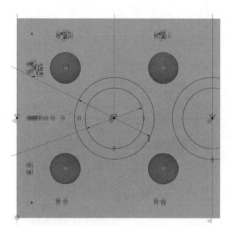

Use the Mirror tool to select all 3 rectangle's edges as the Objects and the Horizontal Construction Line as the Mirror Line, and press OK.

Repeat this process with the Original 3 rectangles and the 3 newly made rectangles and select the Vertical Construction Line as the Mirror Line.

You should now have 12 rectangles.

Finish the Sketch, click the house icon on the View Cube, and type E for Extrude.

Extrude all 12 rectangles and the 3 circular ring profiles -8.4 mm. Verify the Operation is set to Join and press OK.

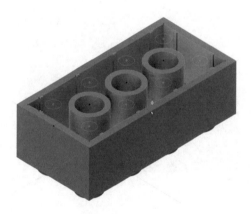

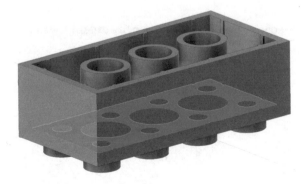

Start a new Sketch on the bottom surface of the inside of the block.

Draw a Vertical Construction Line in the middle of the brick. Draw 2 vertical lines to the left of the Construction Line that touch the outer circle and add a Collinear constraint to these 2 lines.

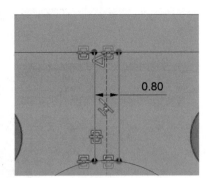

Mirror these 2 lines about the Vertical Construction Line and dimension them to be 0.80 mm apart.

Press P for Project and select the middle circle's ring profile and outer rectangular profile.

Click the area inside to verify you have 2 enclosed profiles.

Extrude the top and bottom profiles up 6.3 mm. Verify that the Operation is set to Join and press OK.

This may be a negative number, depending on your view and orientation.

Type A to open the Appearance tool and search for "red plastic", click and drag Plastic - Glossy (Red) onto the part.

Orbit around the part to see the reflections off the glossy surface.

Select the Draft tool, click the top of the circles as the Pull Direction, and all inner surfaces except for the small rectangular extrusions as the Faces. Change the Angle to 1 degree. The Dialog Box should read 23 faces.

This doesn't look like an important step, but this is part of the genius behind plastic engineering. The plastic building bricks must be perfectly square on the outside but requires angles on the interior to relieve pressure while being pulled from the mold. Interior angles allow the best of both worlds—the correct draft angle and the square outsides.

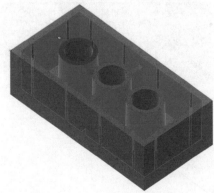

Type M for the Move tool, click on Body 1 in the Browser, and set the Y Angle to 180 degrees to rotate it back to the correct orientation. Notice that although it is rotated correctly, it is not in the correct location.

In the Dialog Box, click on Point to Point, click on a bottom corner of the PLAY Brick, click on the Eye next to Origin in the Browser, and click on the Origin. Click OK. The Move tool's options can look a little intimidating to beginners, but most of the Move commands you will use in this course are simple rotation and Point to Point moves.

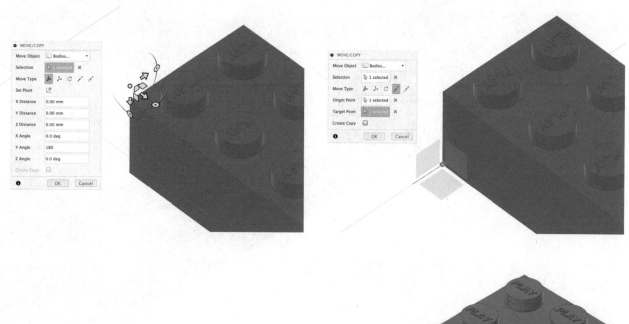

And you are done!

CHALLENGE

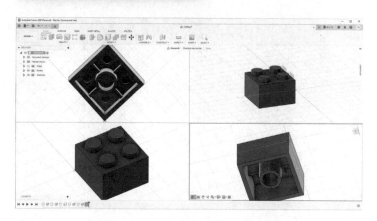

Using these same principles, design another Plastic Construction Brick, such as a 1x4 or 2x2. Apply a different color to it. You may need to research the underside of these bricks to make them accurately.

@ Steel Monkey

User #304

GEOCACHE HIDE

CHAPTER 2

Join the worlds largest treasure hunt and design a 3D printable Geocache hide container.

By adding threads, knurls, and chunky walls, this container should last years through all weather conditions.

DIFFICULTY:
★★☆☆☆

TIME ESTIMATE:
2 HOURS

KEY LEARNING:
- Work with multiple bodies at the same time
- Add a thread or knurl to a part
- Emboss text into a surface
- Emboss an SVG

DISCORD LINK:
Discord.gg/5hbt6xDPqf

INTRODUCTION

Geocaching® is an international treasure-hunting sport that uses GPS and coordinates to hunt for camouflaged hidden containers in urban and rural areas.

In this class, you will learn how to make a 2-piece threaded container that can be 3D printed and screws together easily. While this may sound simple, there are a few design considerations you need to make to ensure your threads unscrew and screw easily. Without enough clearance between the mating threads, the 3D-printed container will not screw together. You will also add a textured grippy surface called a knurl to aid in unscrewing.

In addition, this container will be thicker than most common containers since Geocaching® containers need to survive months or years outside in the elements.

CAD

Verify your Units are set to Millimeters (mm).

Unlike previous examples, you will create a Cylinder instead of drawing a circle and extruding it. You can use the premade geometries in the Create menu for simple shapes like cylinders, boxes, torus, and spheres.

Navigate to Create >> and select the Cylinder tool, select the Top Plane, set the Diameter to 33 mm, the Height to 16 mm, and press OK.

Navigate to the Browser, expand the Bodies tab, double-click on Body1, and rename it Bottom Screw.

When working on projects, it is generally a good idea to name each Body to stay organized.

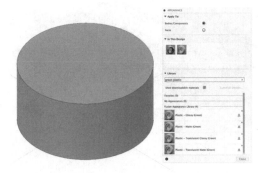

Most Geocache Hides need to be camouflaged to be hidden in plain sight from Muggles (non-Geocaching folk). An easy way to do this is to 3D print this container in a color that matches the surroundings of where you want to hide it. In most cases, green prints blend in very well with the environment. Type A for the Appearance tool, search "Green Plastic", and add Plastic - Glossy (Green) to the cylinder.

Navigate to Modify >> Chamfer, click the top edge of the cylinder, type 3, and click OK.

Navigate to Create >> Thread, select the cylindrical face, check Modeled, and click OK.

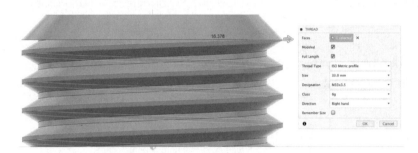

A common mistake beginners make is to chamfer the top edge of a cylinder, add the thread, and then leave it. Unfortunately, as can see, this makes a part that has no entry to the thread and cannot be screwed in.

In the Timeline, click the Thread feature and drag it before the Chamfer feature. Orbit around the chamfered edge to see the start of the thread in the chamfer.

If done correctly, you should be able to see the start of the thread come to a point inside the chamfered surface.

Male and female threads that are exactly the same size will never screw into each other, there needs to be a small gap between the two parts to allow them to screw together firmly. It is almost always easier to do this operation on the male thread since it is easier to access.

Navigate to Modify >> Offset Faces, click the 4 faces of the thread, type -0.25, and click OK.

To make the cavity inside this part for the logbook and maybe a small trinket, navigate to Create >> Cylinder, click the top flat surface to define the plane, click on the Origin, move your cursor away, type 25, press Enter, type -16 and press Enter to cut away a cylinder.

Navigate to Create >> and select Cylinder. Click the bottom of your Body, click its Origin, pull your cursor away, and click.

Set the circle's Diameter to 40 mm in Diameter and either -8 mm or +8 mm in thickness so that it Extrudes away from your other Body.

Now you'll add some grip to the screw cap known as a knurl.

Navigate to Create >> and select Coil. Move your view to the underside of the part. Click the bottom face, select its Origin, and enter 40 mm for Diameter. A red coil and a large Dialog Box will pop up.

Add the following settings:

Type: Revolution and Height
Diameter: 40 mm
Revolutions: 0.1
Height: -10 mm
Angle: 0.0 degrees
Section: Triangle (Internal)
Section Position: Inside
Section Size: 1.0 mm
Operation: Cut

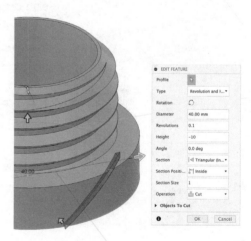

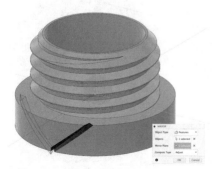

Navigate to Create >> and select Mirror for a 3D Mirror feature. Set the Type to Features and then select the Coil feature in the Timeline.

Use the Front or the Right Plane as the Mirror Plane and click OK. You may need to hide the Body to make this easier.

Navigate to Create >> Pattern >> and select Circular Pattern.
Change the Type to Features. Select the Coil and the Mirror feature in
the Timeline.

Select the Z-axis for Axis. Change the Quantity to 25 and press OK.

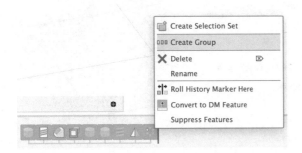

Compress the Timeline to clean it up before moving on.
Select the first feature in the Timeline, hold down the Shift
key, and select the last feature to highlight all the steps.
Right-click and select Create Group to merge them all.
You can always click the small plus sign (+) to expand
this group or the small minus sign (-) to collapse it.

Turn off the part by expanding the Bodies tab in the Browser and clicking the Eye Icon next to Bottom
Screw to Hide the Body.

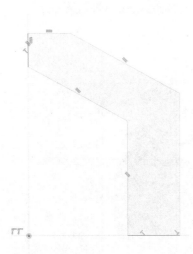

Start a new Sketch on the Front Plane
and draw this shape. Apply a Coincident
constraint between the left vertical line and
the Origin, as well as the bottom horizontal
line and the Origin.

Add a Parallel constraint between the 2
angled lines.

Add the dimensions listed in the picture
and Finish the Sketch.

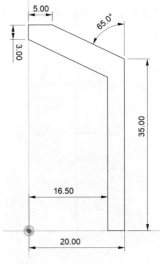

Revolve this profile around the Z-axis and name
this part Top Cap in the Browser.

Add the same green color appearance to this
new Body.

Type F for Fillet, and add 3 mm fillets to the top
2 outer edges.

Click on the Front, Right, Bottom corner of the View Cube, navigate to Modify >> Chamfer, click the inner bottom edge, type 2, and click OK.

Without changing your view, select the Thread tool, click the inner surface below the Origin, check Modeled, uncheck Full Length, set the Length to 18 mm, and click OK.

Click and drag the Thread features in the Timeline before the chamfer. Notice that the start of the thread should now come to a point inside the chamfer.

Start a new Sketch on the Front Plane and use the Line tool to draw the sketch shown in the picture.

Apply a Coincident constraint between the left vertical line and the workspace Origin. Apply a Parallel constraint between the 2 angled lines. Add all the dimensions shown. Mirror this sketch about the left vertical line.

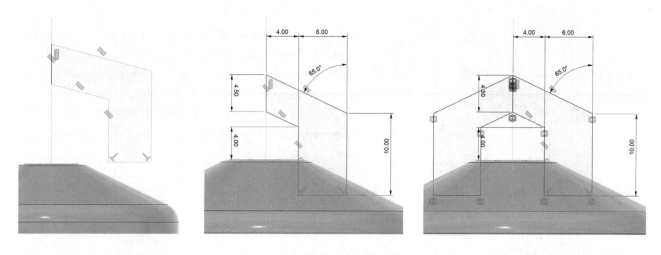

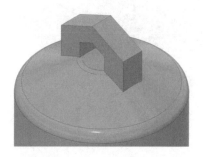

Extrude this profile Symmetrically, change the Measurement to Whole Length, set the Distance to 6 mm, and change the Operation to Join. Press OK.

Apply 0.75 mm fillets to the outer 6 faces to eliminate sharp edges on the part.

To add writing to your container, you will use the Emboss tool by projecting text from an Offset Plane.

Navigate to Construct >> Offset Plane and set it to be -30 mm from the Front Plane and press OK.

Create a new Sketch on this Offset Plane, select the Text tool, and make a text box in front of the cylindrical face of the Top Cap.

Type these words: "UNSCREW CAP OFFICIAL GEOCACHE." Change the Font to Stencil or Impact and set the Height to 7.5 mm. Center and middle align the text, and press OK. You can grab and move the text in whatever location you like.

Navigate to Create >> and select the Emboss tool. Select the text as the Sketch Profile and the cylindrical face as the Face. –Set the depth to 0.75 mm and press OK.

It is good practice in 3D printing to emboss text outwards instead of recessing it into the model on vertical walls. By having text that is proud of the surface, it only adds a tiny amount of material to the entire print. Inversely, if you wanted recessed text, you would need to add more thickness to the entire Body except for the area that has text.

In addition to text, you can also emboss graphics and logos.

Create a new Offset Plane 30 mm from the Front Plane and click OK. Verify this plane is on the opposite side of the embossed text on the front of the Body.

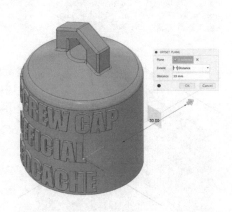

You will add the Geocache Logo to the back of this project by using an SVG (Scalable Vector Graphic). This is a file type used in graphic design that can scaled up without losing quality because it is made of mathematical curves, not pixels like a picture. You can find it in the **FREE DOWNLOAD** tab at **CADclass.org**.

Create a new Sketch on the new Offset Plane and verify the View Cube reads BACK.

Navigate to Insert >> Insert SVG, Insert from Computer, and select the downloaded .SVG file.

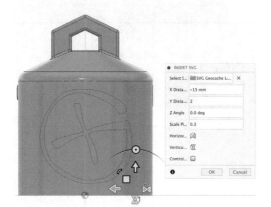

Change the Scale Plane XY to 0.3, click Horizontal Flip and Vertical Flip, set the X Distance to -15 mm and the Y Distance to 2 mm, click OK, and Finish Sketch.

This should put the Geocache® logo in the correct orientation and centralized over the cylindrical face.

In the same process as the Text, select the Emboss tool in the Create menu, select the logo as the Sketch Profile and the cylindrical face as the Face, emboss this logo to 0.75 mm, and click OK.

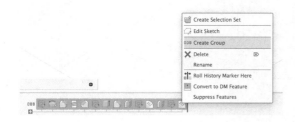

Select all Features in the Timeline that make up the Top Cap, right-click, and click Create Group.

Navigate to Inspect >> Section Analysis to visually cut the project in half to see inside it.

Depending on where you clicked when you made the threads, they may not line up perfectly. The starting point of the threads is randomized, so to some, they will look perfect; to others, they will intersect with each other. Regardless, it doesn't matter as they will screw together perfectly in real life.

To turn this view off, click the Eye Icon next to Analysis in the Browser.

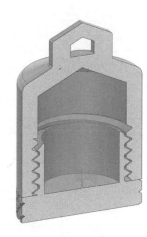

Now, you will export these for 3D printing. Because this file has two Bodies, you cannot just export the entire file as an STL.

Right-click on a Body in the Browser and click Save As Mesh. Select STL Binary format with High Refinement, and press OK to save it. Repeat this process for the other Body.

Your files are now ready to be sliced and 3D printed. Happy printing!

CHALLENGE

Make a custom Geocache® Hide that can be camouflaged to look like an everyday object. A popular hide is a container shaped like an acorn or a bolt. Post this hide and its coordinates on **Geocaching.com.**

@Raluca A
User #794

CHAPTER 2 QUESTIONS

1. Which is an example of a correct metric thread identifier?

    a. 33m

    b. 33M

    c. M33

    d. m33

2. True or False? Text can be sketched on curved and flat surfaces.

3. To turn a Construction Line or Arc into a Sketch Line or Sketch Arc, you would select the geometry, a type … ?

    a. X

    b. Shift+X

    c. C

    d. Shift+C

4. An appearance that is not simply a solid color is known as a…?

    a. Picture Appearance

    b. Decal Appearance

    c. Texture Appearance

    d. Roughness Appearance

5. RGB stands for?

    a. Roughness, Gradience, Blankness

    b. Revolve, Ground, Boundary

    c. Roughness, Gradience, Bump Map

    d. Red, Green, Blue

6. Knurls are … ?

    a. Small hardware similar to nuts

    b. Texture on metal parts used for grip

    c. A defect on the surface of a metal part

    d. Plastic clumps used to make 3D-printed filament

7. A common draft angle in plastic injection molding is …?

    a. 1 degree

    b. 45 degrees

    c. 15 degrees

    d. 10 degrees

8. What is the most common file type for 3D Printing?

    a. 3MF

    b. OBJ

    c. DXF

    d. STL

9. What is the purpose of an Offset on a threaded surface?

    a. It is purely aesthetic

    b. Better printing quality

    c. Allows the threads to screw into each other

    d. To change the thread pitch

10. Compressing multiple Features in the Timeline is accessed by highlighting the Features in the Timeline and … ?

    a. Right-click

    b. Double-click

    c. Left-click

    d. Press C for compress

CHAPTER 3
PARAMETRIC DESIGN

HOW TO CUSTOMIZE YOUR DESIGNS
WITH DIMENSIONS AND PARAMETERS

- METRIC BOLTS
- PROTOTYPE DRONE

PARAMETRIC DESIGN

There are a handful of CAD milestones that separate the beginner from the intermediate modeler. One of those milestones is parametric modeling. For many CAD designers, parametric modeling is a game changer.

Until now, you've entered dimensions manually for each line, angle, or plane in your models. If you need to make changes to your model, you're stuck having to either redo it or make individual edits to each dimension. This works for simple designs with a limited number of dimensions but can quickly get out of hand in more complex models with hundreds or thousands of dimensions.

Parametric modeling allows you to attribute names, values, and equations to dimensions instead of a single number. These names, along with their corresponding values, define a parameter. Parameters store numerical information that can easily be changed, automatically updating the model.

For example, you can manually enter 20" for height and 10" for width to create the rectangles below. Or, you can create a 20" Height parameter and a 10" width parameter and apply them to all 3 rectangles. This way, if you need to change these dimensions later, you only need to edit Height and width, and the changes will automatically update the rectangles.

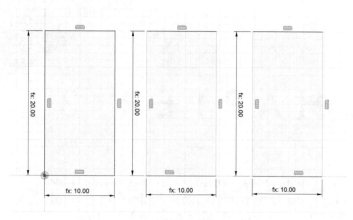

If you change the Height parameter to 30" and the Width parameter to 20", all 6 dimensions update, as shown.

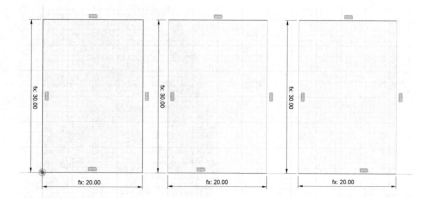

You're now 3-times more efficient. Not bad! If you were using traditional dimensions, you would need to individually change each one of these numbers. That's manageable for 3 rectangles, but what if you have 100? We hope you can see that it quickly gets out of hand.

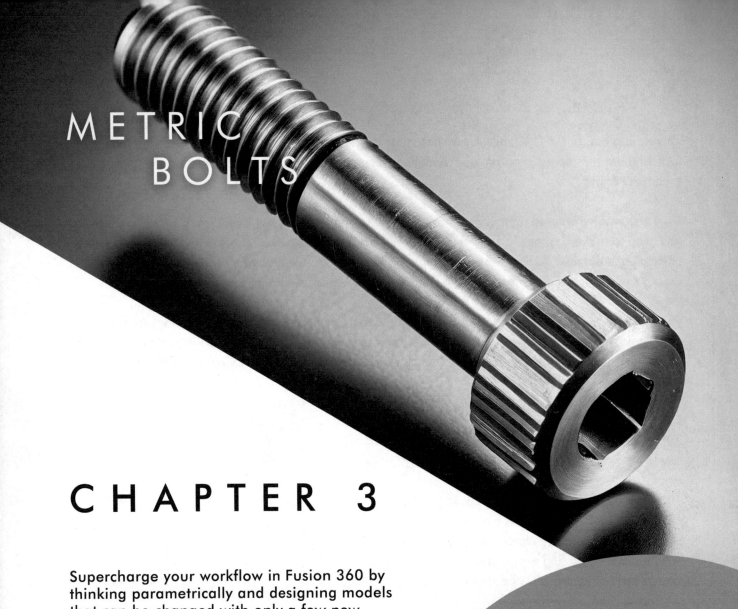

METRIC
BOLTS

CHAPTER 3

Supercharge your workflow in Fusion 360 by
thinking parametrically and designing models
that can be changed with only a few new
dimensions.

DIFFICULTY:

★★☆☆☆

TIME ESTIMATE:
1.5 HOURS

KEY LEARNING:

- Simplify a design parameters
- Add a partial thread to a body
- Where to find importable hardware
  online.

DISCORD LINK:
Discord.gg/5hbt6xDPqf

INTRODUCTION

Bolts are a standard piece of hardware with many variations, making them a great parametric modeling project. Instead of creating each bolt variation from scratch, you can create 1 bolt using parameters and then edit a few parameters to make an entirely new bolt instantaneously. In this lesson, you will parametrically model the commonly found M5x25 bolt and learn parametric design principles.

CAD

Navigate to Modify >> and select Change Parameters. Notice the 3 preset Parameters called Favorites, User, and Model Parameters. Model Parameters list every dimension in a project. User Parameters list all of your custom Parameters. Favorites are a quick list of Parameters you are likely to change often.

Click the plus sign (+) at the top of the Dialog Box, add t`he name, Head_Diam, and the Expression 8.5, and click OK.

Parametric names are case-sensitive and often have underscores to separate names.

An easy mistake is to add a space before a Name.

Add the following Parameters from this table to your User Parameters list.

Note that a Parameter's Expression may also contain another Parameter such as Thread Length always being half of the Shank Length Value.

Note that the last Parameter, Quantity does name have mm as its Unit. Because it is an amount, set the Unit to No Units.

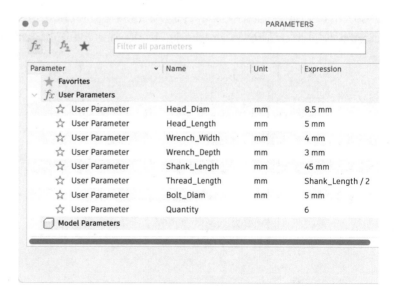

Parameter	Name	Unit	Expression
⭐ Favorites			
ƒx User Parameters			
☆ User Parameter	Head_Diam	mm	8.5 mm
☆ User Parameter	Head_Length	mm	5 mm
☆ User Parameter	Wrench_Width	mm	4 mm
☆ User Parameter	Wrench_Depth	mm	3 mm
☆ User Parameter	Shank_Length	mm	45 mm
☆ User Parameter	Thread_Length	mm	Shank_Length / 2
☆ User Parameter	Bolt_Diam	mm	5 mm
☆ User Parameter	Quantity		6
🗌 Model Parameters			

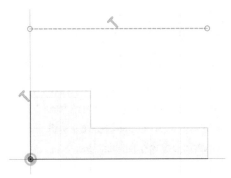

Create a new Sketch on the Front Plane and draw this profile on the horizontal and vertical axes.

Sketch a horizontal Construction line above the profile.

Use the Coincident constraint to constrain the Construction line's endpoints to the left and right edges of the bolt's profile.

Select the bottom horizontal line, click the Sketch Palette (+) symbol to expand it, and click Centerline next to Linetype.

This turns the bottom horizontal line into an Axis of revolution, so every time you dimension geometry to it, it will display the diameter instead of the radius.

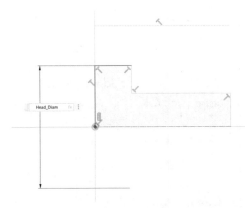

Dimension the top left horizontal line to the Centerline as the Parameter Head_Diam by pressing D for Dimension, selecting the 2 lines, pressing H, and selecting Head_Diam from the dropdown.

When you start typing a Parameter's name in a dimension box, it will only show the parameters that contain the letter you typed. For example, as you type H for Head_Length, it won't show "Bolt_Diam" or "Quantity".

Add the following sketch dimensions. Set the top left horizontal line to Head_Length=fx: 5.00, the middle horizontal line as Shank_Length=fx. 45.00, and the right vertical Parameter as Bolt_Diam=fx: 5.00.

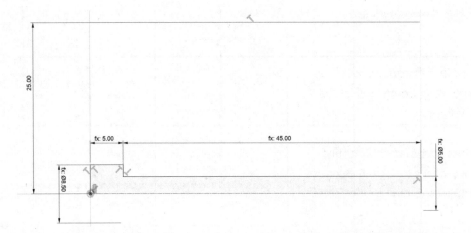

Select the Revolve tool. The Profile and Axis will automatically be selected because there is only 1 profile and a Centerline was set, click OK.

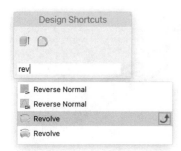

As you get more comfortable with the tools in Fusion, consider using the Search tool. For example, press the S key and type "rev". You can select the Revolve tool here instead of going into the menu. This can be especially useful for tools you don't use often.

Start a new Sketch on the bolt head. Draw a 6-sided polygon in the center and apply a Horizontal/Vertical constraint to the top edge.

Add the Wrench_Width=fx: 4.00 to the edge-to-edge dimension.

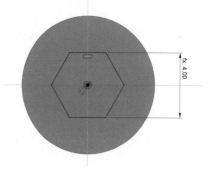

Extrude Cut this profile a Distance of -Wrench_Depth. Remember, the volume will turn a transparent red when cutting the material away. If it doesn't, verify the Operation is set to Cut. Press OK.

Add a 1 mm chamfer to the end of the bolt, click the (+) symbol in the Chamfer Dialog Box, add 0.5 mm chamfers to both of the bolt head's ends, click the (+) symbol again, and add 0.25 mm to the 6 outer edges of the hexagon. Click OK.

Adding threads to a cylinder or hole in Fusion is easy to do but can be tricky when you don't want threads on the entire length. The trick in Fusion is that partial threads will be applied to the section of the cylinder or hole you selected regardless of your view.

Navigate to Create >> Thread and select the right end of the bolt's shank.

Check Modeled, uncheck Full Length, and type Thread_Length in Length. Click OK.

In a similar operation to the Geocache thread in the previous chapter, navigate to the Timeline, and drag the Thread feature before the Chamfer feature.

If you look at a standard metric bolt, you will find some lines around the bolt head, called straight knurls. Knurls add texture that makes it easier to hand screw them in. You can recreate these knurls by extruding a triangular profile and patterning it around our Axis of Revolution.

Create a Sketch on the top of the Bolt's head, project the chamfered edge, sketch a simple upside-down triangle above the bolt, and Equally constrain all 3 sides of the triangle,

Apply a Horizontal/Vertical constraint to the top line, Vertically constrain its bottom point to the Origin, add a Tangent constraint to the top of the triangle and the outer projected circle, and dimension the top edge to 0.10 mm. Finish the Sketch.

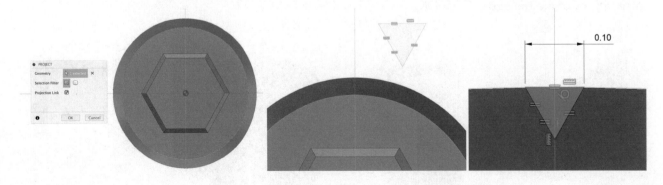

Extrude the triangle through the Bolt's head. Change the Extent Type to To Object and select the Bottom Face of the Bolt's head.

Navigate to Create >> Pattern >> and select Circular Pattern. With the Object Type set to Features, select the most recent extrusion on the Timeline and select the Bolt head's curved surface as the Axis. Change the Quantity to 40. Press OK.

Type A for Appearance, search "Anodized", and click and drag your favorite color onto the Bolt.

Anodization is a manufacturing process of increasing the durability of a metal surface with the benefit of adding interesting colors to the metal.

Navigate to Modify >> Change Parameters and change the Length value to 25 mm and see how the bolts and thread length update automatically without needing to make a brand new part from scratch.

Expand Sketches in the Browser and click the Eye Icon next to Sketch 1 to show the Construction Line above the profile.

Navigate to Create >> Pattern >> Circular Pattern, click on the Bolt, click "Select" next to Axis, click the horizontal Construction line above the bolt, and set the Quantity to the parameter Quantity. Click OK.

And just like that, you have 6 fully customizable bolts!

DISCUSSION

Advanced Units

While this is one example of a parametric model, many other use cases exist. Parameters can represent other information such as mass, cost, viscosity, luminance, and much much more.

Fasteners tool

A new tool to Autodesk Fusion is Fasteners in the Insert menu. It is a vast library of every type of hardware you may need in your project, but it has one flaw: It can be overwhelming for someone unfamiliar with fasteners like bolts and nuts and their truly endless specificities.

CHALLENGE

Design a coffee cup with a parametrically driven height, circumference, and wall thickness.

@Biikjo
User # 160

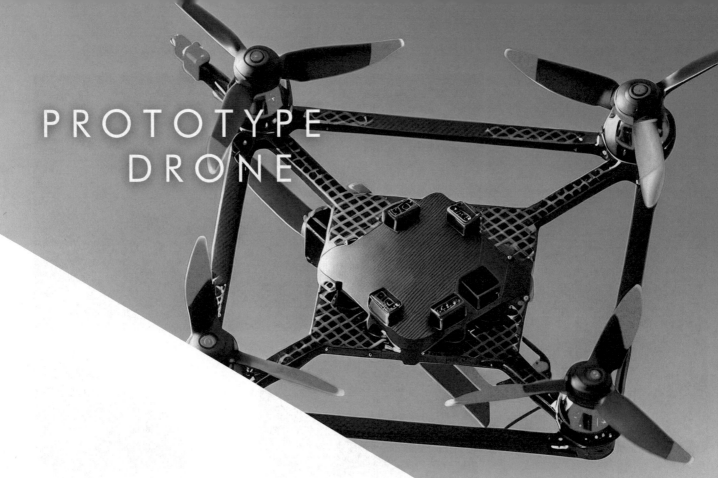

PROTOTYPE
DRONE

CHAPTER 3

Supercharge your workflow in Fusion 360 by thinking parametrically and designing models that can be changed with only a few new dimensions.

DIFFICULTY:
★★★☆☆

TIME ESTIMATE:
2.5 HOURS

KEY LEARNING:
- Import STEP files
- Copy and Mirror components
- Where to find importable hardware online.

DISCORD LINK:
Discord.gg/5hbt6xDPqf

INTRODUCTION

Making a Drone used to be a fantasy. However, thanks to readily available parts, relatively simple CAD models, and 3D printers, many enthusiasts now build and iterate at home.

In this project, you will build a parametric Drone frame connected to off-the-shelf components. By modeling the frame parametrically, you can create a new prototype by changing a few values. This modeling approach is ideal for projects that are likely to be changed in the future.

You will import pre-designed components, apply new material properties, and measure the weight of your build to know if it will be under the 250-gram limit for hobbyists.

This Drone has five major parts: the frame, propellers, motors, AIO (all-in-one) board, and a Li-Po Battery. Combined, these parts must weigh no more than 250g (0.55 lb). If you exceed this weight limit, you may need an official Drone pilot's license to operate in the US and Europe.

Before we begin, let's discuss the critical design considerations.

Learning CAD is an art and science that requires a technical understanding of the programs as well as a real-world understanding of material properties, mechanical and electrical systems, art/design, and more. For this project, our biggest concerns are:

1 - Weight
2 - Strength/Rigidity
3 - Stability

The primary drivers of strength/rigidity are material choice, frame thickness, and arm length. Carbon fiber has a high strength/weight ratio and will behave differently than 3D-printed PLA or PETG, which are weaker. Both may work but will have different CAD design features.

Stability requires a delicate balance between arm-to-arm length, propeller choice, motor choice, weight distribution, material choice, and many more factors. Therefore, a parametric frame design is ideal since getting the balance right on the first few attempts is unlikely.

We encourage you to consider the real-world design implications of your CAD models, as these will impact how you approach your work in Fusion.

CAD

This is the first multi-part assembly project, though this topic will be discussed in more depth in the Joints and Assemblies chapters later.

Make a New Folder named "Prototype Drone" in the 3 - Parametric Design Folder.

Save a new file to this Folder called Prototype Drone.

Verify that you are working in mm.

Navigate to Assemble >> New Component, verify Internal is checked, change the Name to "Drone Frame," and click OK.

Notice in the Browser that the Root Component at the top, Prototype Drone v1, has 3 stacked white cubes denoting it as an assembly.

This is because it houses the Drone Frame component, denoted by a white cube inside it. Also note the anchor icon on the white cube, which means it is grounded and will not move around the workspace.

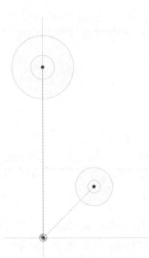

Create a sketch on the Top Plane, press L for Line and X for Construction, and make the following two lines that meet at the Origin.

Press C for circle, then X to deselect Construction geometry, and make two concentric circles on each of the line's endpoints.

Dimension the top circles to 9.2 and 3.5 mm to match the dimensions of the motors, and dimension the inner bottom circle to 1.8 to match the mounting hole on the AIO board.

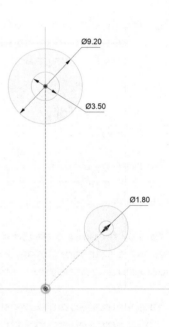

Navigate to Modify >> Change Parameters, click the (+) symbol to Add a new User Parameter called Support_Width, and set the Expression to 4 mm. Click OK to close the Change Parameters Dialog Box.

Press D for Dimension, click the two lower circles, move your cursor away, click again, type S, press Enter to auto-fill the parameter, type /2 to half the value, and press Enter.

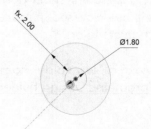

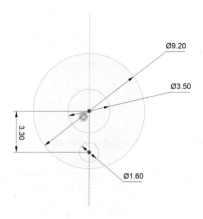

Sketch a circle inside the top circles on the vertical Construction line that is 1.6 mm in diameter and 3.3 mm below the circle's center.

Navigate to Create >> Circular Pattern, click the circle you just sketched, click "Select" next to Center Point, click the large circles center, leave the Quantity at 3, and click OK.

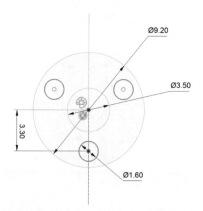

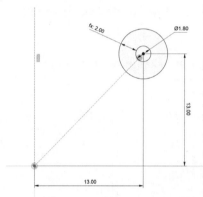

Dimension the center of the lower circles to be 13 mm to the right and up from the Origin.

Sketch two vertical lines on either side of the vertical Construction line that touches the larger outer circle.

Apply the Symmetry constraint by clicking the constraint tool, click the left sketch line, the right sketch line, and the Construction line in the middle.

Dimension the distance between these lines with the parameter Support_Width = fx: 4.00.

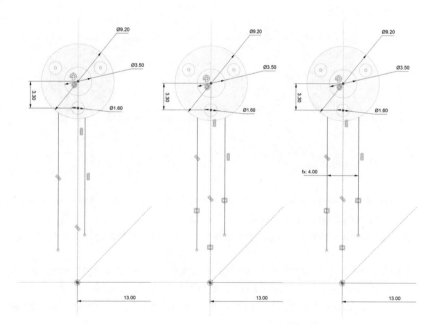

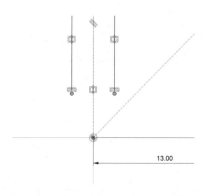

Add Horizontal/Vertical constraints to the bottom 2 endpoints of the lines.

Dimension the left bottom endpoint to the Origin's vertical distance as Support_Width/2 = fx: 2.00.

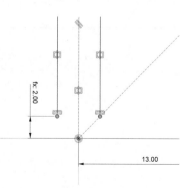

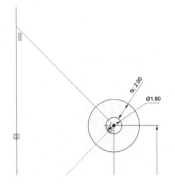

Sketch a Construction line from the lower circle's center to the right vertical line.

Note that you may need to click and drag the upper circle up so this line terminates at the vertical sketched right line.

Add a Perpendicular constraint between this Construction line and the other angled Construction line.

Press X to return to normal sketching. Sketch two angled lines on either side of the new Construction line that touches the outer circle and the right vertical Sketch line, and add two Parallel constraints between the 3 lines.

Add a Symmetric Constraint by clicking the Symmetry constraint, one of the sketch lines, the other sketch line, and the middle Construction line.

Dimension the distance between the two lines as the parameter Support_Width = fx: 4.00.

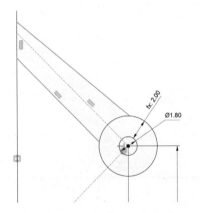
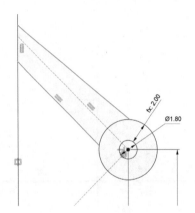
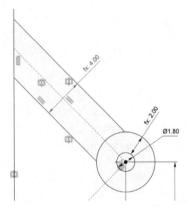

The last dimension to constrain is the height of the vertical constriction line, which defines the Drone's arm length. This is a critical dimension; the propellers will collide if the arms are too short.

If they are too long, it makes for a weaker, flimsier, and heavier design that is harder to fly and more prone to breaking in transportation. For that reason, it is helpful to set upper and lower bounds of this dimension.

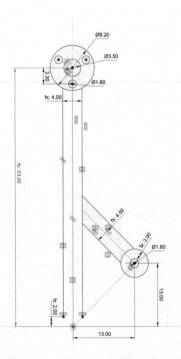

Start by navigating to the Modify >> Change Parameters tool. Create a new User Parameter called "Arm_Length", set the Expression to 53 mm, click OK, and click OK again.

Dimension the length of the vertical Construction line Arm_Length = fx: 53.00.

Navigate back to Change Parameters and click the (+) symbol to make another User Parameter called "Limits_Arm_Length".

In the Expression box, type "min" and press Enter; this will add the minimum function and put your cursor between two parentheses.

Type "100" and a semicolon ";". This number, counterintuitively, defines the maximum value.

Type "max" and press Enter; this will add the maximum function and put your cursor between two parentheses.

Type "45", a semicolon ";", and "Arm_Length".

Support_Width	mm	4 mm
Arm_Length	mm	53 mm
Limits_Arm_Length	mm	min(100 mm; max(45 mm; Arm_Length))

The Expression should read: **min(100;max(45;Arm_Length))**. Click OK and click OK again.

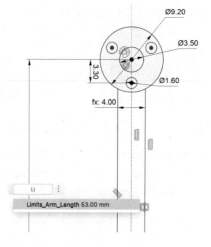

Return to the Sketch, double-click the parameter fx: 53.00, type Limit_Arm_Length, and press Enter.

Open the Change Parameter tool, double-click the Expression of the Arm_Length to 50, and the sketch will automatically shrink.

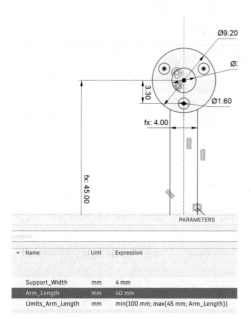

Double-click and change this value to 40 mm, but note that the dimension in the sketch reads 45 mm because that is the minimum value set in the Parameters and will not go any smaller than that.

Change the Arm_Length value to 110 and see that it will max out at 100 mm.

Change this value back to 53 mm and click OK.

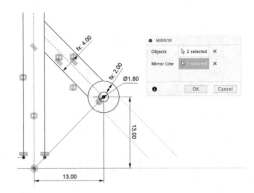

Navigate to Create >> Mirror, click the two angled sketch lines, click "Select" next to Mirror Line, click the highlighted Construction line in the picture, and click OK.

Highlight the entire sketch, navigate to Create >> Circular Pattern, click "Select" next to Center Point, click the Origin, change the Quantity to 4, and click OK.

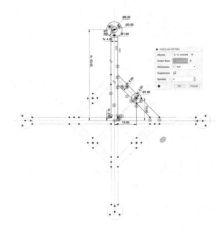

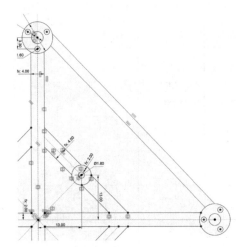

The current design, known as a Toothpick frame, is lightweight but has flimsy arms. You can join the arm ends with supports to make a Square Frame to strengthen them.

Draw two lines that touch the two outer circles of two arms and add a Parallel constraint to the two arms.

Add two Tangent constraints to the upper line and the two circles at either end. Dimension the distance between the two lines with the parameter Support_Width.

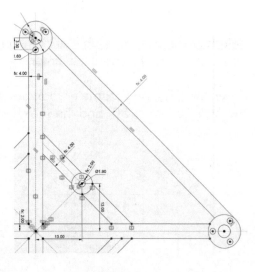

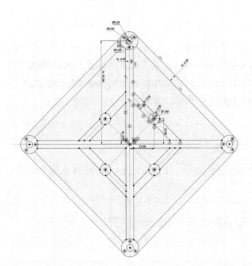

Use the Circular Pattern tool to pattern the two lines about the Origin to a Quantity of 4.

If your patterned lines remain blue, continue to the next step.

Finish the Sketch and get an Isometric View of the Sketch.

Press E for Extrude and click all 21 profiles except for the circle's centers.

In the Distance, type "Thickness= -2.5 mm" to extrude the profile down and click OK.

This is the second and much faster way to create a Parameter: Type the name and value in the dimension box.

The Thickness Parameter has now been added to the Parametric table as a Favorite Parameter.

To add more strength, you can type F for Fillet and add internal 2.5 mm fillets to the vertical lines of the frame where you see fit.

Orbit around the model and click on the corners that you think would benefit from being stronger.

Highlight the entire model, navigate to Modify >> Chamfer, and set the value to 0.25 mm.

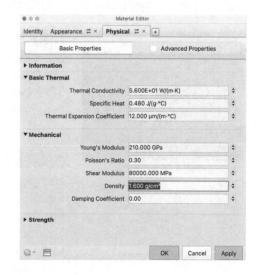

The default material in Autodesk Fusion is steel, which is significantly heavier than Carbon Fiber.

To change this value to the correct density of 1.6 g/mm^3, navigate to Modify >> Physical Material, double-click on the Steel icon in the "In This Design" window.

Click Advanced, Physical, Mechanical, change the Density to 1.6 g/cm^3 click Apply, Cancel and Close.

Type A for Appearance, and apply any of the Carbon Fiber appearances to the frame.

The Drone Frame component is now done.

Right-click "Prototype Drone v1" at the top of the Browser, known as the Root Component, and click Activate or click the small white dot to the right of the it's name.

Activating the Root Component after working on another component will become routine when creating new parts inside Components as you practice modeling complex multi-part assemblies.

Next up in the project is importing and joining the CW (Clockwise) and CCW (Counterclockwise) Propellers & Motors, Li Po Battery, and AIO (All-In-One) Board.

You can find the 4 STEP files for this project on the **FREE DOWNLOADS** tab at **CADclass.org**.

If you are working on a project that requires components for your CAD model, you will want to look for .STEP or .STP files. These are similar to STLs used in 3D Printing but retain some of the CAD model's design information, allowing you to move and edit files between various CAD software. Note, however, STEP files don't transfer information about how the part was made, physical material properties, or decals.

You can find similar files on **GrabCAD.com**, **Printables.com**, and many other online repositories.

There are many places to find and download 3D models, but most models are designed for artistic 3D modeling, 3D Printing, or are expensive.

Download these files onto your computer, open the Data Panel, click the blue Upload button, select the files from your computer, and click Upload. The files will now be saved to the Prototype Drone folder.

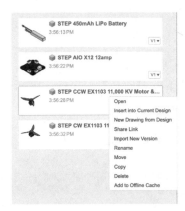

Right-click on "STEP CCW EX1103 11,000 KV Motor & Propeller" in the Data Panel and click Insert into Current Design.

In the Dialog Box, change the Y Distance to Arm_Length.

Orbit to the motor's underside and notice how the 3 mounting holes line up with the holes on the Frame. Click OK.

In Drone building, the CCW (Counter Clockwise) and CW (Clockwise) motors must be diagonal to each other to resist the rotation of the other motors. This is a similar principle to the small blade on the back of a helicopter; without it, the main top blades would have nothing to push against and the helicopter would spin in place without moving up or down.

To duplicate the part, click the CCW Motor & Propeller Component in the Browser, Copy (Ctrl/Cmd+C) & Paste (Ctrl/Cmd+V), change the Y Distance to -2 * Arm_Length, change the Z Angle to 180 to rotate it, and click OK.

Right-click on "STEP CW EX1103 11,000 KV Motor & Propeller" in the Data Panel and click Insert into Current Design.

Change the X Distance to Arm_Length and click OK.

Click the CW Motor & Propeller component in the Browser, Copy (Ctrl/Cmd+C) & Paste (Ctrl/Cmd+V), change the X Distance to -2 * Arm_Length, change the Z Angle to 180 to rotate it, and click OK.

In the Data Panel, right-click the STEP AIO Board X12 12amp, click Insert into Current Design, and click OK.

Orbit above the project and see how the mounting holes on the AIO (All In One) board line up with the holes on the Drone Frame.

Finally, right-click on the STEP 450 mAh Li Po Battery in the Data Panel, click Insert into Current Design, set the X distance to -30 mm, the Y Distance to -7.5 mm, and the Z Distance to -14.5 mm, and click OK.

Due to their small capacity, batteries on hobby Drones are often swapped out during flight days, so temporary holding mechanisms like rubber bands, Velcro straps, and zip ties are often the best choice for securing them to the frame. Hence, there is no strict need to include holding elements in the design.

None of the components are locked in place except the Drone Frame, which was automatically grounded when created.

If you have accidentally moved any parts in the assembly process, you can always undo this move with the shortcut Ctrl/Cmd+Z.

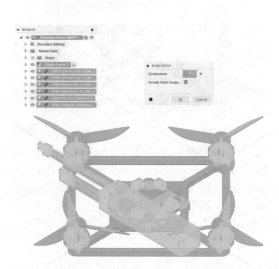

To lock all these parts together, hold down Ctrl/Cmd, click on all 7 components in the Browser, navigate to Assemble >> Rigid Group, and click OK.

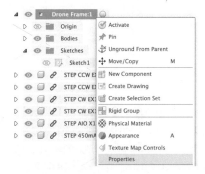

Now that the design is complete, you can analyze the Drone's weight to verify that it doesn't exceed 250g.

As stated before, STEP files do not transfer Physical Material Properties and revert to the default Steel density. The real-world combined weight of the 4x Motors (4x 3.8=15.2g), 4x Propellers (4x 1.3g = 5.2g), AIO Board (5.1g), and Li Po Battery (29g) is 54.5g. As long as the Drone Frame is under 195.5g, then it will be a successful Hobby Drone.

Right-click Drone Frame in the Browser, click Properties, and look at the Mass in the Physical section.

With a density of 0.002 g/mm^3 (rounding from 0.0016 g/mm^3), that leaves you with a final total weight of 65 grams, well under the 195.5 gram limit!

This is a testament to the modern engineering that goes into making materials stronger, lighter, and more accessible for all making projects.

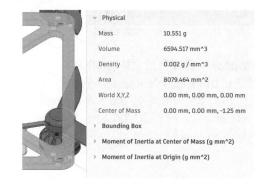

Experiment with your design by changing all parameters and seeing what amazing styles you can create!

Pictures taken by the CADclass community Drone Expert @Dairy Air, cheers mate

DISCUSSION

Components

AIO Board - Esc/FC AIO Board- Happymodel X12 12Amp 1-2S capable 25-400mw VTX ELRS

AIO Board or All In One refers to all of the important electronic components for flight being included on one convenient board. This board contains an Electronic Speed Controller (ESC) for the motors and a Flight Controller (FC). This Happymodel board runs at 12 Amps and supports a 1-2S battery. It is capable of Video Transmission (VTX) for short-range flying at 25 mW to longer-range flying at 400 mW. Express LRS (ELRS) is the low latency and high-performance protocol that is used to pilot a Drone with a remote control.

Motor - EX1103 KV11000

EX is the motor's identifier/series number while the 1103 denotes the size of the brushless motor. 11000 KV, refers to the RPM (revolutions per minute) per Volt. A KV rating of 11000 means the motor will spin at 11,000 RPM for every volt applied. High KV ratings like this are typically used for small, high-speed Drones.

Props - T2.5 X 3.5 X 3

Diameter: 2.5", Pitch: 3.5, Blades: 3. The Pitch number refers to the theoretical linear distance the propeller would move in one revolution. These propellers come in packs of 4, 2 being CW (Clock Wise) and 2 being CCW (Counter-Clock Wise). They are often made of strong materials like polycarbonate but are usually inexpensive as they can be damaged and need to be replaced.

Battery - 2S 450mAh 80/160C

2s refers to the number of cells in the battery that are wired up in series. If one cell was 3.7V, then the combined voltage would be 7.4 V. 450 mAh refers to the battery capacity. The higher this number, the longer it will live, and Drones will be able to fly longer. Paradoxically, the larger the mAh of the battery, the larger and heavier it will be leading to shorter flights. 80/160C is the discharge rate of the battery, or how quickly the electricity can "leave" the battery. This battery can be safely discharged at a rate of 80 times its capacity; 80 * 450mA = 36,000 mA = 36A. Think of this value as the rate of electricity going from the battery to the motor when it is casually flying. 160C refers to the burst discharge rate which the battery can only handle for a few seconds of high acceleration; 160 * 450 mA = 72,000 mA = 72A. Think of this value as the rate of electricity going from the battery to the motor when it is quickly accelerating from resting to full speed.

CHALLENGE

Add a top frame, connected with stand offs above the AIO Board to add more stability to the Drone and protect the delicate parts.

Use an AI image generator, like **DALL-E** or **Newarc.ai**, to get inspiration on how to make this project look better or to render it in an epic background.

CHAPTER 3 QUESTIONS

1. STEP files are most similar to…?

    a. Sketches

    b. JPEG

    c. STL

    d. DXF

2. The name of the item at the top of the Browser is called the …?

    a. Root Component

    b. Top Component

    c. It doesn't have a name

    d. Root File

3. True or False? All parameters require dimensions.

4. What are Model Parameters?

    a. Parameters you enter in yourself

    b. Parameters from dimensions

    c. Parameters you favorite/star

5. True or False? Sketches need to be fully defined to be used in Create feature.

6. True or False? Dimensions can include both parameters and mathematics.

7. Before making a New Component, you should … ?

    a. Activate the top Assembly component

    b. Activate the current component

    c. Do nothing in specific, proceed as normal

    d. Insert a mesh

8. True or False? Parameters that are edited will update the model immediately without needing to update the entire file.

9. If a formula in a dimension box is red, it may be … ?

    a. Contains spelling mistake

    b. Does not have a closing parenthesis

    c. Multiple algebraic symbols next to each other

    d. All of the above

10. The Combine tool is used for … ?

    a. Combining components or Bodies

    b. Cutting one component/Body from another

    c. Neither

    d. Both

CHAPTER 4
ASSEMBLIES

HOW TO BUILD YOUR PROJECT WITH
MULTIPLE PARTS

- FIRE PISTON
- 3D PRINTER HOT END

ASSEMBLIES

Assemblies are a collection of components joined together. For example, a nut and a bolt are individual components and become an assembly, as shown.

There are two primary ways to make Assemblies in Autodesk Fusion: using Internal Components and External Components.

External Components

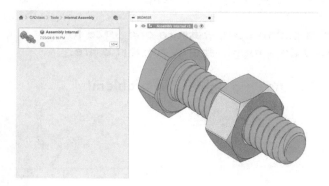

External Components are individual files that can be organized in a folder, imported into a separate Assembly file, and joined together.

Internal Components

Alternatively, Internal Components are all housed inside a single Assembly file, not in a separate folder. This is easier to manage for assemblies with fewer components, but it can be computationally heavy for larger assemblies.

It is your personal preference about which type to choose. This chapter's projects will teach you why we used Internal vs. External Components.

Free vs. Paid

If you are using a free Hobbyist or personal Autodesk Fusion trial, you will have trouble making these and any future projects using External Components.

If you want the full functionality of Autodesk Fusion, consider purchasing it for a monthly, annual, or lifetime fee. You may also want to see if you are eligible for an Education or Start-Up License, which will give you free access to the paid version.

FIRE PISTON

CHAPTER 4

Use knowledge about thermodynamics and physics to survive in the wild.

A fire piston uses pressure and force to generate enough energy to start a fire.

No matches, no lighter, no problem!

DIFFICULTY:
★★★☆☆

TIME ESTIMATE:
2.5 HOURS

KEY LEARNING:

- Add a rigid joint to two components
- Cylindrical Joints
- Joint Limits

DISCORD LINK:
Discord.gg/5hbt6xDPqf

INTRODUCTION

There are various ways to make fire on demand, but few are as exciting as the fire piston. Load flammable fuel inside the cylinder, smash the piston down, and you'll have a smoking piece of tinder if all goes well. The spike in pressure leads to an increase in temperature high enough to start a fire.

In this class, you will design a fire piston as you begin to learn about advanced CAD design using Assemblies. Although you have already created New Components, you will better understand how to connect different Components while keeping your designs organized and your parts working correctly.

CAD

Set your Units to Inches and save this file to the 4 - Assemblies Folder as Fire Piston.

Navigate to Assemble >> New Component. Name this component Piston Body and set it to Internal.

Notice the small anchor icon next to the new component, indicating that it is Grounded and cannot move.

Piston Body

Create a new Sketch on the Front Plane and draw this rough sketch with the Line tool. Set the bottom horizontal line to be a Centerline using the Sketch Palette and make its endpoints coincident with the vertical lines above it.

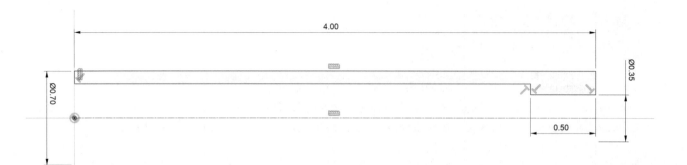

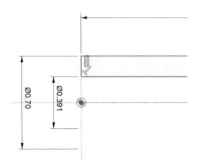

Add the following dimensions from the picture:

The diameter of the highlighted horizontal line to the Centerline is 25/64". This odd number is 1/64" larger than the 3/8" piston that will pass through it.

Revolve this profile around the Construction Line and add an internal 3/8" thread to the right side of the hole. Keep the Thread as Modeled and click OK.

Because this model won't be 3D printed, the threads can remain as a decal instead of being set as Modeled.

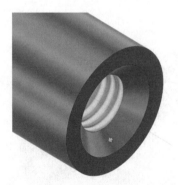

Chamfer the inner edge on the right face to 3/32", click the (+) symbol, and set the outer right edge and the left face to 0.02".

Navigate to Construct >> Offset Plane, select the left face, and Offset the plane -0.5" into the Body.

Navigate to Create >> Coil, click the Offset Plane, click on its Origin, and make a circle to start the knurl.

Click and drag your mouse from the Origin to the outer edge. Start the Coil by dragging the axial arrow, so it travels down the length of the Piston Body, and type in the following settings:

Diameter: 0.70"
Revolutions: 1.5
Height: -3.00"
Section: Triangular Internal
Section Position: Inside
Section Size: 0.02"

Select the Mirror tool, set the Object Type to Features, select the Coil feature in the Timeline, and select the Front Plane as the Mirror Plane. Click OK.

Navigate to Create >> Patterns >> Circular Pattern. Change the Object Type to Features and select the Coil and Mirror features from the Timeline.

Set the Axis as the X-axis and the Quantity to 6.

Search Anodized in the Appearance tool and add any anodized appearance to this component or make your own custom colors.

This component is completed, so before you make the next one, you must activate the entire assembly file.

Click on the white dot to the right of the Root Component at the top of the Browser to Activate it.

You can also right-click the Root Component and select Activate.

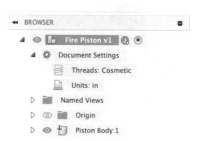

Click the first feature in the Timeline, hold down the Shift key, select the last feature, right-click, and Create a Group. Right-click the Group in the Timeline and rename it as the component's name. Do this step for all of the components in this project.

Body End Cap

Create a new Internal Component by clicking New Component in the Assemble menu and name it Body End Cap. This part will have mating threads that affix to the Piston Body that has an O-ring in between it.

Make a new sketch on the Front Plane and draw the rough shape of the Body End Cap away from the Piston Body. Make the bottom horizontal line a Centerline using the Sketch Palette, set the Centerline to be Coincident with the Origin, and add 2 Tangent constraints to the arc and their connecting lines. Add the following dimensions from the picture and note that the left edge is positioned 4.5" from the Origin.

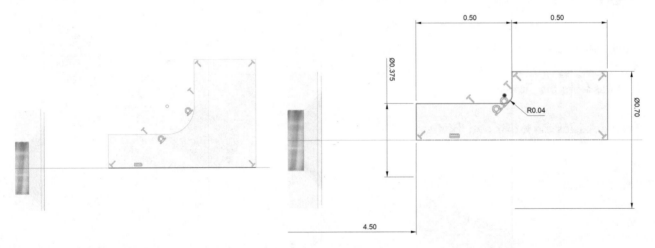

Revolve this part about the Centerline, add a Polished Brass Appearance, add a 0.05" chamfer to the left edge to 0.05", two 0.02" chamfers to the bolt's head's edges, and add a Decal Thread to the shank.

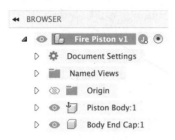

This component is completed, so click on the white dot to the right of the Root Component at the top of the Browser and Create a Group in the Timeline of the features that make up this Component.

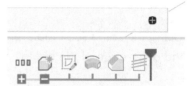

As there is no joint that connects the Piston Body and the Piston End Cap, you can click and drag the End Cap away and then type Ctrl/Cmd + Z to undo this movement.

Because the Piston Body is grounded (note the anchor icon in the Browser), it is unmovable.

You will now add the O-ring that will go in between these parts. Navigate to Insert >> McMaster Carr Component, and search for part: 9452K19.

Download the 3D STEP file. This will automatically insert the part at the Origin.

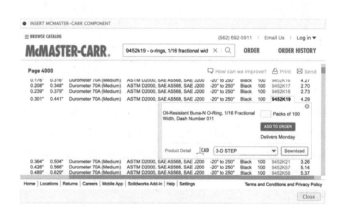

Change the Y Angle to 90 degrees and click and drag the X Distance arrow down the length of the Piston Body till it is in between the two components.

Select the Joints tool in the Assemble menu; click the O-ring and the curved surface at the end of the threads on the Body End Cap.

When making joints, the first object you click moves to the second object you click.

It is important to note that, in Fusion, you can only make joints between 2 components, not between 2 Bodies.

Using the same Joint tool, select the circular edge on the underside of the Body End Cap's head and on the outer edge of the Piston.

Note that when you select this edge, a circular icon known as the Joint Origin appears at the center of the circle. When joining any 2 components, 1 Joint Origin will move to another and become Coincident.

If you do a Section Analysis of the Front Face, you can see the O-ring interfering with the Body End Cap. Because this is a rubber part that can deform and stretch over rigid metals, you don't need to worry about this. As you can see, the O-ring would squish to form an air-tight seal by the chamfer on the Piston Body.

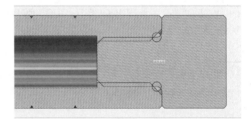

Piston End

Make a new Internal Component called Piston End.

Hide the other 2 components and start a new Sketch on the Front Plane of the following profile.

Set the center of the circle at the midpoint of the top horizontal line, the vertical highlighted line is Coincident to the Origin, and set the bottom horizontal line to be a Centerline.

Verify the Centerline is Coincident with the Origin.

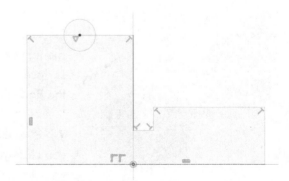

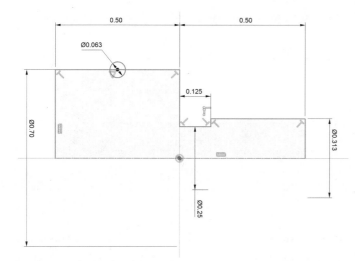

Add the following dimensions to the sketch.

Type the 0.313" dimension as 5/16" and set the circle's diameter to 1/16".

The 0.125" wide groove, commonly known as a gutter in machining, is a handy way to establish the end of the threads during a lathe operation known as Threading.

Revolve this part about the Centerline, add a Polished Brass Appearance, add the same chamfers to this component that you did on the Body End Cap component, and add a thread to the bolt's shank.

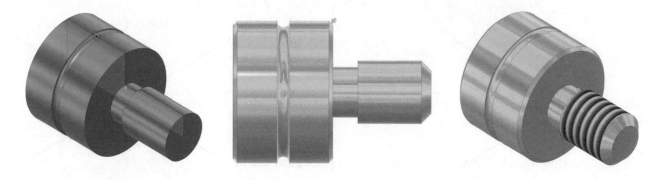

Activate the Root Component at the top of the Browser and Create a Group in the Timeline of the features that make up the Piston End.

Piston

The Piston will screw into the Piston End, hold onto an O-ring, and have a small cavity to hold flammable material.

Make a new Internal Component called Piston, right-click the component in the Browser, and click Isolate. This will hide all of the components except for the one you have Activated.

Make a new Sketch on the Front Plane of the profile and set the bottom horizontal line as a Centerline.

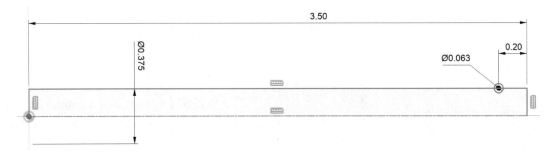

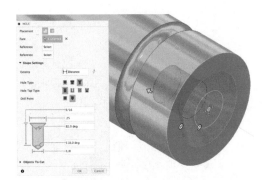

Type H for Hole and select the right face next to the groove. Click the drag the blue circle to the center, where it will snap in place.

Change the Hole Type to Countersink. Set the Countersink Diameter to 0.25", the total depth to 3/16", and the hole diameter to 1/8". This hole will have the geometry that can hold onto the tinder. Click OK.

Make a new threaded hole and center it on the left face of the Piston. This hole will screw into the Piston End.

Change the Hole Type to Simple, the Hole Type to Tapped, the size to 0.3125", and the Depth to 0.5". Change it to Modeled and click OK.

Add a 0.02" chamfer to the right outer edge of the Piston to make it easier to insert into the bore of the Piston Body.

Click on the white dot to the right of the Root Component at the top of the Browser and Create a Group of the features that make up the Piston.

Click the Eye Icon next to the Piston End component to Show it.

Navigate to Assemble >> As-Built Joint and click on the two components to add a Rigid joint. Click OK.

The As-Built Joint was chosen over the Joint tool because the 2 components are already in the correct location.

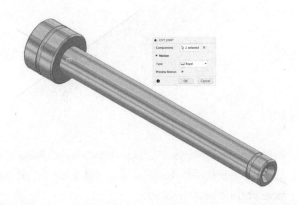

Insert another McMaster Carr O-ring by going to Insert >> McMaster Carr and downloading part: 9452K16.

Rotate it 90 degrees and place it roughly in the correct location.

Press J to open the Joint tool, select the O-ring, and the grooved surface and the O-ring will slide into place.

O-rings are made of flexible rubber, so the part will interfere with the Piston to the point where you can barely see it. This O-ring will stretch over the part in real life, so there's no need to worry about this error.

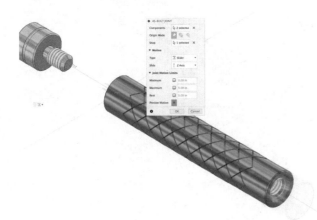

Right-click the Piston component in the Browser and click Unisolate to show the other components.

Navigate to Assemble >> As-Built Joint, click the Piston End, then the Piston Body, then select any circular edge on the Piston End. Click OK.

In Slider joints, the direction that the component moves runs parallel to the axis of revolution of the circular edge you selected.

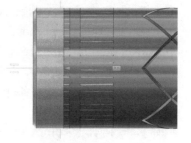

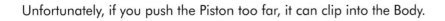

Click and drag the Piston and notice how it realistically moves in and out of the Piston Body.

Unfortunately, if you push the Piston too far, it can clip into the Body.

To fix this, expand Joints in Browser, hover your cursor over Slider joint, and click on the orange arrow pop-up called Edit Motion Limits. Check Minimum and Rest, and press the Preview Limits button.

Depending on your view's orientation, the Piston End may clip through the Piston Body, which is obviously incorrect. Click Flip which checks Maximum and press Preview Limits again to see the Piston End moving away from the Piston Body. Click OK.

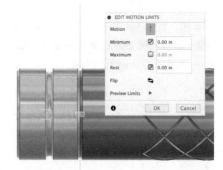

By having Rest set at 0", when you click and drag the Piston away from the Body and release, it will automatically reset back to the starting position.

To see this movement better, right-click Piston Body in the Browser >> Opacity Control >> 70% and click and drag the Piston again.

And you are done!

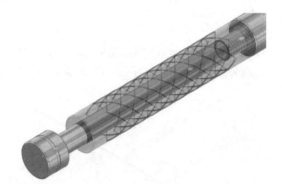

DISCUSSION

Anodized Aluminum

The Piston Body is Anodized Aluminum. Anodizing is an electrolytic process that encourages an oxide to form on the outside of metals. Oxide is usually bad, like rust on steel, which degrades the material rapidly. However, aluminum oxide is more durable against impact and scratches and incredibly durable against thermal (heat) energy. Anodizing increases the oxide layer in a controlled way, often by submerging it in a bath of sulfuric acid while passing a current through it. This process also makes it easier to add dyes. Chances are you own an anodized aluminum part. Look for carabiners on backpacks, colorful keys, or heat sinks in your computer.

CHALLENGE

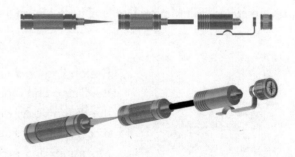

Design and recreate another camping/survival tool with multiple parts, such as a multi-tool, a compass, or a wood-splitting hatchet.

@Raluca A   User #794

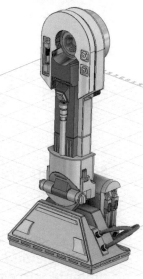

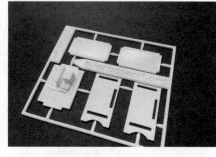

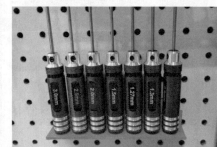
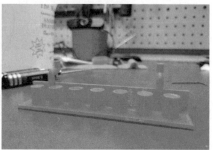

3D PRINTING HOT END

CHAPTER 4

3D printers are amazing machines, turning spools of plastic into real 3D objects.

The hot end is the component that melts the plastic and is critical for the rise and ultimate success of 3D printing.

In this project you will learn how they work, what their main components are, and how to model one from scratch.

DIFFICULTY:
★★★★☆

TIME ESTIMATE:
3 HOURS

KEY LEARNING:
- Add dual chamfers to edges
- As built joints and how they differ from standard joints
- When to use rigid joints

INTRODUCTION

3D printing has revolutionized the manufacturing industry and captured the imagination of millions. Robust, inexpensive printers now cost under $200 and are used for prototyping projects and making parts on demand. Chances are you either already have a printer or are considering purchasing one.

In this project, you will make a 3D Printer (3DP) hot end. The hot end is responsible for melting the plastic filament and is vital to the proper function of a filament-based printer. There will be many components, so staying organized is essential.

CAD

Verify you are working in Millimeters (mm). Save the file and name it 3DP Hot End Assembly.

0.4 mm Nozzle

Create a new Internal Component and name it 0.4 mm Nozzle. It is important to name each part to stay organized.

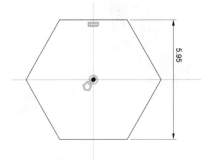

Create a hexagon on the Top Plane that is 5.95 mm tall with a Horizontally Constrained top edge. Extrude this profile up 13 mm and hide this new Body.

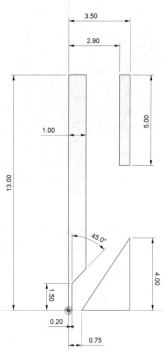

Draw a rectangle, a triangle, and the 6-sided shape on the Front Plane as shown in the picture.

Add 3 Collinear constraints to the top, right, and bottom sets of lines.

Dimension the Sketch and verify it is fully Constrained.

Revolve the 3 profiles around the vertical Axis.

Set the Operation to Cut, ignore the error, turn the Body back on, and click OK.

Navigate to Modify >> Physical Material >> Metal >> and drag Brass onto the Nozzle.

Add a 0.75 mm chamfer to the top outer edge of the Nozzle, click the (+) symbol, and add 0.1 mm fillets to the top inner hole and the bottom outside edge of the Nozzle.

Create a Modeled Thread on the top cylinder to make an M6 thread.

Start a Sketch on the hexagon's front face, create a text box that reads 0.4 that is 1.5 mm in Height.

This value refers to the outlet Nozzle diameter. 0.4 mm is the most common size in 3D printing.

Extrude Cut this text into the component -0.1 mm.

Click the white dot to the right of the Root Component at the top of the Browser to Activate it, and Create a Group in the Timeline of all the component's features.

Again, notice the anchor icon, next to the 0.4 mm Nozzle component. This indicated that it is a grounded part that is fixed in place.

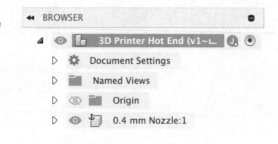

Click the Gear Icon in the bottom right corner of your screen and check Component Color Swatch.

This will add a colored marker to each component in the Browser and a corresponding header in the Timeline, making it easier to see which features correspond to which components.

Heater Block

The heater block is a brick of aluminum that connects the Nozzle and the heat break. It also holds the heating element and the thermistor, which melts the plastic.

Create a new Internal Component called Heater Block.

Make an Offset Plane 9 mm above the Top Plane. This puts the plane 1 mm above the hexagonal face on the Nozzle, which is quite hard to select when it is transparent.

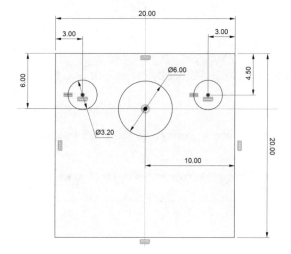

Click the Eye Icon to Hide the Nozzle.

Start a new Sketch on this Offset Plane, and sketch a rectangle and three circles. Verify that the View Cube reads TOP in the correct orientation; if the text is upside down, rotate your view.

Apply a Horizontal and Equal constraint to the 2 outer circles.

Constrain the middle circle to the Origin and dimension the sketch.

Extrude the profile up 10 mm and set the Physical Material to Aluminum.

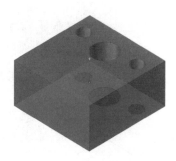

Aluminum conducts heat very well, so the energy from the Heater Element can be transferred to the Nozzle to melt filament efficiently.

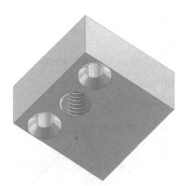

Orbit to the underside of the component and add 1.375 mm chamfers to the hole's edges for 2 countersunk bolts and add a Modeled M6 thread to the center hole to screw into the 0.4 mm Nozzle.

Create this Sketch on the right side of the block.

Vertically Constrain the 2 smaller circles and Finish the Sketch.

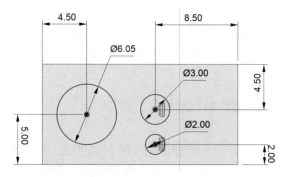

Show Sketch 2 during the next 3 extrusions and Hide it when you have completed the following. Extrude Cut the top right circle -4 mm and the bottom right circle -5 mm. Extrude Cut the left circle by setting the Extend Type to All and clicking Flip to flip the direction of the extrusion.

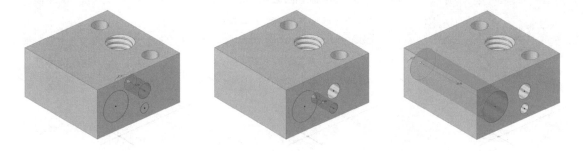

Create a new Sketch on the underside of the Heater Block, sketch a circle, Vertically constraint it to the Origin, dimension it and Finish the Sketch.

Extrude the circle, change the Extent Type to To Object, and select the inside surface of the 6.05 mm hole.

Add a Modeled M3 thread to this hole, this hole will house a small M3 set screw to hold the Heater Element in place in a later step.

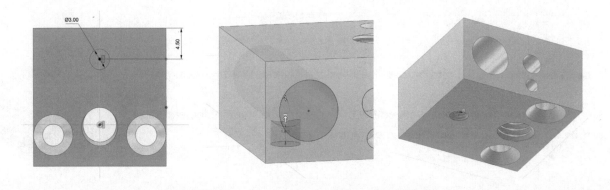

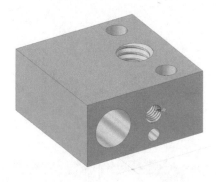

Add a Modeled M3 thread to the top right hole.

Unfortunately, you can't add a chamfer to Threaded holes.

Click and drag the 1st Threading feature next to the most recent two in the Timeline.

Move the Timeline Playhead to the left of the first Threading features. Now, you can edit the holes without the threads.

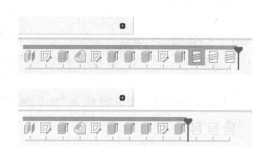

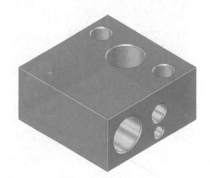

Using the Chamfer tool, select the top, 4 side faces, and the outer edge of the small circle on the bottom. Set the value to 0.25 mm.

Move the Timeline back to the end of the features.

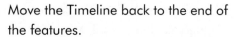

Click the white dot to the right of the Root Component at the top of the Browser to Activate it and Create a Group of the Heater Block features.

Show the 0.4 mm Nozzle component and add a Rigid As-Built Joint between the 2 components.

If the Joint icons become distracting, turn them off in the Navigation Bar by going to Display Settings >> Object Visibility >> and uncheck Joints.

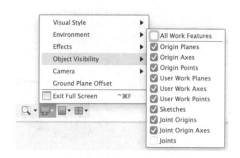

Thermistor

Thermistors are electric thermometers. This thermistor is a small, delicate glass bead with an electric current passing through it. As it heats up, the current passing through it changes, and the motherboard measures this change. This value is interpreted as the temperature of the Nozzle.

Two wires extend out of this part, which supplies resistive thermal information.

Go to **CADclass.org,** navigate to the **FREE DOWNLOADS** tab, and download the three STEP files for this project: STEP Heater Element, STEP Thermistor, and STEP Bowden Connector.

Open the Data Panel and click the blue Upload button, select the 3 STEP files from your computer, and click Upload.

Right-click the STEP Thermistor file and click Insert Into Current Design.

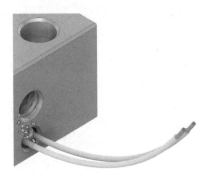

Move the component: X Distance: 7.0 mm, Y Distance: -2.50 mm, Z Distance: 11 mm.

Navigate to Assemble >> As-Built Joint, select the Heater Block and the Thermistor, and click OK. Because Rigid joints don't move, the order in which you select the components doesn't matter.

Heater Element

This part converts electrical energy into thermal energy to melt the plastic in the Hot End. Heating elements are often made from ceramic, which can reach high temperatures without failing.

Right-click the STEP Heater Element file in the Data Panel, click Insert Into Current Design, and click OK.

Type J for Joint and select the outer edge of the silver cylinder. Note how you can also select the inner silver edge because the Joint Origin would be in the same location, its center.

Click the outer edge of the large hole on the Heater Block. Note that if you clicked the inner edge of the hole's chamfer, the Heater Element would be incorrectly joined deeper into the hole.

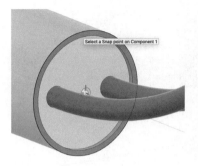

Heat Break

Heat Breaks are thin-walled couplers that connect the Heater Block to the Heat Sink.

Its purpose is to limit the heat traveling up from the Heating Element and prematurely melting the plastic. The thin-walled section limits thermal transfer due to a smaller cross-sectional area.

This part often gets broken when replacing a clogged Nozzle, as some people unscrew it while it is still cold, causing it to become over-torqued and sheer off.

Create a new Internal Component called Heat Break.

Hide all components except for the Heat Break and 0.4 mm Nozzle.

Make a new Sketch on the Front Plane and draw the profile and the vertical Centerline from the midpoint of the Nozzle's projected top face.

Project a Point on the Nozzle's top surface. Add a Coincident constraint to a Projected Point on the Nozzle's top and the bottom horizontal line.

Add a Parallel constraint to the two angled lines.

Add the following dimensions and Finish the Sketch.

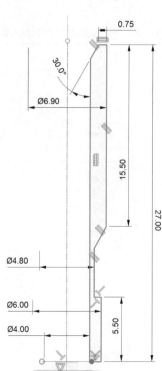

Revolve the part about the Z-axis and add a Modeled M6 thread to the bottom cylinder. Activate the Root Component, Create a Group in the Timeline, and add a Rigid As-Built Joint between the Heat Break and the 0.4 mm Nozzle.

Heat Sink

Heat Sinks are heat exchangers that move energy away from electronic parts to avoid overheating. These parts are common in computing hardware to prevent failure (thermal runaway). Often heat sinks are immediately next to a fan to blow the hot air that clings to surfaces, known as the boundary layer effect. This part is also made of aluminum (an excellent thermal conductor) to translate as much heat as possible.

Make a new Internal Component called Heat Sink and start a new Sketch on the Front Plane.

Project the top of the Heat Break and add a vertical Centerline from the Origin.

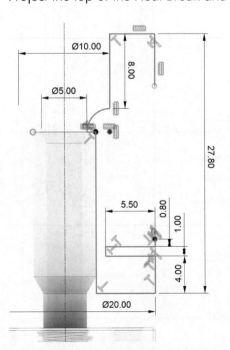

Add a Collinear constraint to the 3 selected lines in the rough sketch.

Add two Horizontal/Vertical constraints between the ends of the 3-point arc and the arc's center to form a quarter of a circle.

Add a Coincident constraint between the two selected points in the rough sketch.

Now add all dimensions.

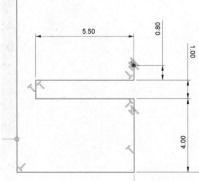

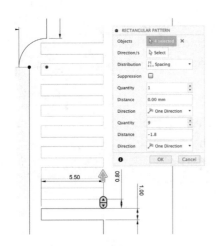

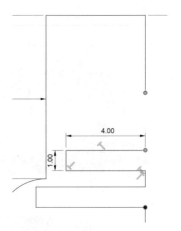

Use the Rectangular Pattern tool to make the snake pattern by selecting the 4 highlighted lines and patterning them upwards. Change the Distribution to Spacing, the Quantity to 9, and the Distance to 1.8 mm.

Draw the three blue lines shown. Add a Coincident constraint between the 2 blue points and add the dimensions.

Verify your Sketch is fully Constrained, then revolve this profile about the Z-axis.

Change the Physical Material to aluminum, anodized, red.

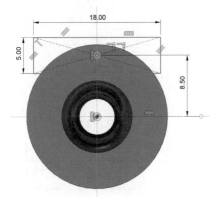

To make the cutouts for the flat front and back faces, make a new Sketch on the top surface, sketch a Center Rectangle that is Vertically Constrained to the Origin, and add the dimensions.

Extrude Cut this profile, set the Extent to To Object, and select the underside of the Heat Sink. Mirror this Extrude Cut feature about the Front Plane.

Add a 0.5 mm chamfer on the top hole edge.

Add an M10 thread to the top hole for the Bowden Connector.

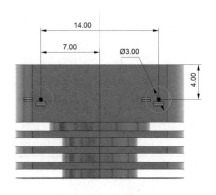

Sketch two circles on the Heat Sink's front face of the Heat Sink. Equally and Horizontally constrain the circles, and add the following dimensions.

Extrude Cut these holes to the back side of the Heat Sink. The circles overlap with the curved edge of the part, so you'll have to select 4 profiles for the two holes.

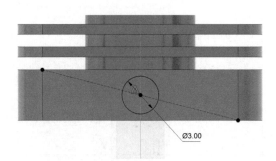

Start a Sketch on the back face of the Heat Sink and sketch a diagonal Construction line and a 3 mm circle at its midpoint.

This hole will house a set screw that will tighten the Heat Sink to the Heat Brake.

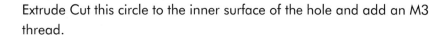

Extrude Cut this circle to the inner surface of the hole and add an M3 thread.

Show the Heater Block by clicking its Eye Icon. Start a Sketch on the Heat Sink's bottom face.

Project the holes on the Heater Block onto the underside of the Heat Sink.

Select the circles and Extrude Cut them to the underside of the bottom rib.

Add an M3 thread to the 2 holes by holding down Ctrl/Cmd and clicking both holes' surfaces.

Click the white dot to the right of the Root Component at the top of the Browser to Activate it, add a Rigid As-Built Joint to the Heat Break, and Create a Group of the Heat Sink features.

Bowden Connector

The Bowden Connector holds the PTFE tube, which guides the filament into the hot end. This fitting has a mating M10 thread to go into the Heat Sink. It has a plunger mechanism, which, when depressed, will retract teeth, allowing the PTFE tube to be removed.

Right-click the STEP Bowden Connector file in the Data Panel and click Insert Into Current Design. Click and drag the Bowden Connector upwards 44.50 mm.

Add a Rigid As-Built Joint to lock it in place.

PTFE Tube

The last component to model is the PTFE tube. PTFE, more commonly known as Teflon, is a low-friction plastic used to direct filament from the cold end to the hot end of a 3D printer.

To visualize how far the PTFE tube goes into the Assembly, show all the components, and make a Section Analysis on the Front Plane. Hide this analysis from the Browser.

The PTFE Tube is inserted at the top and rests on top of the Nozzle.

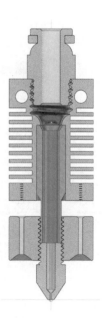

Hide all components other than the Nozzle, make a new Internal Component called PTFE Tube, and make a Sketch on the Nozzle's top.

Draw the 2 circles at the Origin that are 2 and 4 mm in diameter and Finish the Sketch.

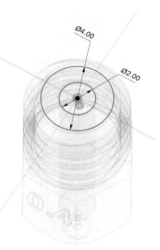

Make a new Sketch on the Front Plane of an 80 mm vertical line from the center of the Nozzle's top face, hold down the left mouse button, and make a tangential 3-point arc. Finish the Sketch.

The arc length of the arc can be left undefined.

Using the Sweep tool, select the circles shown as the profile, and the line and arc as the Path.

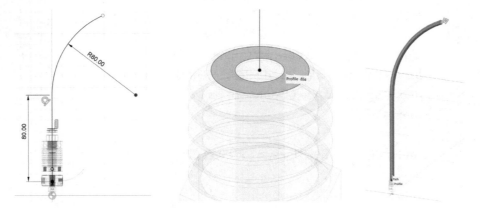

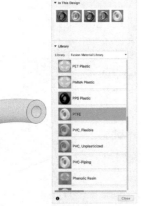

Change the Physical Material to PTFE under the plastic tab for this component.

Double-click the PTFE icon in the In This Design window, click Advanced, navigate to the Appearances tab, click Color, change the color wheel or slider to royal blue, and apply it to the Component.

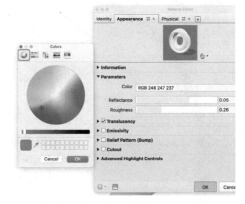

Add a Rigid As-Built Joint between the PTFE Tube and the Bowden Connector. Note that you can add As-Built Joints between any two components even if they don't touch.

Show all the components in the Browser and Activate the Root Component.

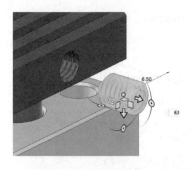

Use the McMaster Carr plugin to add all the hardware. Download the 3D STEP file for the M3 x 4 mm Set Screw: 91390A098.

This set screw will be used to hold the Heating Element in place. Move this screw near the heat block as shown. Click OK.

Navigate to Assemble >> and select Joint. Click the circular edge on the screw's head next to the Hexagon. The Joint Origin should float in the middle of the circle.

Select the outer edge of the threaded hole on the Heater Block so the Joint Origin is at the center. This will move the screw so the two Joint Origins are Coincident.

Click and drag the blue arrow to position the screw, as shown in the picture. Click OK.

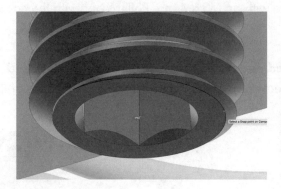

Click the Set Screw in the Browser and copy and paste it into the workspace. Move and rotate the part so it lines up as shown on the back face of the Heat Sink.

Add a joint between the duplicated set screw and the Heat Sink. Click OK.

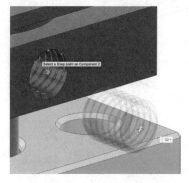
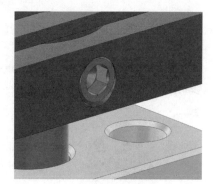

Import a M3x20 countersunk bolt with the code 91294A136 to pass through the Heat Block and screw into the Heat Sink.

Add joints to the bolts by selecting the top edge on the bolt's head and the outer chamfered edge on the Heater Block. Copy and Paste the bolt 14 mm to the other hole and add an As-Built Joint.

The next bolt will hold the Glass Bead Thermistor in place with an M3 x 4 mm Phillips bolt with the code: 92000A113.

Add a joint to the circle of the underside of the bolt's head and the outer circular edge of the threaded hole on the Heater Block. If the screw is in the wrong orientation, click the Flip button at the bottom of the Dialog Box.

Finally, add the M3 x 16 mm button head bolt, 92095A184, that will pass through the Heat Sink. Copy, Paste, and Join a second bolt to the other hole on the Heat Sink.

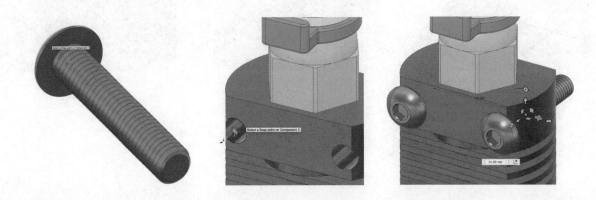

Congratulations, this project is done!

DISCUSSION

6061 Aluminum

Aluminum is an excellent thermal conductor, meaning the heat from the heating element goes into the Nozzle with little thermal resistance. 6061 is a common aluminum alloy in machining. Most alloys have a 4-digit code which defines which metals are present. 6061 has about 1% magnesium, 0.8% silicone, and trace amounts of copper and chromium. You may also see T6 after its name, indicating that it has undergone a treatment (T) where it has been tempered (6) or hardened from its Original annealed softened state.

CHALLENGE

Recreate a tool made of multiple parts. Measure each component and add joints between all components. Examples: Adjustable Wrench, Box Knife, Lineman Pliers, or Combination Square.

@Conny
User #485

@Moses Shaib
User #681

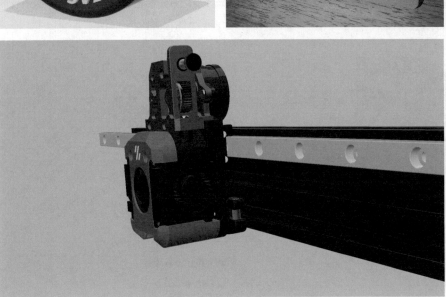

CHAPTER 4 QUESTIONS

1. To apply a Rigid As-Built Joint to more than 2 components in one feature, you would choose which tool?

    a. Contact sets

    b. Rigid group

    c. Joints

    d. Multi-joints

2. Which of these choices only applies to As-Built Joints?

    a. The first component clicked will move to the other

    b. Linear movement in X,Y,Z is available

    c. Rotational movement can be set in the Angle box

    d. The components don't move at all

3. Internal Components would be the best choice for which project?

    a. A large project with hundreds of components

    b. A simple project with a small number of components

    c. A project where each component may need to drastically change

    d. A project that is shared across a large team of CAD engineers

4. To not accidentally make a subassembly under an assembly file when making a new component, you should … ?

    a. Activate the top Assembly file

    b. Activate the current component

    c. Activate the next component you're about to make

    d. Fusion 360 does this automatically

5. What does the Rest setting do?

    a. Stops a Joint from moving

    b. There is no setting called Rest, only Reset

    c. Returns a Joint's movement to this location

    d. Darkens the screen slightly for easier viewing.

6. The McMaster Carr tool is a great tool for importing … ?

    a. New environments to view your project in

    b. Other users projects

    c. Hardware like bolts, motors and springs

    d. STLs from 3D printer hubs like Thingiverse

7. If two components are already in the right location, you would join them with which tool?

    a. As-Built Joint

    b. Joint tool

    c. Join

    d. Fix / Unfix

8. To edit a joint type (ex. Change a Rigid joint to a revolute joint), you would…?

    a. Click on the joint icon in the model

    b. Right click on the Joint in the Browser

    c. Either

    d. None of the above

9. What does a Grounded Component mean?

    a. Moves a component below the other components

    b. Places the component on the Top Plane

    c. Locks the component in place

    d. Automatically makes its physical material a non-conductive default

10. What does Enable Contact Sets do?

    a. Allows for haptic capabilities to be incorporated

    b. Allows components to push each other

    c. Adds a reference contact to each model to track its progression

    d. Allows you to save sign in information for your account

CHAPTER 5
JOINTS

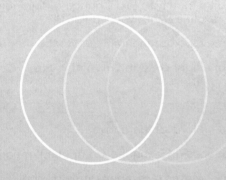

HOW TO JOIN PARTS FOR REALISTIC
MOVEMENT

- PIZZA CUTTER
- TESLA TURBINE

JOINTS

Joints are static or dynamic connections between components. It is important to note that Joints can only be added between components, not Bodies.

Here is a list of available Joint types within Autodesk Fusion:

- **Rigid:** Locks 2 or more parts together. If one component is Grounded, neither will move. Example: two wooden boards glued together.
- **Revolute:** Allows a component to spin about a central Axis that can be adjusted to spin a full 360 degrees or just a part of an arc. Example: A spinning car tire on an axle.
- **Slider:** A linear movement along a single dimension. Example: a piston traveling up and down in a cylinder.
- **Cylindrical:** Allows parts to rotate and move linearly at the same time. Example: a woodworking clamp; the clamping screw mechanism requires cylindrical spinning and linear movement.
- **Pin Slot:** A component can rotate about one Axis and move linearly along a different axis. Example: A rolling pin on some pizza dough; the pin's axle is perpendicular to the direction of travel.
- **Planar:** Allows a component to rotate but is confined to only being able to move in one plane. Example: An object placed on a desk that can be moved around the desk and can rotate but can't pass through the table or be lifted upwards.
- **Ball:** A component can rotate in all 3 axes of rotation. Example: a ball joint on top of a camera mount.

Adding Joints in Autodesk Fusion places a Joint Origin on both components and connects them. For example, the nut's circular edge and the bolt's circular edge join, as shown. Notice the Joint Origin in the center of each circle and how they connect.

PIZZA CUTTER

CHAPTER 5

There's nothing like the smell of a sizzling pizza fresh out of the oven.

In this project you will join multiple parts together to make a pizza cutter, ready for slicing up a fresh pie.

DIFFICULTY:
★★★☆☆

TIME ESTIMATE:
120 MINUTES

KEY LEARNING:

- How and when to use different types of joints
- Make a plane for mirroring operations
- Move revolute joints
- Add eccentricity to a joint

DISCORD LINK:
Discord.gg/5hbt6xDPqf

A Pizza Cutter is a simple project that illustrates the power of different Joint types inside Autodesk Fusion. With a few clicks of a button, you will learn how to rotate the blade as if you were slicing a fresh piece of pizza. You will continue practicing with Assemblies in this lesson and for the remainder of the program.

CAD

Set your default Units to Inches.

End Cap

Make a new Internal Component called End Cap.

Draw this shape on the Front Plane using the Line tool and a 3-point arc.

Make the bottom horizontal line a Centerline by expanding the Sketch Palette, selecting the line, and clicking Centerline.

Coincidently constrain the arc's center and the Centerline; this effectively makes the arc tangent to the vertical Z-axis without needing to open and close the Origin tab in the Browser.

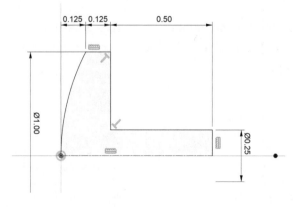

Add the dimensions shown, set the 1.00" dimension as the distance from the top horizontal line to the Centerline, and Finish the Sketch.

Click the home icon on the View Cube, revolve the profile about the Centerline, add a 0.04" chamfer to the end of the shank, add a Modeled ¼"-20 Thread to the shank, and drag the Thread features before the Chamfer feature in the Timeline.

Add a Brushed Stainless-Steel Appearance to the part.

Most metal products in the food industry are made from stainless steel for its hygienic properties.

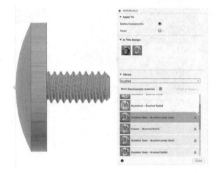

Inner Body

Activate the Root Component and make a new Internal Component called Inner Body.

This inner metal core will add stability to the Pizza Cutter.

Start a Sketch on the Front Plane, Project the right face of the End Cap's head, and hide the End Cap Component.

Sketch a rectangle from the midpoint of the purple projected line, make the bottom horizontal line a Centerline, and add the following dimensions.

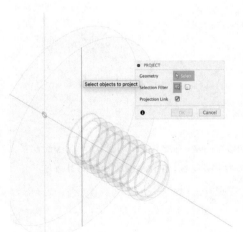

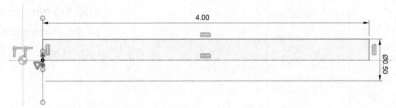

Revolve this Profile about the Centerline to make a cylinder.

Add a 0.02" chamfer to either edge of the cylinder by clicking the cylindrical face.

You can make a threaded hole with a light countersink in 1 feature using the Hole tool. Select either of the cylinder's faces and drag the hole's blue dot to the circle's center.

Add a Countersunk, Tapped hole with the following values: 0.625" depth, 0.25" chamfer, and a size 0.25" hole 1/4"-20 Thread.

Instead of duplicating this operation, mirror it. That way, if one hole's dimensions change, the other will update as well.

Since there is no plane that bisects the middle of the cylinder, make one using the Midplane tool in the Construct menu. Select both end caps of the cylinder, and click OK.

Use the Mirror tool to mirror this hole feature to the other side.

Expand Construction in the Browser and Hide Plane 1 and add a Brushed Stainless Steel Appearance.

Activate the Root Component, show the End Cap, navigate to Assembly >> As-Built Joint, select both components, verify the joint is set to Rigid, and click OK.

Right-click the End Cap component in the Browser and select Unground From Parent.

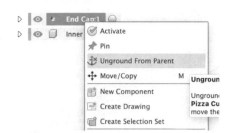

Without moving the components, right-click the Inner Body component in the Browser, and click Ground To Parent. The small anchor icon should now be on the Inner Body component.

Wooden Handle

Make a new Internal Component called Wooden Handle.

This will be made out of teak wood, a dense, water-resistant wood with a high oil content that is often used for high-quality cutting boards or on boat decks due to its waterproof nature.

Hide the Inner Body and project the cylindrical face of the End Cap's head. Sketch a horizontal line from the top right projected point and make the rest of the sketch using three 3-point arcs and Lines. Note that the top left horizontal line is coincident with the projected point.

Hold down Ctrl/Cmd, select all 4 top horizontal lines, and apply Collinear and Equal constraints.

Hold down Ctrl/Cmd, select all 3 arcs, and add Equal constraints.

Hold down Ctrl/Cmd, select all 4 horizontal lines, and apply Equal constraints.

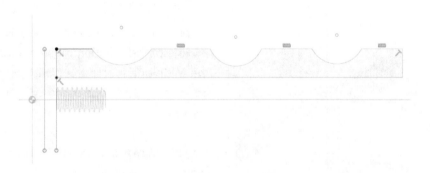

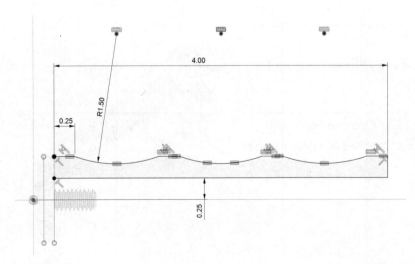

Hold down Ctrl/Cmd, select all 3 arc's centers, and apply a Horizontal/Vertical constraint.

Dimension the total length of the sketch to 4.00" first, then dimensions the left horizontal line to be 0.25", the arc's radius to 1.50", and the bottom horizontal line to be 0.25" above the Origin.

Revolve this Profile about the X-axis.

Add a 0.25" fillet to the curve's inner edges.

This can be done by selecting the 3 curved surfaces or the 6 curved edges.

Mahogany is the closest-looking wood to teak in the Autodesk Fusion Library. Drag this Appearance onto the part.

Double-click the Wood Appearance and change the rotation to 90 degrees and the scale to 40% to look more realistic.

Activate the Root Component at the top of the Browser and Show The Inner Body.

Add an As-Built Joint between the Wooden Handle and the Inner Body.

Wheel Bracket

The next component is the Wheel Bracket which joins the Blade to the Handle.

Make a new Internal Component called Wheel Bracket.

Make a new Sketch on the Front Plane and Project the Wooden Handle's right face.

Right-click the Wheel Bracket component in the Browser and click Isolate to hide the other parts.

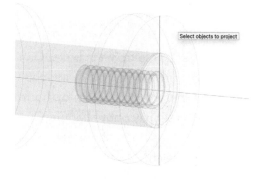

Make the rough Sketch and Horizontally constrain both arc's centers to the Origin.

Add a Tangent constraint between the right arc and the horizontal line.

Set the bottom horizontal line to be a Centerline.

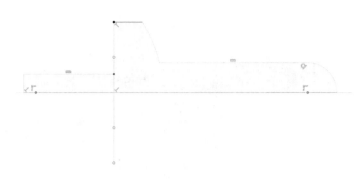

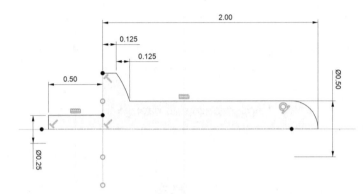

Add dimensions to the Sketch and Finish it.

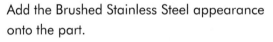

Revolve the profile, add a 0.04" chamfer to the shank of the Wheel Bracket, add a ¼"-20 Modeled Thread to the shank, and drag the Thread feature before the Chamfer feature in the Timeline.

Add the Brushed Stainless Steel appearance onto the part.

Start a sketch on the Top Plane and project the cylindrical surface of the component.

Sketch a rectangle from the bottom left projected point that is 1.75" wide and 0.28" tall. Note that the rectangle's top horizontal line extends slightly above the Origin.

Finish the Sketch.

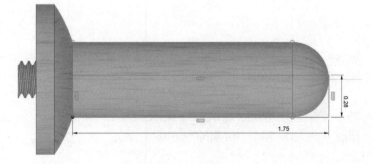

Symmetrically Extrude the Rectangle through All in both directions.

Add a Hole to the center of the hemispherical end. Click on the new flat face you just made. Add the same dimensions as the previous countersunk threaded hole. 0.625" deep, 0.25" countersink, 0.25" size, 1/4"-20 designation.

Add a 0.02" fillet to the flat face.

Activate the Root Component and add a Rigid As-Built Joint to the Wooden Handle and the Wheel Bracket.

Shoulder Bolt

The next component is the shouldered bolt that passes through the Blade while allowing it to spin.

Make a new Internal Component called Shoulder Bolt and Isolate the Shoulder Bolt component.

Make a new Sketch on the Right Plane and sketch this profile to the left of the Origin.

Make the bottom horizontal line a Centerline and Coincident to the Origin.

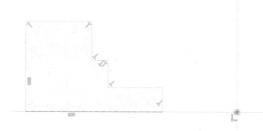

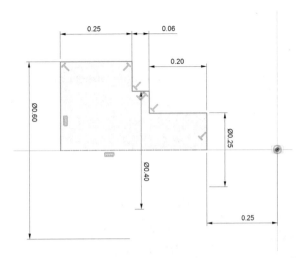

Add the following dimensions:

Revolve this part about the Centerline and give it a Brushed Stainless Steel Appearance.

Add a 0.04" chamfer to the shank's end, add a thread to the smallest cylinder, set it as a 1/4"-20 Thread, and move the Thread feature before the Chamfer feature.

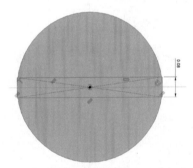

Make a sketch on the bolt head and make a 0.08" tall Center Rectangle at the Origin. Make one of the vertical lines tangent to the outer circle.

Extrude Cut this into the head 0.16". This is a standard-size slot for a flat-head screwdriver.

Add 0.01" chamfers to the Bolt head's round and front surfaces.

Activate the Root Component and move the Shoulder Bolt near the threaded hole on the Wheel Bracket.

Add the Rigid joint to the shoulder edge and the threaded hole.

This component has a 0.06" wide shoulder, which will join with the Blade and leave a small gap to allow for rotation.

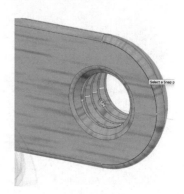

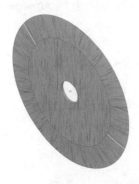

Blade

The last component is the Blade, which you will make from 18 gauge (0.050") stainless steel. This will allow enough tolerance for the blade to spin freely but not wobble side to side. Sheet metal comes in gauges; the higher the gauge, the thinner the material. These numbers change based on the type of metal you choose.

Make a new Internal Component called Blade, Isolate the component, and make the rough Sketch on the Right Plane.

Mirror the 3 lines about a vertical Centerline that is coincident to the Origin. Add the following dimensions and note that the 1.375" will give you a 2.75" diameter Blade.

This 0.05" wide blade will sit on the 0.06" wide shoulder of the Shoulder Bolt allowing enough tolerance to spin freely.

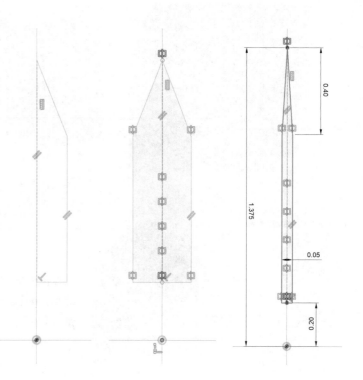

Revolve this profile about the Y-axis and add a Brushed Stainless Steel Appearance.

Activate the Root Component and move the Blade nearer the Shoulder Bolt.

Type J for Joint, change the Joint Type to Revolute, select the front edge of the Blade's hole, orbit your view to the back, and select the back edge of the shoulder on the Shoulder Bolt.

Before clicking OK, click and drag the Y-axis 0.005" so the Blade sits symmetrically on the Shoulder Bolt.

You can animate this motion by selecting the Motion tab in the Dialog Box and clicking the play button.

Activate the Root Component and save the file.

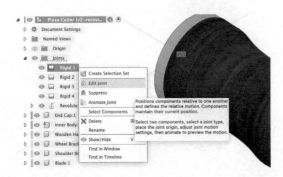

Expand Joints in Browser, right-click on Rigid 1, Edit Joint, change the Type to Cylindrical which will allow it to rotate and linearly move.

Click on the round edge of the End Cap which defines the axis that the End Cap will linearly move along, and click OK.

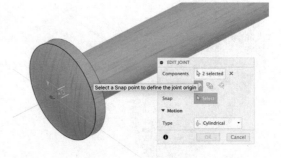

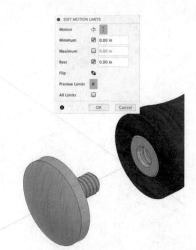

Right-click Cylindrical 1 in the Browser, click Edit Motion Limits, change Motion from Rotate to Slide, check Minimum and Rest, and click Preview Limits to verify that the End Cap is moving away from the Pizza Cutter, not into it. Click OK.

Click and drag the End Cap and notice that it can move outwards and rotate, but not like a bolt would, so let's fix that.

Navigate to Assemble >> Motion Link, click Cylindrical 1 in the Browser, check Link with Same Joint, set Distance to 1/20 because this thread makes 20 revolutions per inch, and click OK.

Now, you can click and rotate the End Cap to unscrew it from the Pizza Cutter, just like in real life!

This project is all done and is a sign from the universe for you to go out and grab a slice!

CHALLENGE

Recreate another kitchen utensil with moving parts. For example, a can opener, tongs, or an ice cream scoop.

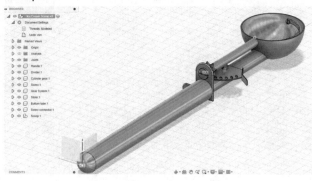

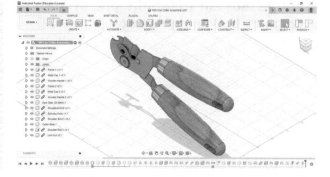

@Maximusber
User #338

@Moses Shaib
User #681

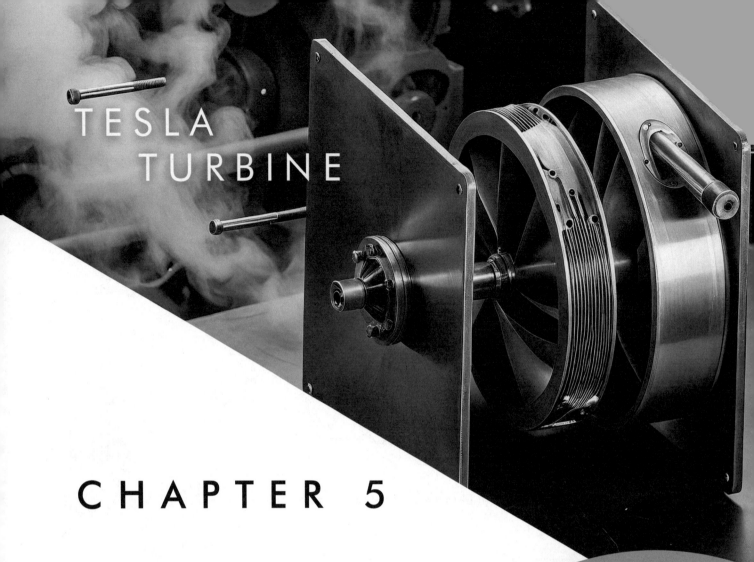

TESLA TURBINE

CHAPTER 5

This project is a tribute to Nikola Tesla, one of the most prominent inventors the world has ever known.

It is also a compelling Autodesk Fusion build, bringing together many concepts you've learned so far into one of the complex builds of this book.

DIFFICULTY:
★★★★★

TIME ESTIMATE:
4 HOURS

KEY LEARNING:
- Make Subassemblies
- Move components to make copies
- Pattern or mirror a component

DISCORD LINK:
Discord.gg/5hbt6xDPqf

INTRODUCTION

Nikola Tesla was one of the most prolific inventors of all time, developing many ingenious devices and ideas throughout his life. One of those inventions was a new type of blade-less turbine that relied on the drag force of fluids passing over a surface. This is the same force you feel when you put your hand out the window of a car.

This Tesla Turbine will be made closely to scale to Nikola Tesla's Original patent. It should be noted that when Tesla designed this turbine, it was impossible for it to work due to the limiting material sciences of his time.

In this lesson, you will build a Tesla Turbines scaled down to be manufacturable in a small machine shop. You will continue to explore the use of Joints and Components and gain a deeper understanding of how they work together.

This is one of the longer and more difficult builds in this book, so stick with it, and good luck! If you can complete this project, it's easy sailing from here on out!

CAD

Because Nikola Tesla filed a U.S. Patent on this turbine, this model will be designed in inches, so verify your Units are set to inches.

This project can be broken down into 2 main parts: the Stator and the Rotor. The Stator will consist of the Housing, the Inlet and the Outlet, all parts that are stationary that direct the flow of the fluid, i.e. Steam. The Rotor subassembly will consist of the Discs, Spacers, and Axle, all parts that rotate and convert the flow of fluid into harnessable energy.

Housing & Inlet Tube

The Housing & Inlet Tube is a large ring that encompasses the turbine discs while allowing steam into to enter through tangentially. Holes in the Inlet Tube allow the steam to be accelerated to spin the turbine discs faster to generate more power.

Make a new Internal Component called Stator Subassembly and make another new Internal Component called Housing & Inlet Tube inside it.

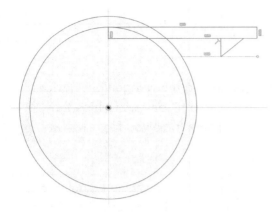

Make the following sketch on the Front Plane of 2 Concentric circles, a rectangle, a triangle, and a horizontal Centerline.

Set the rectangle's top left point to be Coincident with the inner circle and Vertically constrained to the Origin.

Add a Coincident constraint between the bottom point of the triangle and the Centerline.

Dimension the inner circle to be 9.00" * 1.02. This makes the inner surface 2% larger than the spinning 9" Disc's diameter you will make later. This tight tolerance improves the turbine's efficiency.

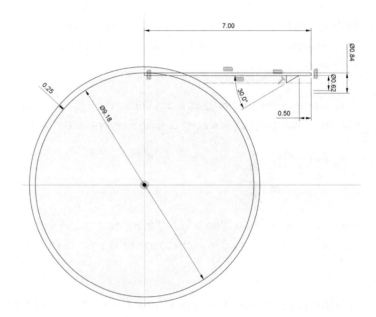

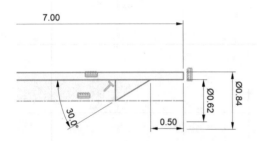

Finish the Sketch and Symmetrically Extrude the 2 profiles that make up the ring to a Whole Length of 2.25".

This Housing must have a thick Wall to handle high rpm vibrations and large thermal loads and be able to stand up to welds without melting.

Note that you are designing this project symmetrically about the Origin and the Front Plane to mirror and pattern parts more easily. This is a big part of becoming better at CAD and how you can make life easier for yourself down the line. Several components in this project are mirrored about the Front Plane, so symmetrically extruding this part is beneficial.

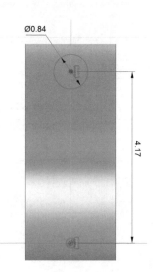

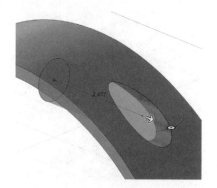

Make a Sketch on the Right Plane of a 0.84" diameter circle that is Vertically constrained and 4.17" above the Origin.

Finish this Sketch and Extrude Cut it through the right side of the Housing Body.

Show Sketch 1, revolve the 4 Profiles that make up the Inlet Tube, and set the Operation to Join.

Extrude cut the inner circle's profile symmetrically to a Whole Length of 2.25" to cut away the revolved section.

Add a Polished Aluminum Appearance to the Body.

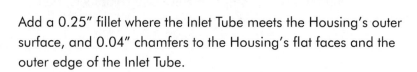

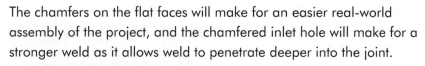

Add a 0.25" fillet where the Inlet Tube meets the Housing's outer surface, and 0.04" chamfers to the Housing's flat faces and the outer edge of the Inlet Tube.

The chamfers on the flat faces will make for an easier real-world assembly of the project, and the chamfered inlet hole will make for a stronger weld as it allows weld to penetrate deeper into the joint.

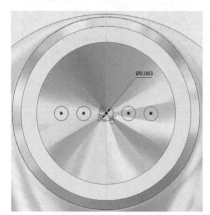

Make a new Sketch on the right face of the Inlet Tube, sketch a 1/16" circle at its center, select the Rectangular Pattern tool, select the 1/16" circle, change the Distribution to Spacing, set the Quantity to 5, the Spacing to 0.1", the Direction to Symmetric, and click OK.

Extrude Cut the 5 profiles -1.25" into the Inlet Tube.

These holes more evenly distribute the airflow to the rest of the Discs instead of a single central hole, which only forces fluid at the middle Discs.

Click the house icon on the View Cube so the end of the Inlet Tube faces you, and apply a Thread to the Tube. Uncheck Full Length, set the Length to 0.75", and change the Thread Type to ISO Pipe Thread.

In the real world, this Inlet Tube would receive a 1/2" NPT (National Standard Pipe Thread Taper) thread. This feature is currently available for internal threads but not external threads.

Housing Gaskets

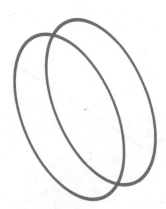

Two rubber Gaskets will be placed on either side of the Housing to seal it. A Gasket is a thin sheet of material that seals off a cavity, usually made from rubber or cork.

They are commonly found in engine compartments, food containers, and water-tight appliances, among many other things.

Activate the Stator Subassembly and make a new Internal Component called Housing Gaskets.

Note that you Activated the Subassembly, not the Root Component at the top of the Browser, which will place the Housing Gaskets component inside the Subassembly, not on the same level as it.

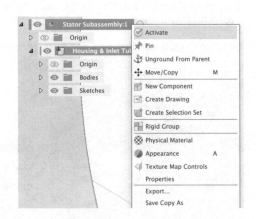

You will mirror these parts on either side of the Front Plane, meaning you can make one and duplicate it to the other side. If you need to change it in the future, you can adjust the 1st one, and the 2nd will automatically update.

Extrude the front face of the Housing to 0.025" and verify the Operation is set to New Body.

Open the Appearance tool, search for Rubber-Soft, and drag it onto the component. Double-click the Soft Rubber Appearance in the menu and change the color slider to red in the top left corner.

Navigate to Create >> Mirror, select the Housing Gasket, verify the Object Type is set to Bodies, and Mirror about the Front Plane. Expand Bodies under the component and notice that there are 2 Bodies in 1 Component. Click and drag one of the Gaskets and notice that the other will move with it because both Bodies are inside 1 Component.

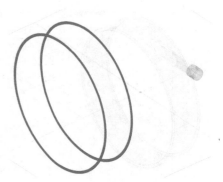

Ctrl/Cmd + Z to undo that movement, activate the Stator Subassembly, and add a Rigid As-Built Joint between the Housing Gasket and the Housing & Inlet Tube.

Power Side Wall

To cap off the Housing, you will need 2 Walls on either side with a circular recess to accept the Housing, the Gaskets, and a bearing in the middle to reduce friction when spinning. This Wall is where the Axle will extend to attach to a generator. The other Wall is where excess steam will exit.

Make a new Internal Component called Power Side Wall.

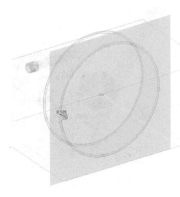

Orbit to the back side of the Stator and make an Offset Plane 0.125" from the back Gasket.

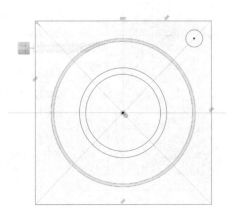

Make a new Sketch on this Offset Plane, sketch a Center Rectangle, two concentric circles at the Origin, and a circle on the Center Rectangle's diagonal lines in the top right corner.

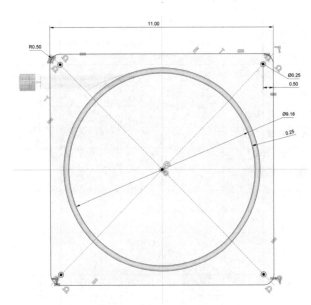

Navigate to Modify >> Fillet, click 2 edges to see the red fillet preview, repeat on the other 3 corners, and set the Fillets to 0.50".

Add Equal constraints to the rectangle's edges, add the following dimensions, and Circularly Pattern the 0.25" circle about the Origin to a Quantity of 4.

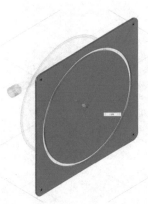

Finish the Sketch and extrude the outer and inner profiles -0.125"into the Turbine.

Show Sketch 1 in the Browser, extrude all 3 profiles away from the turbine 0.125", Hide Sketch 1, and add a Polished Aluminum Appearance.

Type H for Hole, click on the back face of the component, and click and drag the hole till it snaps on the center white dot.

Set the Hole Type to Counterbore and add the following dimensions: 0.25" in depth, 0.625" in top diameter, 0.2 in Counterbore depth, and 0.55" in bottom diameter.

This stepped hole will allow for a bearing to be seated.

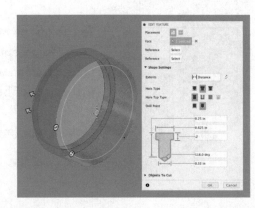

Hold down Ctrl/Cmd, select all 4 holes' inner faces, select the Thread tool to apply a ¼"-20 Thread, and click OK.

Activate the Stator Subassembly and add a Rigid As-Built Joint between the Power Side Wall and the Housing Gaskets.

With the McMaster Carr tool, import the sealed bearing 3759T58, and rotate and move it to the back side of the Power Side Wall.

Type J for Joint, click the outer edge of the bearing, the outer edge of the counterbore hole, and click OK.

Steam Side Wall

This Wall is almost identical to the Power Side Wall but has holes that allow steam to escape and threaded holes for attaching an exit funnel.

Activate the Stator Subassembly, navigate to Create >> Mirror, set the Object Type to Components, select the Power Side Wall and the bearing in the Browser, select the Front Plane as the Mirror Plane, and click OK.

Double-click the Power Side Wall (Mirror) component in the Browser and rename it Steam Side Wall.

Add a Rigid As-Built Joint between the Steam Side Wall component and its bearing.

Select the As-Built Joint tool, change the Type to Slider, select the Steam Side Wall component, select the Housing & Inlet Tube component, and click any circular edge on the bearing so the Steam Side Wall slides away from the turbine.

Right-click the Slider joint feature in the Timeline, click Edit Motion Limits, check Minimum and Rest, and verify the Steam Side Wall is sliding away from the turbine, not into it. If it is passing through the Turbine, click Flip.

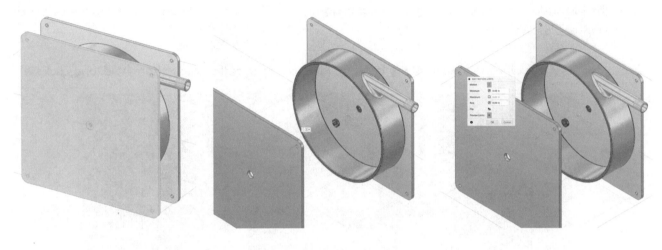

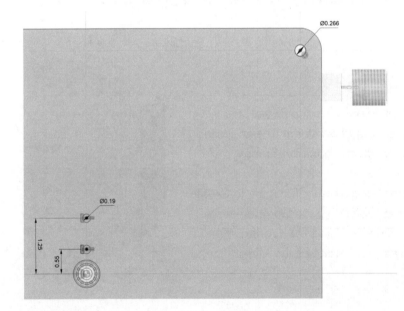

Activate the Steam Side Wall component in the Browser and make a new Sketch on its front face.

Sketch a 0.266" circle that is concentric with the top right hole and two 0.19" circles that are Vertically constrained to the Origin and 1.25" and 0.55" above the Origin.

Extrude Cut the 2 circles and the ring profile -0.25".

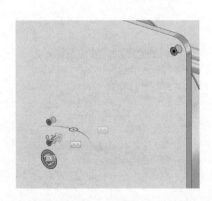

Perform 3 Circular Patterns by changing the Object Type to faces and selecting the hole's inner surface: the 0.266" hole to a Quantity of 4, the top 0.19" hole to a Quantity of 6, and the bottom 0.19" hole to a Quantity of 12.

Hold down Ctrl/Cmd, select the 6 Circularly Patterned holes, select the Thread tool, change the Designation to 10-32, and click OK.

   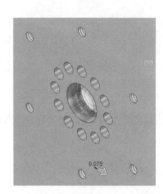

Activate the Stator Subassembly in the Browser, import 91251A553, a ¼"-20 x 2.75" bolt from the McMaster Carr tool, and rotate and move it near the top left hole of the Steam Side Wall.

Type J for Joint, change the Joint Type to Slider, click an edge on the underside of the bolt's head, and click on the front edge of the hole.

Click the Motion tab on the Joint Dialog Box, check Minimum and Rest, and verify the bolt is moving away from the turbine.

Expand Joints in the Browser under the Stator Subassembly. Navigate to Assemble >> Motion Link. Click Slider 5, then Slider 6, Type 1.00" in the top Distance and 2.00" in the bottom Distance to make for a 1:2 movement ratio.

Now, when you click and drag the Steam Side Wall, the bolt will move twice as far.

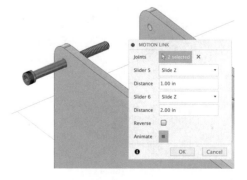

Navigate to Create >> Circular Patter, set the Object Type to Components, select the ¼"-20 x 2.75" bolt, select the Y-axis as the Axis, and set the Quantity to 4.

Navigate to Assemble >> Rigid Group, select all 4 bolts and click OK. Now, when you click and drag the Steam Side Wall, all 4 bolts will be joined together without needing to make individual Motion Links on each bolt.

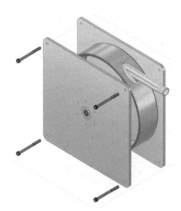

Outlet Nozzle and Gasket

The last 2 components in the Stator are the Outlet Nozzle and Gasket.

The Nozzle directs steam from the 12 circles on the Steam Side Wall into a central pipe with the same NPT pipe thread as the Inlet. If the Inlet and the Outlet don't have the same cross-sectional area, efficiency will decrease by throttling the steam.

Make a new Internal Component called Outlet Gasket, make a new Sketch on the front face of the Steam Side Wall, and make the following sketch of 3 circles. Note the top 0.25" circle is coincident to the threaded hole in the Steam Side Wall.

Circularly Pattern the 0.25" circle about the Origin to a Quantity of 6 around each bolt hole.

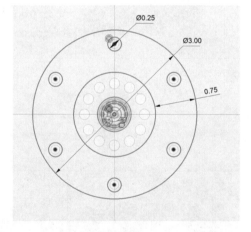

Extrude the Profile 0.025" and add the Red Rubber Appearance used on the Housing Gaskets.

Activate the Stator Subassembly and add a Rigid As-Built Joint between the Outlet Gasket and the Steam Side Wall.

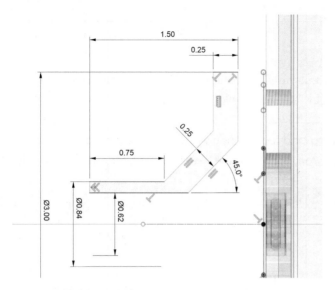

Make a new Internal Component called Outlet Nozzle and make a new Sketch on the Right Plane.

Project the front face of the Outlet Gasket and make the following sketch that includes 2 parallel lines and a Centerline. Coincidently constrain the sketch's right line to a projected point, and Finish the Sketch.

Revolve this profile about the Centerline and add a Polished Aluminum Appearance.

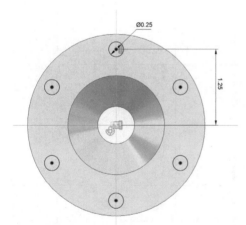

Right-click the Outlet Nozzle in the Browser and Isolate it. Make a new Sketch on the back face of the component of a circle that is Vertically Constrained to the Origin, dimensioned, and Circularly Patterned about the Origin 6 times.

Extrude Cut the 6 Profiles through the entire component.

Highlight the entire part and add a 0.02" chamfer.

Add an ISO Pipe Thread to the cylinder, which should be the same as the Inlet Tube.

Activate the Stator Subassembly, Unisolate the Outlet Nozzle, and add a Rigid As-Built Joint to between the Outlet Nozzle and the Steam Side Wall.

Note that you could also add the As-Built Joint between the Outlet Nozzle and the Outlet Gasket, too, for the same result, but the Steam Side Wall is easier to select.

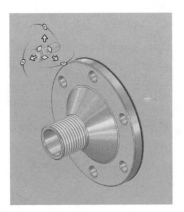

Using the McMaster Carr tool, import the 10-32 ½" bolt, 91251A342, and rotate and position it near the Outlet Nozzle.

Add a Rigid joint between the underside of the bolt's head and the Outlet Nozzle's top hole's outer edge.

Navigate to Assemble >> Duplicated with Joints, click the 10-32 bolt, and select the other 5 outer edges of the Outlet Nozzle.

This new tool patterns the components and adds the joints at the same time. It is most effective when all the duplicated components need to be facing the same direction.

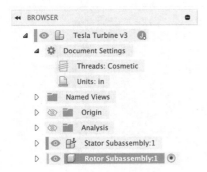

Collapse the Stator Subassembly, activate the Root Component at the top of the Browser, and create a new Internal Component called Rotor Subassembly.

Central Axle

This part rotates and holds the Discs, Spacers, and Brass Shoulders.

It supports the weight of the spinning Discs and must be made from a hard material, such as stainless steel.

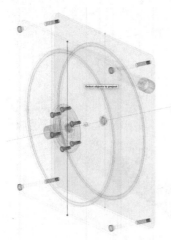

With the Rotor Subassembly still Activated, make another new Internal Component called Central Axle.

Make a new Sketch on the Right Plane and project the Front face of the Steam Side Wall and the back face of the Power Side Wall.

Click the Eye Icon of the Stator Assembly to Hide it.

Sketch a rectangle whose bottom horizontal line is coincident with the Origin and a Centerline. Dimension its left edge to be 0.25" to the left of the left projected line and 1" to the right of the right projected line.

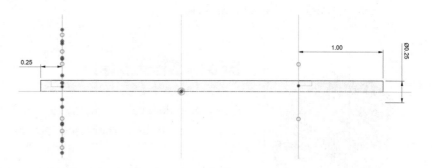

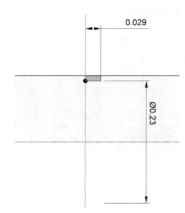

Sketch 2 more smaller rectangles inside the Central Axle profile that are on the outside of the projected lines. Add Equal constraints to the width and height of the rectangles.

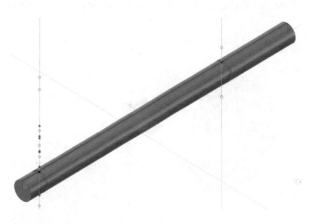

Revolve the 3 profiles about the Centerline. This will leave you with a cylinder with square grooves to accept two retaining rings.

Make a new Sketch on the Right Plane of four equally sized rectangles with four sets of Collinear constraints. Dimension the sketch as the following:

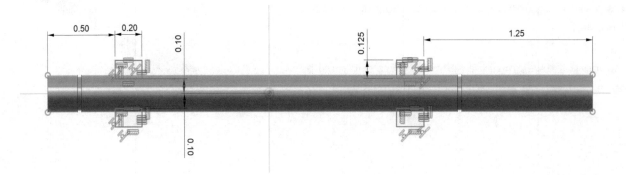

Extrude the four profiles Symmetrically to a Whole Length of 0.25" and add a Polished Stainless Steel Appearance.

You cannot use the All Extent Type because you have a curved surface.

These cutouts are the flat surfaces that 4 set screws screw down into. If you tighten screws onto a round surface, they can easily slip and rotate with the Axle.

Brass Shoulders

Brass Shoulders will be rigidly locked to the Central Axle, allowing the Discs and Spacers to be compressed together and secured in place.

Activate the Rotor Subassembly and make a New Component called Brass Shoulders.

Make a Sketch on the Right Plane, Project the front face of the Central Axle, and make the following Sketch of six lines:

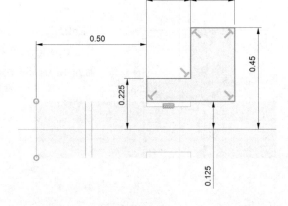

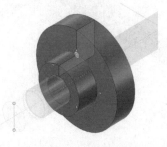

Revolve this part about the Y-axis. This part will attach to the Central Axle, hence having a hole the same diameter as the Axle.

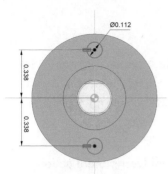

Sketch two Vertically and Equally constrained 0.112" circles on the stepped face and extrude cut these profiles through the component.

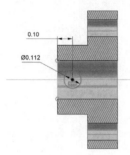

Make a new Sketch on the Right Plane, check Slice in the Sketch Palette for a bisected view, and sketch and dimension a 0.112" circle that is Horizontally Constrained to the Origin.

Finish the Sketch and Symmetrically Extrude Cut the profile to a Whole Length of 0.5".

Highlight the entire component and add 0.01" chamfer to all edges.

Hold down Ctrl/Cmd, select the four hole faces, and add 4-40 Threads.

4-40 is often the smallest size bolts you will find in machine shops.

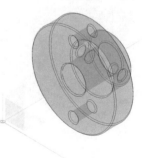

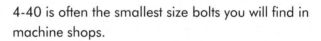

Select the Mirror tool, change the Object type to Bodies, select the Brass Shoulder, and Mirror it about the Front Plane.

Again, because this step will make 2 Bodies inside 1 Component, when you move one Brass Shoulder, the other will move with it.

Rotor Discs

The Rotor Discs are the most essential part of a Tesla Turbine, as they rotate when steam is let into the system. The Disc is made from thin sheet metal with a central hole for the Central Axle, 2 eccentric holes for long 4-40 bolts, and 6 patterned holes to allow the steam to escape.

Activate the Rotor Subassembly and make a new Internal Component called Rotor Discs.

Make a new Sketch on the Front face of the Mirrored Brass Shoulder and Isolate the Rotor Disc component.

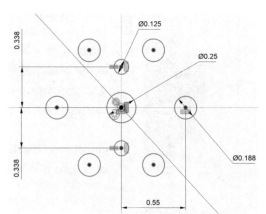

Sketch a large 9.00" circle at the Origin and the following geometries inside it.

Extrude the Profiles 1/32" and add a Polished Aluminum Appearance.

Rotor Spacers

Spacers between the Rotor Discs allow steam to enter, spinning the turbine. Ideally, the gap between the Discs is equal to 2 boundary layers; any more than that and there is free-flowing steam that doesn't contact the Discs. This boundary layer is a function of the turbulence and the viscosity of the steam entering the turbine. Conveniently for this turbine, the boundary layer is roughly equal to the Disc's thickness, so having 2 Spacers between Discs works well.

Activate the Rotor Subassembly and make a new Internal Component called Rotor Spacers.

Make a new Sketch on the front face of the Rotor Disc, Project the front face, and sketch a 0.90" circle.

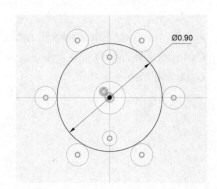

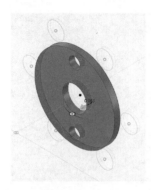

Extrude this profile 1/16".

For Tesla Turbines, it is critical that the Rotor Spacers are double the thickness of the Rotor Discs for the best transfer of energy from the steam to rotational energy.

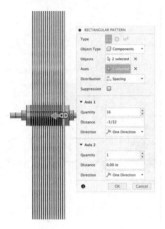

Activate the Rotor Subassembly and Show all components inside the Subassembly.

Navigate to Create >> Pattern >> Rectangular Pattern, set the Object Type to Component, select the Rotor Disc and Rotor Spacer components, select the Y-axis as the Axes, set the Distribution to Spacing, set the Quantity to 16 and the Distance to -3/32" (1/32" Disc + 1/16" Spacer).

Notice that the Browser is now very long with 16 Spacers and 16 Discs. To compress this, make a new Internal Component called Discs and Spacers, click the top Rotor Disc in the Browser, hold down the Shift key, click the bottom Rotor Spacer to highlight them all, and click and drag the selected list into the new Internal Component.

Use the McMaster Carr tool to import a 4-40 x 1-7/8" bolt, 91772A516, rotate it, and move it in front of the Rotor Assembly. Add a Rigid joint by clicking an edge on the underside of the bolt's head, and the Brass Shoulder's top outer edge.

Select the Duplicate With Joint tool, select the bolt, and click the bottom hole's outer edge.

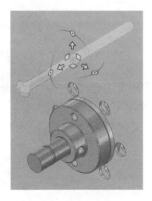

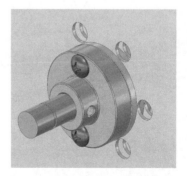

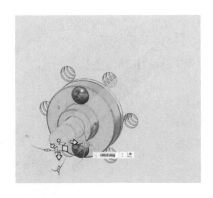

Type M for Move, click the front face of the Central Axle, and rotate it 90 degrees so the flat faces line up with the radial threaded holes.

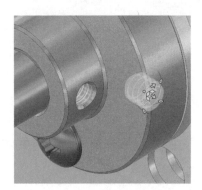

Use the McMaster Carr tool to import a 4-40 x 1/8" set screw, 94355A130, rotate it, and position it near the threaded hole on the Brass Shoulder.

Add a joint to the center of the flat face on the underside of the 4-40 set screw, and the center of the flat face on the Central Axle.

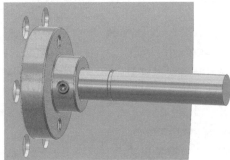

Use the Duplicate With Joint tool to duplicate this set screw to the other flat face on the right side of the Central Axle.

Use the Mirror tool to mirror the 2 set screw components about the Right Plane.

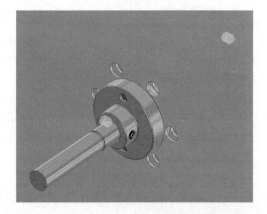

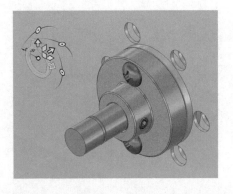

Use the McMaster Carr tool to import a Retaining Ring, 97633A130, to prevent the Axle from moving axially when spinning.

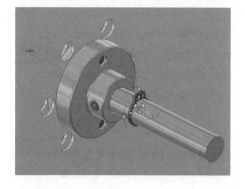

Select the retaining ring component in the Browser,
Ctrl/Cmd + C (Copy), Ctrl/Cmd + V (Paste) the component, and
set the X distance to 2.833" to the other groove.

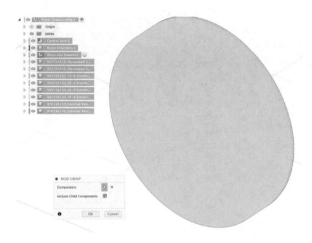

Select the Rigid Group tool, select the Rotor
Subassembly in the Browser, and click OK to join all
parts together.

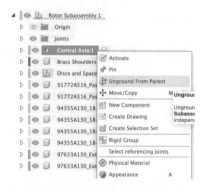

Activate the Root Component at the top of the Browser, right-click the
Central Axle component, click Unground From Parent, and expand the
Stator Subassembly.

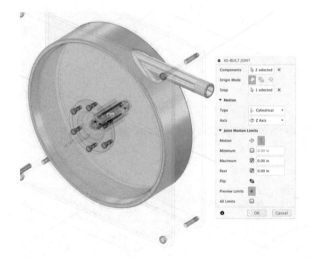

Select As-Built Joint, change the Type to Cylindrical,
select the Central Axle and the Housing component
in the Browser, set the Motion to Slide, and check
Maximum and Rest so the Axle is rotating and moving
away from the turbine.

Select the Motion Link tool, expand Joints
under the Root Component and under the
Stator Subassembly, click on the first Slider
joint under the Stator Subassembly, then the
Cylindrical joint under the Root Component, set
the Distances to 2.00" and 1.00" respectively,
check Reverse and click Animate to verify that
the Rotor Assembly moves out of the Stator
Subassembly at half the speed of the Steam
Side Wall.

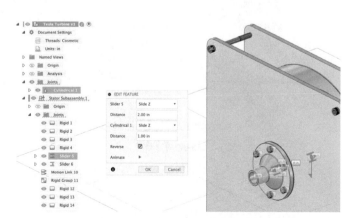

Select the Motion Link tool again, select the Cylindrical joint under the Root Component, check Link with Same Joint, and click OK.

Now, when you click and drag the Steam Side Wall, the 4 bolts will eject, and the Rotor Subassembly will come out of the Housing and rotate at the same time!

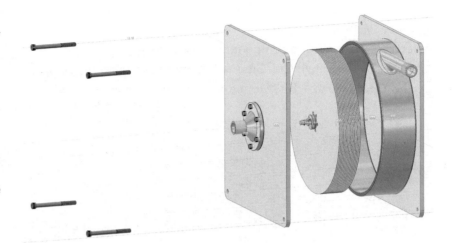

DISCUSSION

Laser Cutter File Type

DXF files are commonly used for laser cutting. You can right-click any sketch and save it as a DXF from the Browser. In this project, you can save the Gasket Sketch as a DXF, since laser cutters are sometimes used to produce them.

CHALLENGE

Find one of the mechanical mechanisms on **507movements.com**. Recreate it and apply moving, Revolute, and Slider joints.

@Paul Hobbiest
User #763

@Moses Shaib
User #681

CHAPTER 5 QUESTIONS

1. Which one of these is not a type of joint?

    a. Revolute

    b. Planar

    c. Ball

    d. Coaxial

2. Which of these is not an example of a revolute joint?

    a. Rack and pinion gears

    b. Bicycle wheel

    c. Pizza cutter wheel

    d. Spur gears

3. How many degrees of freedom does a Planar Joint have?

    a. 3: 2 rotational, 1 linear

    b. 2: 2 rotational

    c. 3: 1 rotational, 2 linear

    d. 2: 2 linear

4. True or False? Joint Origins can only be placed on corners, centers or midpoints.

5. True or False? External components require a folder to house components, internal assemblies do not.

6. True or False? A component that is rigidly joined to grounded component will not move.

7. If a component is inconvenient to make in place in the assembly you should … ?

    a. Make the component in a separate stand-alone file and import it later

    b. Push through and make it in place

    c. Make it in a separate assembly file and import it

    d. Import a premade file from a 3D model hub

8. Which of these is not a way to duplicate components?

    a. Pattern tools

    b. Copy and paste

    c. Duplicate

    d. Create Copy

9. To change the starting position of an extrusion you would adjust the … ?

    a. Starting Offset

    b. Ending Offset

    c. Extent type

    d. Distance Type

10. To measure the distance between two components, you would use which tool?

    a. Distance

    b. Measure

    c. Inspect

    d. Inspect Distance

CHAPTER 6
MOTION ANIMATION

HOW TO MAKE YOUR MODEL MOVE
AND COME ALIVE

- STRANDBEEST
- GEAR TRAIN
- ROBOTIC HAND

MOTION ANIMATION

Now that you are comfortable with Assemblies and Joints, the next step is animating them.

All Joints, except for Rigid joints, allow a degree of freedom linearly, rotationally, or a combination of both. In this chapter, you will make a motion study to learn how to animate these Joints and see how your entire project moves.

Motion studies are helpful for hobbyist robotics, product prototypes, gears, kinetic art, and more.

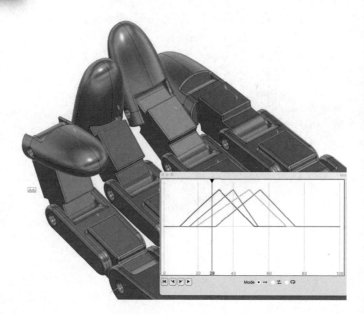

STRANDBEEST

CHAPTER 6

A sciency, nerdy, bioengineered sculpture, the Strandbeest is truly a mythic creature, walking along beaches using only the wind.

Theo Jansen's creations have captured the imagination of many.

In this project, you will recreate some of the beast's joints and explore its movement.

DIFFICULTY:
★★☆☆☆

TIME ESTIMATE:
1 HOUR

KEY LEARNING:

- How multiple revolute joints affect each other
- Animate a model's joints

DISCORD LINK:
Discord.gg/5hbt6xDPqf

INTRODUCTION

Strandbeests, or beach beasts, are animal analogs designed by Dutch mathematician Theo Jansen.

These "animals" are self-moving creatures made from recycled material, wind-powered, and walk by mimicking quadruped animals.

By utilizing Autodesk Fusion's movement animation capabilities, you will apply motion to a Strandbeest Leg.

CAD

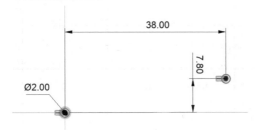

Set the Units to Millimeters (mm) and make a new Internal Component called Pins.

Make the following Sketch on the Front Plane of 2 Equally Constrained 2 mm circles and dimension them as follows.

Extrude these 2 profiles -6 mm towards you.

Since the Original Stranbeests (roughly translated from Dutch to Beach Beasts) are made of PVC, they eventually become sun-bleached and yellowed as they walk across the beaches of the Netherlands. To make your Strandbeest look more realistic, search ABS, drag it onto both cylinders, double-click the ABS icon, and change the color to be more yellowed.

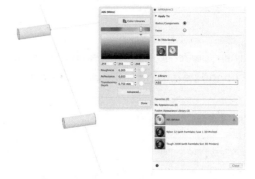

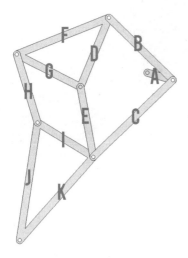

This project consists of several stacked arms linked with Revolute joints and driven by one axis. You will design each part layer by layer and join them together later, so do not worry about the exact location of your sketches, as they will be moved.

This diagram shows the component names of all the parts of this Strandbeest Leg.

Activate the Root Component, make a new Internal Component called A Link, and make a Sketch on the Front Plane.

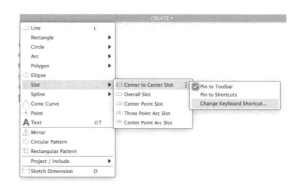

This project will contain many Center to Center Slots. To save time, you can make a custom shortcut.

Select the 3 vertical dots next to Center to Center Slot and select Change Keyboard Shortcut. Since S is already taken with the search tool, type Shift+S and click OK.

Other common custom Sketch Shortcuts include: Shift+R for the Center Rectangle tool, Shift+T for the Text tool, and Shift+P for the Polygon tool.

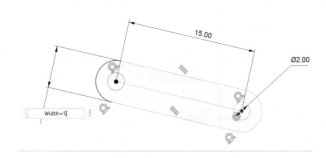

Type Shift+S to select the C2C Slot (Center To Center Slot) tool, click the center of the right Pin's profile, move your cursor down and to the right, click again, move your cursor away, and click again to define the width.

Sketch a 2mm circle at the other arc center, dimension the C2C distance at 15 mm, and set the slot's width as the Parameter: Width=5mm.

Their Center-to-Center lengths will be the only difference. This slot can be left undefined as the angle will change as it rotates. Because this component will move, it is not necessary to fully define this sketch.

Extrude this profile with the Parameter, Thickness = -2 mm and add the yellow ABS appearance.

Revolute joints will be added once all components in each layer are completed.

Activate the Root Component, make a new Internal Component called DGF Plate, and make a sketch on the Front Plane.

Sketch a triangle of three C2C Slots from the Origin, sketch three 2 mm circles at each corner, dimension the slot's width with the Parameter Width, and dimension the length of the C2C slots: D = 41.5 mm (Right), F = 55.8 mm (Left), G = 40.1 mm (Bottom).

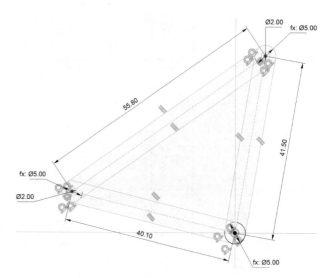

Extrude the 6 profiles the Parameter Thickness and add the yellow appearance.

Verify that the Pin's back and the Plate's back are coplanar.

Activate the Root Component, make a new Internal Component called IJK Plate, and make a sketch on the Front Plane.

Make a similar sketch to the DGF Plate of an upside-down triangle of C2C slots, sketch three 2 mm circles at each corner, dimension the slot's width with the Parameter Width, and dimension the length of the C2C slots: I = 36.7 mm (Top), J = 65.7 mm (Left), K = 61.9 mm (Right). Activate the Root Component.

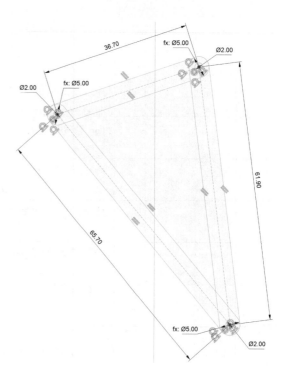

Extrude the 6 profiles the Parameter Thickness and add the yellow appearance.

Add a Revolute As-Built Joint between the right Pin and A Link and snap to any circular edge on the right Pin.

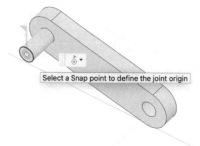

Select a Snap point to define the joint origin

Add a Revolute As-Built Joint between the left Pin and DFG Plate and snap to any circular edge on the left Pin.

Now, A Link and DFG Plate can both rotate about their respective Pins; do not move the IJK Plate as it needs to be planar to the other Link and Plate.

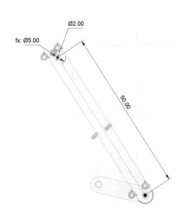

Make a new Internal Component called B Link, make a new Sketch on the front face of A Link, and project the right circle of A Link.

Make a 50 mm C2C Slot from A_Link's hole up to the left. Add the 2 mm circle and the dimensions shown.

Extrude the 2 profiles -Thickness away from the first layer of components and change its appearance to the yellow ABS.

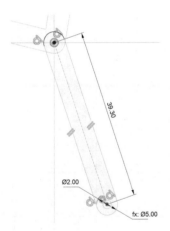

Activate the Root Component, make a new Internal Component called E Link, and make a new Sketch on the front face of the DFG Plate.

Project the right Pin, sketch a 39.3 mm C2C slot from the projected point downwards, and sketch a 2 mm circle.

Extrude the profile -Thickness away from the first layer and change its appearance to the yellow ABS.

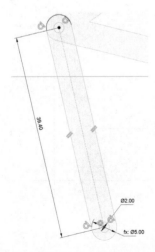

Activate the Root Component, make a new Internal Component called H Link, and make a new Sketch on the front face of the DGF Plate.

Project the left hole of the DFG Plate, sketch a 39.4 mm C2C slot from the projected point downwards, and sketch a 2 mm circle.

Extrude the profile -Thickness away from the first layer of components, change its appearance to the yellow ABS, and Activate the Root Component.

Add a Revolute As-Built Joint to A Link and B Link and click on any circular edge they share.

Add a Revolute As-Built Joint to E Link and DFG Plate and click on any circular edge they share.

Add a Revolute As-Built Joint to H Link and DFG Plate and click on any circular edge they share.

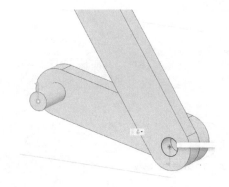 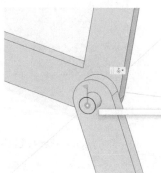 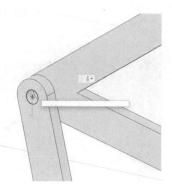

Type J for Joint, verify the Joint Type is set to Revolute, click the back edge of B Link's top hole, click the front edge of DFG Plate's top hole, and click OK.

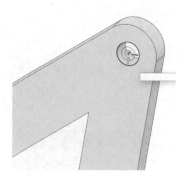

Verify you are joining your parts correctly by clicking and rotating A Link to see DFG Plate move back and forth.

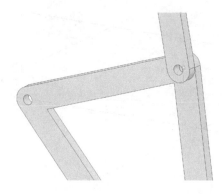

Type J for Joint, click the front edge of IJK Plate's top right hole, click the back edge of E Link's bottom hole, and click OK.

Click and drag E Link so the holes on H Link and IJK Plate are much closer together.

Type J for Joint, click the front edge of IJK Plate's top left hole, click the back edge of H Link's bottom hole, and click OK.

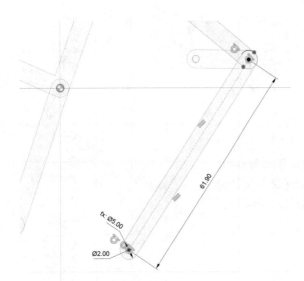

Move the A Link into a horizontal position, make a new Internal Component called C Link, and make a sketch on the front face of B Link.

Project the front face of B Link and sketch a 61.9 mm long C2C Slot and a 2 mm circle.

Extrude the profile -Thickness away from the second layer and change its appearance to the yellow ABS.

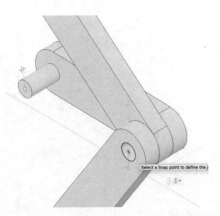

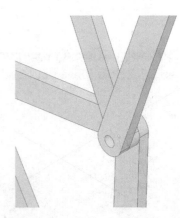

Add a Revolute As-Built Joint to C Link and B Link and click on any circular edge they share.

Type J for Joint, click the front edge of E Link's bottom hole, click the back edge of C Link's bottom hole, and click OK.

MOTION ANIMATION

The simplest form of motion animation in Autodesk Fusion is to animate a single joint that runs an entire system of joints.

In this project, the joint where A_Link revolves around its Pin is the driving joint. If you animate this joint, the entire model moves.

If the model doesn't move, 1 of the joints was likely accidentally set to Rigid instead of Revolute.

To animate this system, expand the Joints in the Browser, right-click Joint Revolute 1, Animate Joint. This will activate that joint alone and suppress the other joints and Components. Press Esc.

Since you want the entire system of joints to move, right-click the Joint Revolute 1 again, and select Animate Joint Relationship. Now everything should move.

Pan around and check it out!

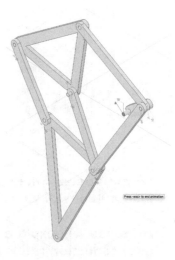

CHALLENGE

Make a double-sided Strandbeest with a leg on the left and the right powered by only 1 input.

@Dairy Air
User #569

GEAR TRAIN

CHAPTER 6

What happens when gears interact? It can take millions of years to make 1 revolution!

Here you will explore the world of gears and gear reduction ratios by building a gear train.

DIFFICULTY:
★★★☆

TIME ESTIMATE:
2.5 HOURS

KEY LEARNING:
- Fusion Plugins and where to find them
- Mathematics behind gear trains
- Add multiple motion links to a complex project

DISCORD LINK:
Discord.gg/5hbt6xDPqf

INTRODUCTION

Gear trains are gear systems that transmit power by reducing speed in exchange for higher torque and vice versa. They can be found in stand mixers, hand drills, and bicycles, to name a few popular items.

The math for gear systems is simple. For example, a 25-tooth input gear spinning at 1 rpm and Meshing with a 50-tooth output gear has a gear ratio of 25:50, or 1:2. The output gear spins at 1/2 rpm.

In this lesson, you will practice animations using components and joints as you build a gear reduction system called a gear train. You will use the pre-built library that comes standard with Autodesk Fusion. We highly recommend making this in real life if you can access a 3D printer.

CAD

Two gears attached to each other that share the same axis are known as a Compound Gear. Make as an Internal Component called Compound Gear.

Set your Units to Millimeters (mm) and select the Utilities tab at the top of the screen.

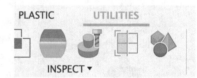

Navigate to Add-Ins >> and select Scripts and Add-Ins. Scroll down to the bottom, click either of the Spur Gear tools, and Click Run.

Make a Metric gear, 20 Deg, 1.5 Module, 20 Teeth, 0 Backlash, 0.88 mm Root Fillet, 8 mm Thick, and an 4 mm Hole Diameter.

This will produce a pitch diameter of 30 mm. See the Discussion at the end of the chapter for more information and definitions.

Click OK and notice the feature group in the Timeline.

Also, notice the green Construction circle. This is the pitch circle and defines the ideal distance between 2 meshing gears which will be used later in the Gear Rack component.

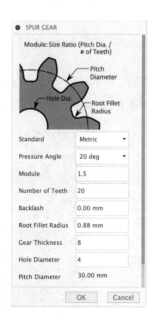

Make another gear with the same values except use 100 teeth and 4 mm thick. This will produce a 150 mm pitch diameter gear, giving you a 1:5 gear ratio; 20:100 = 1:5. Click OK. Hold down Ctrl/Cmd, select both Spur Gear components, and drag them into the Compound Gear component.

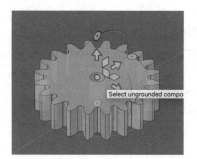

Type M for Move, click the center of the 20 teeth Spur Gear's hole, set the Z Distance to 4 mm, and the Z Angle to 360/20/2 for a half tooth rotation.

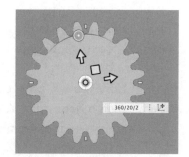

Navigate to the SOLID Tab, add a Rigid As-Built Joint to the 2 Spur Gears. Expand the Compound Gear component.

The large and small gears pitch diameter's sum is 180 mm, half of this value, 90 mm, is the ideal distance between the meshing gears centers.

Type M for Move, click the Spur Gear (100 Teeth) component in the Browser, click Set Pivot, orbit to the underside of the gear, select the bottom edge of the hole, and click the green check mark next to Set Pivot in the Dialog Box. Set the X Angle to 90 degrees which will rotate about the Origin, the location of the newly selected Pivot.

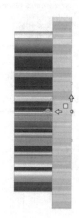

Make the following Sketch on the front face of the 20 Tooth Spur Gear.

Extrude this ring profile 4 mm, the difference in thickness of the gears, and add a 2 mm chamfer on the top edge. This reduces surface area and friction between spinning gears that are stacked on each other.

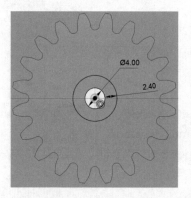

Create a Sketch on the front face of the 100 Tooth Spur Gear to reduce weight. Draw a vertical and angled Construction line from the Origin, 2 lines parallel to the Construction lines, 2 Concentric arcs, and add the following dimensions. Circularly sections the profile about the Origin and Extrude Cut all 6 profiles.

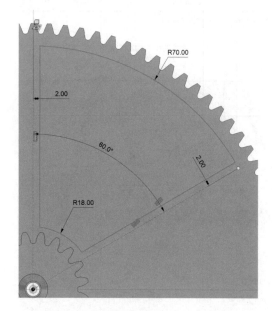

This Gear Train is a reduction system, meaning that the speed of each successive gear is exponentially slower than the previous one. To track how slowly the Compound Gears are spinning, you will make one tooth a different color that can be 3D Printed separately to the rest of the gear.

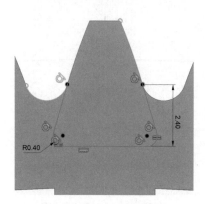

Make the following Sketch on top of the large gear's front face, add Tangent constraints to the angled lines and the curved edges of the teeth, and 0.4 mm fillets to the bottom corners.

Navigate to Modify >> Split Body, select the large gear as the Body To Split, select the Sketch as the Splitting Tool(s), uncheck Extend Splitting Tool(s), and click OK.

Open the Appearance tool and apply ABS to the Compound Gear and a contrasting accent color to the gear tooth.

Collapse the Compound Gear component, activate the Root Component, and make a new Internal component called Gear Rack.

Hide the Compound Gear component, start a new Sketch on the Front Plane, and sketch and dimension this sketch. Sketch the top left 4.00 mm circle at the Origin.

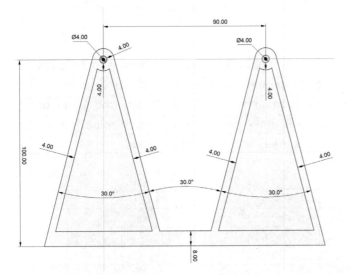

Extrude the profile 4 mm away from the Compound Gear and add 4 mm chamfers to the 6 lower edges for strength.

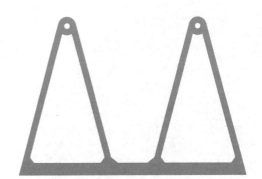

Show the Compound Gear component and Copy and Paste it 90 mm in the X Distance and -8 mm in the Y Distance.

Orbit around the meshing and note how the gear teeth mesh perfectly. This is due to the gears Pitch Diameters mentioned earlier. (30 mm + 150 mm) / 2 = 90 mm Pitch Radius found on the Gear Rack sketch and the half tooth rotation.

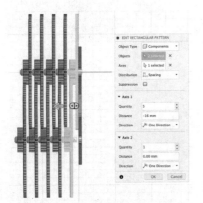

Navigate to Create >> Rectangular Pattern, select both Compound Gear components, set the Y-axis as the Axis, set the Distribution to Spacing, the Quantity to 5, the Distance to -16 (the height of 2 Compound Gears), and click OK.

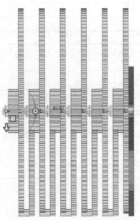

Copy and Paste the first Compound Gear component and move it -80 mm along the Y-axis to make a total of 11 Compound Gears. This will make the last gear in the train spin at 1 Revolution Per Year! If you're interested in the math of how to find out how many gears you need for this Gear Train, then refer to the Discussion section of this project.

Activate the Gear Rack component, expand Bodies, and Copy and Paste the Gear Rack Body -100 mm along the Y-axis.

Right-click the Gear Rack component and Isolate it, start a new Sketch on the front face of the new Body, and sketch 3 center point arc slots that are equal in diameter and horizontally constrained to the hole's center.

Add the following dimensions, mirror to the other hole, and Extrude Cut through the Body. This springed joint is an effective way to hold onto metal rods with 3D Printed parts; as you push the rod in, the arms flex out of the way and then hold a metal rod tightly without the need for glue or hardware.

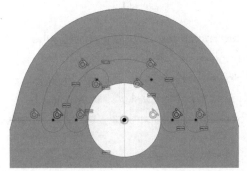 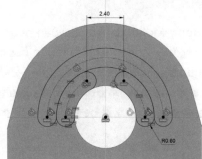 

Start a Sketch on the bottom face of a Rack and sketch a rectangle that is coincident to the inner corners. Extrude this profile upwards 8 mm and Verify the Operation is set to Join.

Extrude cut the small triangles on either side of the Gear Rack's base through all and change its Appearance.

Unisolate the Gear Rack component and Activate the Root Component at the top of the Browser.

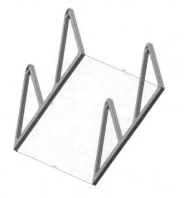  

Make a new Internal Component called 4 mm Rods, sketch two 4 mm circles on the front of the Gear Rack that are coincident to the Compound Gear's centers.

Extrude these profiles to the back face of the Gear Rack, add the Polished Aluminum Appearance to the two Bodies, and Activate the Root Component.

Add a Rigid As-Built Joint between the Gear Rack and the 4mm Rod component.

Hold down Ctrl/Cmd, select all 11 Compound Gear components in the Browser, right-click, select Unground From Parent, and right-click the Gear Rack component and select Ground To Parent.

MOTION ANIMATION

The purpose of this project is to apply Motion Links between gears that match the 5:1 gear ratio so they spin in realistic ways. Unfortunately, the Motion Animation in Fusion only lasts a few seconds. This is enough time to see the first few gears successively spin slower and slower but not long enough to see all gears move. Because of this, you will only be applying Revolute joints and Motion Links to the first 5 Compound Gears, as they are only ones you will be able to see move although technically, all of them are moving, just incredibly slowly.

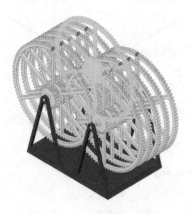

Select the Revolute As-Built tool, set the Joint Type to Revolute, select Compound Gear:1 in the Browser, then the 4 mm Rods component in the Browser, click the round edge of left 4mm Rod and click OK. Now your first gear can revolve.

Perform the same operation on Compound Gear:2 and the right 4 mm Rod.

Expand Joints in the Browser, navigate to Assemble >> Motion Link, click Revolute 2, Revolute 3, check Reverse and set the second Angle to 360/5 because of the 1:5 gear reduction.

Click and drag the first gear and see how the second gear rotates at a fifth of the speed but in the opposite direction.

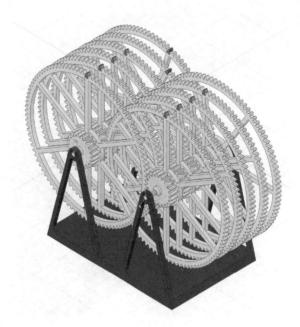

Continue this pattern of steps: Add a Revolute As-Built Joint to the 3rd Compound Gear and the 4 mm Rods, add a 5:1 Motion Link between Compound Gear 2 and 3, and continue until you Motion Link the 5th Compound Gear.

Right-click the first Revolute joint in the Browser, click Animate Motion Relationship, and see the gears spin!

DISCUSSION

Gear System Math

To achieve a 1 year per revolution speed for the last gear, you need to know 3 pieces of important information: the input speed, the gear ratios, and how many gears are in the gear train.

An input speed of 100 RPM from a hobby motor will drive the first compound gear. The gear ratios of 5:1 mean that the 2nd gear will spin at 20 RPM, then the 3rd 4 RPM and so on.

The formula for this gear train is: Input RPM / Output RPM = $5 \wedge X$, where X is the number of gears. The Output RPM is 1/ (60 mins * 24 hours * 365 days). The gear ratio (Output RPM / input RPM) for this train is 52,560,000.

To solve for the number of gears: log(52,560,000) / log(5) = approx. 11 gears. To move the last gear 1 gear tooth, you would need to spin the first gear for over 810 miles!

CHALLENGE

Make an animated piston system that mimics the movements of a car's engine. This will require Revolute and Slider joints. Add complexity to this model by designing an engine Body with 8 pistons for a V8 configuration.

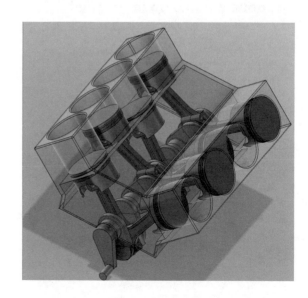

@Vasile
User #498

ROBOTIC HAND

CHAPTER 6

Explore the world of robotics and add a touch of humanity to this metal hand.

Control the motors to replicate a human hand wave.

Master the movement of this hand and you'll be well on your way to making a robotic automaton in no time!

DIFFICULTY:
★★★☆

TIME ESTIMATE:
3 HOURS

KEY LEARNING:
- What selection box is and how to change it
- Pattern a joint
- Make a construction axis component
- Perform a motion study

INTRODUCTION

The advancement of hobby robotics is a testament to the development of computer science and inexpensive, robust hardware. Microcontrollers like Arduino paired with inexpensive motors, sensors, and other hardware can be programmed in a single afternoon.

In this project, you will make a robotic hand that can be 3D printed and affixed with servos to move like a human hand. You will apply a Motion Study to Motion Links that will mimic the necessary information to make this hand in real life.

CAD

Digit 1

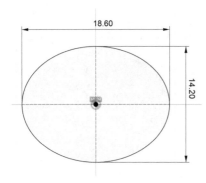

Set the file to mm, make an Internal Component called Digit 1, and start a new Sketch on the Front Plane. Make an ellipse at the Origin and add the following dimensions. Finish the Sketch

If you have a pair of calipers, you can measure your fingers and adapt the project to make a robot replica of your own hand!

Start a new Sketch on the Top Plane and project the ellipse.

Make a Construction rectangle that starts from the Origin, is 28 mm tall, and has its corner Coincident with the right projected point.

Make a Fit Point Spline from the top left to the bottom right corner of the rectangle and adjust the vertices to make a top-down finger profile.

Add a Tangent constraint to the Spline and the right vertical line, and between the Spline and the top vertical line. Mirror the Spline about the left vertical line.

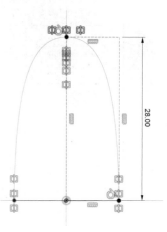

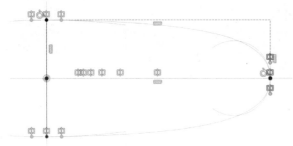

Make a new Sketch on the Right Plane and make a similar profile with the same Constraints.

Note that splines that are too sharp may cause issues in later steps.

Open the Loft tool. Select the ellipse and the point directly across from the Origin.

Click on the cursor icon next to Rails and select the 4 Fit Point Splines. Click OK.

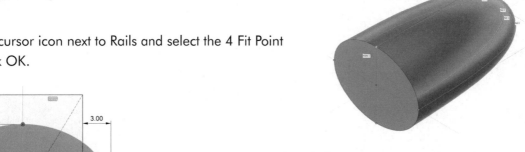

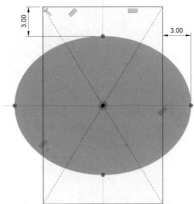

Create a sketch on the Front Plane of a center rectangle at the Origin. Project the ellipse.

Show the previous sketch and Extrude the left and right profiles 5 mm away from the Body. Click OK.

Extrude Cut the middle profile -5 mm into the Body.

Start a sketch on the Right Plane and draw a 3 mm circle at the Origin, extrude this profile Symmetrically through All in both directions. Highlight the entire component and add a 0.5 mm fillet to it.

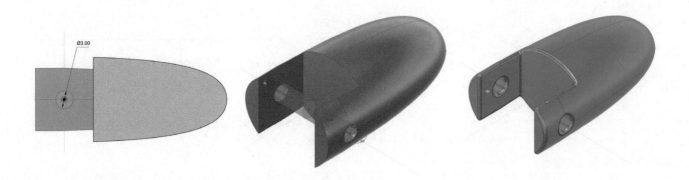

Digit 2

Activate the Root Component and make an Internal Component called Digit 2.

Start a sketch on the Right Plane and project Digit 1's inside face and the fingertip point.

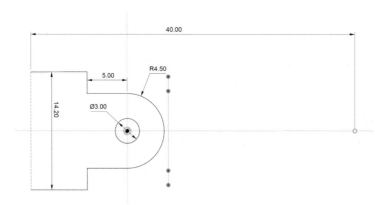

Make the Sketch of a 3 mm circle at the Workspace Origin, a center arc, 6 sketched lines, and 1 Construction Line.

Add the appropriate Equal, Tangent, and Collinear constraints to make this sketch horizontally symmetric.

Add the dimensions shown and Mirror the 8 lines and arcs about the vertical Construction Line.

Extrude this profile symmetrically to a Whole Length of 12 mm.

Highlight this component and add a 1 mm fillet to all edges.

Digit 3

Activate the Root Component and make an Internal Component called Digit 3.

Show Digit 1 & 2. Start a sketch on the Right Plane and project the tip point of the finger and the leftmost arc.

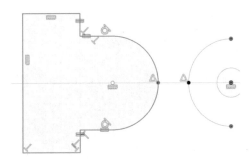

Make the following sketch of an arc, 6 sketched lines, and a vertical Construction Line.

Make the 2 right vertical lines Equal and Collinear, the 2 right horizontal lines Tangent with the arc, and the arc's center Horizontally Constrained to the Origin. Add a midpoint to the projected arc and the new arc as shown.

Add the following dimensions to the Sketch and note the distance from the vertical Construction line to the finger's tip is 76 mm.

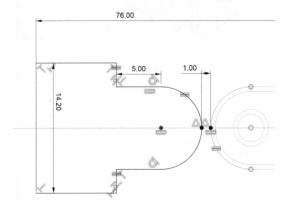

Mirror this sketch about the Construction Line and add a 3 mm circle on the new left arc's midpoint.

Symmetrically Extrude this profile to a Whole Length of 12 mm.

Make a new Sketch on the right face of this component and project Digit 2's left circle. Draw a 25 mm Center to Center Slot 9 mm wide from the projected center point.

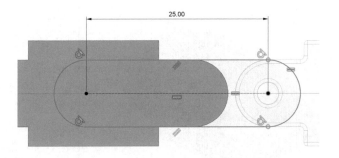

Extrude this profile outwards 3 mm, mirror it about the Right Plane, Hide Digit 1 & 2, highlight the entire component, and add a 1 mm fillet.

Palm

Activate the Root Component and make an Internal Component named Palm.

Create a new Sketch on the Top Plane and project Digit 3's leftmost hole (while looking from the Right Plane)

Make the following vertically symmetric sketch around the projected purple edges of the hole using two points that are Vertically Constrained.

Add Equal and Collinear constraints to the top horizontal lines and Horizontal Constraints to the bottom 2 points. Add the dimensions shown.

Rectangularly Pattern the 7 lines, set the Distribution to a Spacing of 24 mm, and a Quantity of 4.

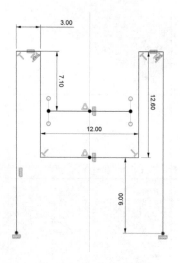

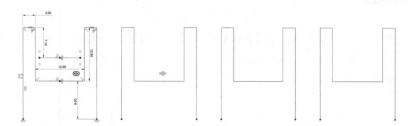

Make the rest of the Palm by drawing an additional 3 lines and dimensioning them as the following:

If you want to add other geometry that makes it look more hand-like, now is the time.

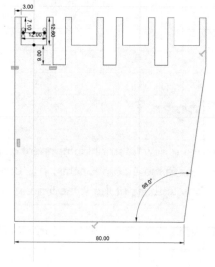

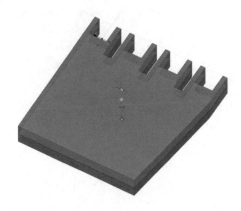

Extrude this profile Symmetrically to a Whole Length of 14.2 mm to match the thickness of the other components.

Add fillets to the Finger Extrusion's top and bottom edges. Set this fillet to 14.2mm/2 to make a full 180-degree arc.

Type H for Hole, select the right face of the Palm, move the blue dot to the center of the fillet, set the Extent to All, and the diameter to 3 mm.

Highlight the entire component and add a 1 mm fillet to all edges.

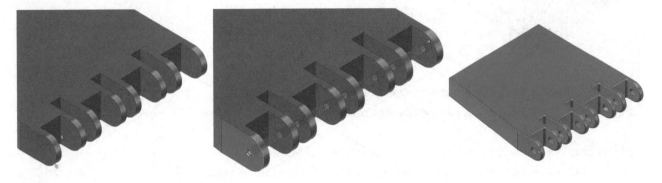

Axle

Activate the Root Component and make the last modeled Internal Component called Axle. This component will contain only a Construction Line.

Open the Axis Running Through Cylinder tool in the Construct menu and select the hole on the first finger slot on the palm.

Unground Digit 1 component, Ground the Palm component, and Show all of the components.

Finger 1

Make a new Internal Component called Finger 1. This is a subassembly to house the 4 components. This process is how to pattern both Joints and subassemblies at the same time. Activate the Root Component.

Drag Digit 1, 2, 3, and Axle into the Finger 1 component.

Click on the View Cube's house icon, add Revolute As-Built Joints between Digit 1 and Digit 2, Digit 2 and Digit 3, and Digit 3 and Axle, and a Rigid As-Built Joint between Axle and Palm.

Notice that the Revolve icon's flag must be facing the same way on each joint, very important!

Expand Joints in the Finger 1 Subassembly and rename the Joints Revolute 1, Revolute 2, and Revolute 3.

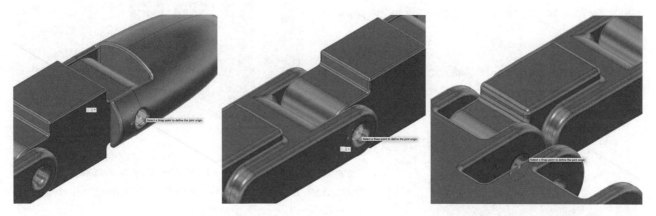

Without changing your view, right-click Revolute 1, Edit Motion Limits, check both Minimum and Maximum, set the Minimum to 0.0 deg, and the Maximum to 120 deg.

Repeat these steps for Revolute 2 & 3 but set the Maximums to: 72 deg and 12 deg respectively.

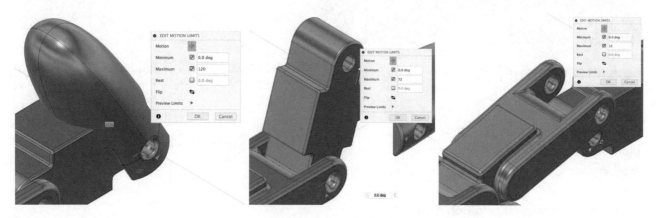

To mimic how a finger curls in, you will add 2 Motion links to the 3 Revolute joints.

Navigate to the Assemble >> Motion Link, select Revolute 1 and Revolute 2 in that order, and set the Angles to 600 and 360. Click OK.

Repeat the process for Revolute 2 and Revolute 3, and set the Angles to 360 and 60. Click OK.

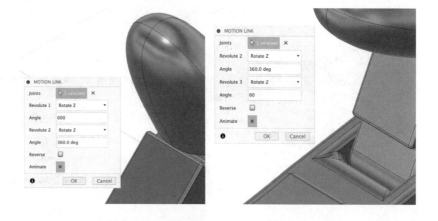

Now, you can click and move Digit 3 up and down to curl the entire finger inwards.

Rectangularly Pattern the Finger 1 Subassembly, set the Distribution to Spacing set to 24 mm, and set the Quantity to 4 so the Fingers are already in the right location.

The Rigid joints between the Axles in Fingers 2-4 must be joined with As-Built Joints not just Joints.

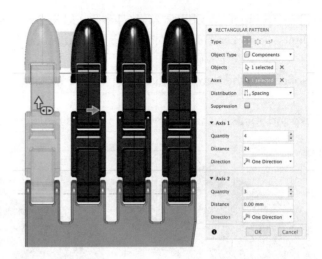

Because all of the Joints in the Subassemblies are Patterned, the Motion Links and the Motion Limits are automatically applied to the other fingers.

Expand Finger Subassemblies 2-4 and add 3 Rigid As-Built Joints between each Axle and the Palm.

MOTION ANIMATION

Navigate to the Motion Study tool in the Assemble menu.

This Timeline, from 0 to 100 steps, plots the degree of rotation or linear motion over time.

Each joint will make a line graph. The more points, the more complex its movement is.

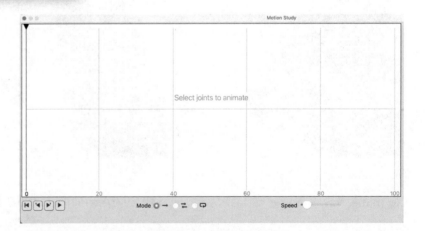

For example, if you wanted a gear to make a half revolution and then return to its start, you would start a point at 0 degrees at step 0, 180 degrees at step 50, and end at 0 degrees at step 100.

You can fast-forward, reverse, start over, or play using the button on the bottom left. You can also loop the animation or change from forwards to reverse and back again.
The speed adjustment bar is at the bottom.

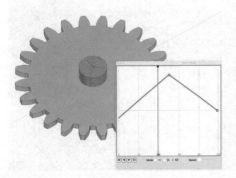

Named Views
Origin
Motion Studies
MotionStudy-1
Joints

Important Note: Click OK to save this motion study. You can always reopen it in the Browser.

However, if you make the project and accidentally click Cancel, your work will be lost.

An good way to think about Motion Studies is to imagine them as a Timeline in a video editing software, at a certain time code, an event will happen, i.e. at Step X the Angle will be at Y deg.

Select Revolute 3 in Finger 1, which will put a flat line on the Timeline representing 0 degrees of movement from Step 0 to Step 100.

Move your cursor along the line and click on Step 9 and set the Angle to 0 degrees.

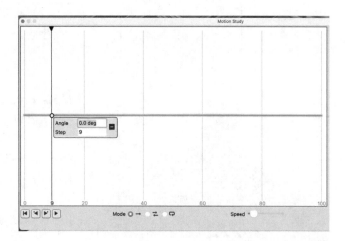

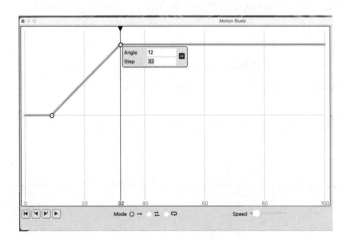

Move your cursor to step 32 and set the Angle to 12.

As you can see, positive angle rotations are above and negative rotations would be below.

Finally, click on Step 52 to return to 0 degrees.

Reduce the Speed to its minimum, set the Mode to Loop, and watch the animation of the finger curling up and down.

Note that the loop ends at the last point instead of 100 steps. Finger 4 will fix this with an additional point at 100 steps.

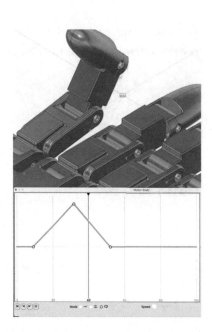

Finger	Step @ 0 deg	Step @ 12 deg	Step @ 0 deg	Step @ 0 deg
1	9	32	52	
2	15	40	54	
3	19	49	70	
4	30	55	75	100

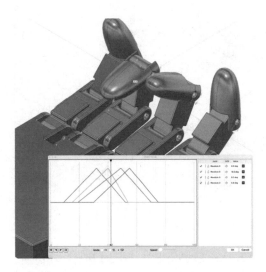

Move onto Revolute 3 on Finger 2, and you will see a different colored line; perform the same operation editing the 3 points.

Use the following chart to change the 3 points for all 4 fingers to 0 deg, -12 deg, and 0 deg.

In the end, your Motion Study should look like this.

It's a good idea to press OK after each line, saving the Motion Study.

You can always bring it back up by right-clicking on the Motion Study and clicking Edit in the Browser.

Press play with a loop, reduce the speed all the way down, and notice how realistically the hand curls and then releases.

You can apply a motion study to various Joints. The Slider joint allows for linear and rotational movement that can be manipulated in both axes at the same time.

This tool is so powerful that you can even incorporate it into a rendering project so you can see your project moving as realistically as possible!

CHALLENGE

Add a thumb to this robotic hand. This will require you to make a thumb with only 2 digits, a new palm, and a new motion study path.

@iks
User #239

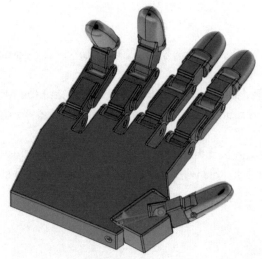

CHAPTER 6 QUESTIONS

1. Which tool would be used to animate an entire project?

    a. Animate Joint

    b. Animate Joint Relationship

    c. Animate workspace

    d. Move

2. In which scenario would Contact Sets not be a good idea to use?

    a. Projects with several components

    b. Projects with Bodies joined, not components

    c. Projects with only a couple of components

    d. Projects with imported components

3. What are rails?

    a. Another word for a path in the Sweep tool

    b. Another word for the Slider joint

    c. The outer surface of a lofted part

    d. The path of a lofted surface

4. Motion links work with gears if you know which piece of information?

    a. Their hole diameter

    b. Both of their number of teeth

    c. The outer diameters of the gears

    d. None of the above

5. True or False? Construction Geometry (Ex. Offset Planes) can also be components.

6. Direction of rotation of a revolute joint being in the positive or negative direction can be caused by … ?

    a. Your camera's view

    b. 50/50 random choice by the software

7. A Motion Study of a wheel with a flat line would produce what effect?

    a. CW rotation

    b. CCW rotation

    c. An error message

    d. No motion

8. To increase the speed of a Motion Study of a rotating wheel, you can … ?

    a. Increase the rotation degree

    b. Decrease the rotation degree

    c. Decrease the time interval

    d. Increase the time interval

    e. Both A and C

    f. Both B and D

9. To reopen a Motion Study, navigate to the … ?

    a. Timeline

    b. Browser

    c. Motion Study tool

    d. Animation workspace

10. If joint icons disappear, you could turn them back on in the … ?

    a. Browser

    b. Data Panel

    c. Preferences

    d. Navigation bar

CHAPTER 7
APPEARANCES

HOW TO GIVE YOUR 3D MODELS
COLOR, TEXTURE, AND DECALS

- AMERICAN FOOTBALL
- SMARTPHONE CASE

APPEARANCES

The simplest way to bring your CAD projects to life is to add colors, textures, and other physical Appearances as you go. With minimal effort, you can transform a default gray-steel colored rectangle into something that looks like any material.

In future lessons, you will work in the Render workspace to bring even more life into your projects. Below is an example of the default color, an Appearance, and a render.

Appearances are loosely broken up into two categories: those without decal images (e.g. Steel), and those with decal images (e.g. Cherry Wood). There are a variety of editable visual properties, such as:

- Reflectivity
- Roughness
- Emissivity luminance
- Transparency
- Bump Maps
- Cutouts

After this chapter, you should consider adding appearances to your own projects to bring them to life!

AMERICAN FOOTBALL

CHAPTER 7

In this lesson, you will model a football and then attempt to make it look as realistic as possible.

This is a great way to show off models before making them in real life.

DIFFICULTY:

★★☆☆☆

TIME ESTIMATE:

2 HOURS

KEY LEARNING:

- Make custom appearances
- Calibrate the size of a canvas
- Explore the rendering workspace
- Pattern a feature along a path

DISCORD LINK:
Discord.gg/5hbt6xDPqf

INTRODUCTION

An American Football is often made from leather and played with on fields, beaches, and backyards worldwide. Even if you've never touched one, you can likely picture the roughness of the leather, the shape of the curve, and the worn-in feel of the materials. For these reasons, it is a great appearance project because if something doesn't look "right," it will be apparent.

CAD

Create a Sketch on the Front Plane and set your Units to Inches.

Navigate to Insert >> and select Canvas and upload the JPEG Football Canvas found at:
CADclass.org in the **FREE DOWNLOADS** tab.

You can leave the Canvas in the current location but set the rotation to 1 degree.

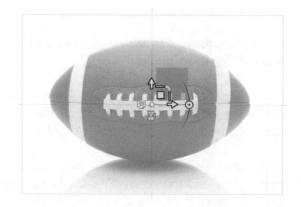

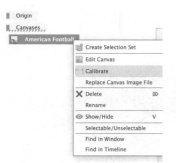

Navigate to Browser >> Canvases >> Football, right-click the American Football Canvas, and click Calibrate.

Select either end of the football as close to the tips as possible and type 11.25" to set the length of the part.

Note: If you use this tool in one of your projects, consider taking a picture with a ruler in the frame.

Navigate to the Browser, right-click the image, click Edit Canvas, and use the square moving icon to position the left point of the football over to the Origin.

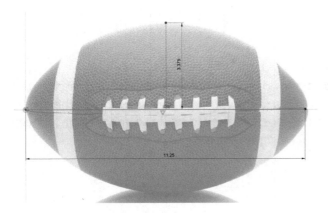

Draw an 11.25" line from the Origin to the right-hand side of the ball and a 3.375" vertical Construction line from the midpoint.

Select the Fit Point Spline tool, click on the Origin, click the top point of the vertical Construction line, and press Enter.

Use the Mirror tool to Mirror the Spline about the vertical Construction line.

Add a Tangent constraint to both Splines and adjust the left Spline's green vertexes till it matches the American Football's profile.

This iterative approach requires changing each line slightly and then correcting for that change until the curve is perfect. Once you're done, apply a Fix/Unfix constraint to the Splines and click Finish Sketch.

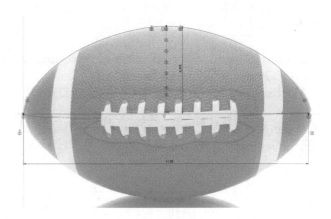

Navigate to the Browser and turn off the Canvas by clicking the Eye Icon next to Canvases.

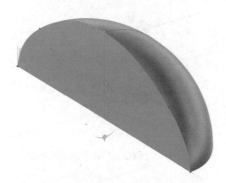

Navigate to Create >> and select Revolve. Revolve this shape 90 degrees around the line on the X-axis to make 1/4 of the football shape.

Add a 1/8" fillet on the outer 2 curved edges.

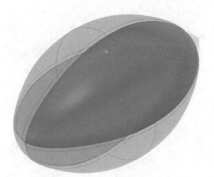

Circularly Pattern the Body about X-axis and set the Quantity to 4.

Use the Combine tool to combine the 4 Bodies into 1.

Navigate to the Navigation Bar at the bottom of the screen.

Click Display Settings >> Visual Style >> and choose Shaded.

Press A for Appearance, expand the Leather and Cloth section, and add the Leather-Matte (Red) to the Football at 75% Scale.

To add a custom leather appearance to this project, download the Brown and White leather files from the **FREE DOWNLOADS** tab on **CADclass.org**.

You should see the 4K image of the brown leather, the Roughness map, the bump map titled _disp, and the EXR file.

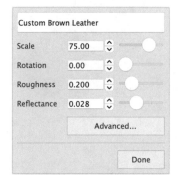

Right-click the Red Leather icon in the Appearance menu, and select Duplicate.

Double-click the new Appearance icon and rename it Custom Brown Leather.

Click Advanced and click on the image title 1_mats_leather_colors_red. This will bring up your File Browser. Find the files you downloaded and select Brown Leather Image.jpg.

Repeat this process for Roughness and the Bump Map images. Click Apply and then click Cancel.

Select the Render workspace by clicking the gray box in the top left-hand corner and selecting Render.

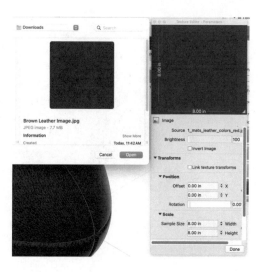

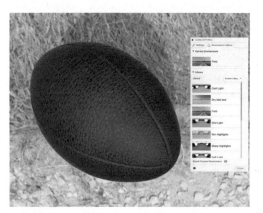

Navigate to Setup >> and click Scene Settings.

Click on the Environment Library tab and download the Field Environment. Drag this Environment into the background.

From here, you can press A for Appearance again, cycle between your two Leather options, and pick which one you think looks best.

Navigate back to the Design workspace, Hide Body 1, and Show Sketch 1.

Make a new Sketch on the Front Plane and Project the Spline and the vertical line.

Type O for Offset, select the Spline, and type 3/32".

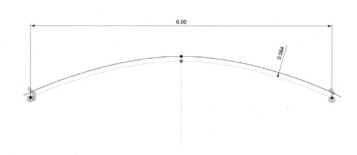

Draw two vertical sketch lines that join these curves, dimension them to 6.00" apart, and apply the Symmetric Constraint about the vertical line.

Extrude this 0.25" and add a 1/16" fillet to the top face and the 4 vertical edges.

If you have trouble adding fillets to this part, try adding them individually.

Hide Sketch 1

Mirror this Body about the Front Plane and note that if you had Extruded this face Symmetrically, you couldn't add the fillets in the middle. This fillet makes it look like two laces.

Construct a New Offset Plane 11.25"/2 from the Right Plane.

Create a new Sketch on the New Plane. Draw two 3-point arcs and connect them with lines to complete the shape.

Add a Concentric constraint to the two arcs. Add a Coincident constraint between the Origin and the arc's center. Add Coincident constraints between the lines and the Origin.

Add the following dimensions and click Finish Sketch.

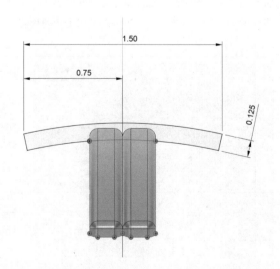

Navigate to Create >> and select Sweep. Select the new shape as the Profile and the Projected Spline as the Path.

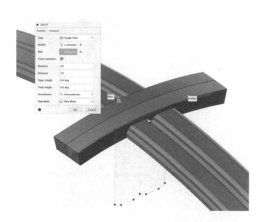

Set the Distances to 0.05 on either side. This isn't a dimension but rather a percentage of the length of the path.

Finally, change the Orientation from Parallel to Perpendicular and the Operation to New Body. Click OK.

Add a fillet and add a 1/16" fillet to the top face and the 4 vertical edges of the lace.

Again, if you are running into issues with this operation, experiment with the order of how you add the fillets.

Navigate to Create >> Pattern >> and select Pattern Along Arc. Change Object Type to Features and select the two most recent features in the Timeline as the Objects. Select the Projected Spline you traced the football with for the path.

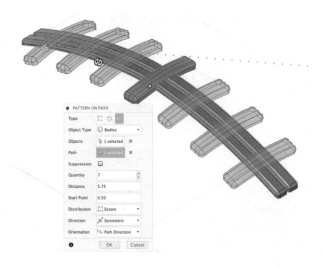

Change the Direction to Symmetric and the Orientation to Path Direction. Set the Distribution to Extent, the Quantity to 7, and the Distance to 5.75". Click OK.

Combine the 8 laces into 1 Body by selecting them in the Browser using the Combine tool.

Open the Appearance menu, right-click your Custom Leather and click Duplicate.

Double-click on the new Appearance and change its name to Custom White Leather.

Open the Advanced section and add the White Leather 4K picture and the new Roughness Map.

Once again, these files can be found at:
CADclass.org in the **FREE DOWNLOADS** tab.

Set the new White Leather's scale to 50% and apply this new Appearance to the Laces.

Finally, select Shaded Lines from the Navigation Bar, open the part in the Render workspace, and check out your final product!

DISCUSSION

Delete Appearances

You can right-click the empty space in the In This Design window and Delete All Unused Appearances.

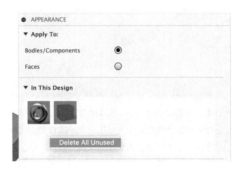

Roughness and Reflectiveness

You also have the option to change the Roughness or reflectiveness of a surface. A high Reflectiveness and a low Roughness will result in the shiniest possible surface.

In contrast, a low reflection and a high Roughness will be matte but will also take longer to render as there is now data about surface texture to take into account.

Advanced Images

Woods, fabrics, leathers, and stones have images of their respective materials inside the Advanced Settings. You can double-click the image in the Parameters area and import a new picture to make custom materials. Note that for an effective end product, this pattern should be a repeating image to avoid a distracting grid of pictures.

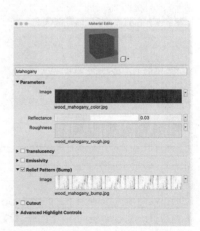

Roughness Image

The Roughness Image is a gray-scale version of the image and reflects light in realistic ways. Without it, you will see a flat glare off a rough image like rocky terrain, which won't look realistic.

Translucency vs Emissivity

Translucency defines the opacity of an object and is often only applied to glasses and some clear plastics like acrylic.

Emissivity refers to how much light is produced by an object, like LEDs, LCD screens, or lightbulb filaments. Much like Translucency, this effect only looks correct in the Render workspace.

Relief Patterns (AKA Bump Maps)

Bump Maps is another type of image that can be superimposed on a surface and acts as a raised texture. This is only a 2D representation but allows the part to cast shadows onto itself.

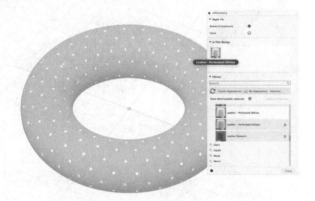

Cutouts are images similar to relief patterns but are PNGs that allow light through the model. For example, adding perforated leather to this torus allows you to see through the model, like in the picture.

CHALLENGE

Download a brick wall texture from **PolyHaven. com** (not affiliated with CADclass) and make a custom Appearance.

Recreate your room or office with a tape measure and apply the custom Brick Appearance to the walls.

@Conny

User #485

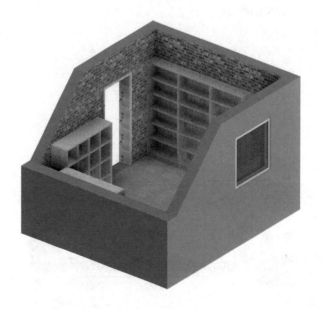

SMARTPHONE CASE

CHAPTER 7

Explore texturing, map controls, grain direction, and more as you design a phone case and phone holder.

Use this project to test your reverse engineering skills by recreating your own phone and adapting a custom case around it!

DIFFICULTY:
★★★☆☆

TIME ESTIMATE:
2.5 HOURS

KEY LEARNING:
- Import a STEP file
- Detect if two components are interfering with each other
- Texture Map Controls and how to adjust them

DISCORD LINK:
Discord.gg/5hbt6xDPqf

INTRODUCTION

Phone cases are great for combining pre-made CAD models with custom designs. In this class, you will work with a CAD file that can be downloaded from **CADclass.org** in the **FREE DOWNLOADS** tab, but you are also encouraged to recreate your phone and make a custom case.

This project will have less information since your skillset is advancing. If you plan to model your phone, you can find CAD files and dimensions for almost any product with a simple Google search.

CAD

Navigate to the Data Panel and make a Smartphone Case folder. Open this new folder and click Upload.

Upload the F3D Phone 16 Plus file from the **FREE DOWNLOADS** tab at **CADclass.org**.

Save your blank workspace to this folder called Smartphone Case.

Right-click the F3D Phone 16 Plus file and click Insert into Current Design.

Note that you will see a chain-link icon next to the name of this component to show that it is externally linked to the Assembly file, known as an External Component.

Activate the Root Component and make a new Internal Component called Phone Case.

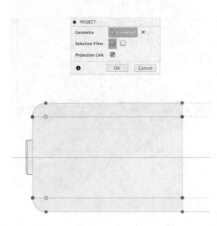

Verify you are working in Millimeters (mm).

Start a new Sketch on the Top Plane and Project the 3 faces as shown in the picture.

This Sketch will house the Profile used to Sweep along a Path to make a bumper around the Phone model.

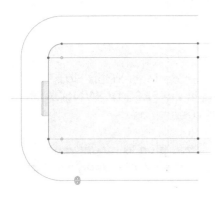

Type O for Offset, uncheck Chain Selection, select the projected 5 lines and curves of the outer perimeter, type 2 mm, and click OK.

Draw 2 Collinear vertical lines 2 mm to the right of the projected vertical line.

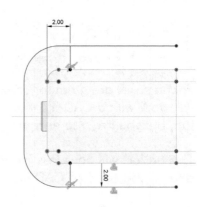

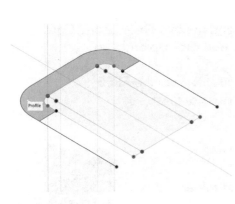

Finish the Sketch and verify your enclosed Profile matches the one in the picture.

Navigate to Create >> and select Sweep.

Sweep the Offset profile about the phone's perimeter. As the Phone's file is transparent, it may be hard to see the edges.

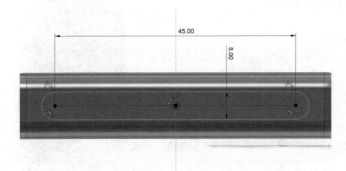

Create a new Sketch on the bottom of the phone case.

Navigate Create >> Slot >> Center Point Slot at the Origin that is 5 mm tall and 45 mm Center to Center.

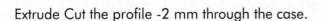

Extrude Cut the profile -2 mm through the case.

Orbit to the of the Phone Case, verify with the View Cube, start a Sketch on the back face of the F3D Phone 16 Plus model, not the Phone Case component, and Project the Phone's back surface.

Sketch a 35 mm circle at the Origin, extrude this profile 2 mm, and set the Operation to Join.

Navigate to Inspect >> Interference, select both components, click Compute, and notice the red volume indicated where the Phone and Case model overlap with each other.

The Power, Volume, and Action Buttons are interfering with the Case.

To cut the Phone model overlaps from the Phone Case model, Navigate to Modify >> Combine, select the Case as the Target Body, select the Phone as the Tool Body, the Operation as Cut, and click OK.

Now, when you use the Interference tool, it should read No Interferences Detected.

Activate the Root Component, hide the Phone component, type E and Extrude Cut all 4 buttons through the entire Phone Case from the inside.

Add 1 mm fillets to the outer edges of the 4 button holes.

Add one of the Carbon Fiber Appearances to the case.

Download the Carbon Fiber – Twill and drag it onto your case.

Double-click the new Appearance and notice the Bump Map is a blue/purple color.

This is a common way to display this data rather than the black-and-white version used in the American Football project.

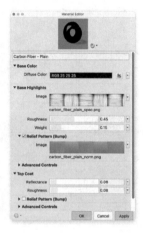

To add any image onto the flat or curved surface, navigate to Insert >> Decal, select any PNG file (we have supplied the CADclass Logo as a test for you), and click the back surface of the Phone Case.

Click and drag the gray square around and see how the image conforms around curves accurately as if it were a sticker on a final product.

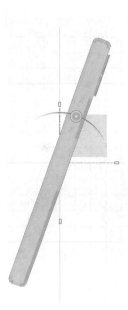

Right-click the Smartphone component and click Unground From Parent, type M for Move, change the Object to Component, select both components, and tilt them back 20 degrees about the X-axis.

Create a new Internal Component called Wooden Stand. Make a new Sketch on the Right Plane and capture the position. Project the back and bottom edges of the phone case.

Use this projected geometry to draw a phone stand. Dimension and constrain the sketch, so it touches the edges of the projected geometries.

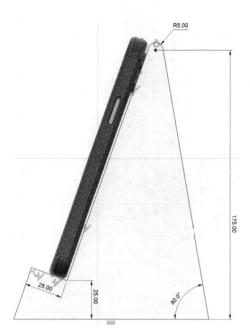

Symmetrically Extrude the Profile to a Whole Length of 100 mm, apply the Oak Wood Appearance onto the stand at 28% Scale, and add a 5 mm fillet to all external faces of the Stand.

Activate the Root Component so you can see all components.

Right-click any surface on the Wooden Block and click Texture Map Controls.

With this tool, you can make the wood pattern look more accurate.

Change the Projection Type to Box and play around with the ring icon to change the grain pattern direction until it looks more realistic.

Navigate to the Render workspace in the top left corner and check out your final phone case and stand!

DISCUSSION

3D model resources

GrabCAD, **Turbosquid**, and **Gallery.autodesk** are all great resources for finding premade CAD models. Some models are free, and some are paid.

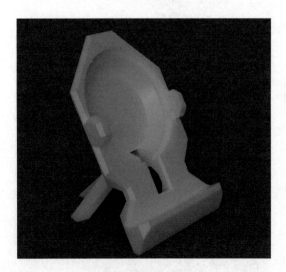

@Ughh
User #592

CHALLENGE

Recreate another tech you use daily and add a realistic Appearance, material properties, and other accessories. Examples: computer mice, smart watches, headphones, and laptops.

CHAPTER 7 QUESTIONS

1. Which of the following is true about Decals and Canvases?

    a. Canvases cannot be placed on curved surface

    b. Decals cannot be placed on curved surfaces

    c. Decals can be calibrated just like Canvases

    d. Canvases should always be centered on the Origin

2. True or False? Calibrating between points will always be either a vertical or a horizontal line.

3. What can you apply appearances to?

    a. Components

    b. Bodies

    c. Both

    d. Neither

4. Sweeping distance is defined by…?

    a. Inches or mm

    b. Percentage of distance of the path

5. To clean up the Appearance dialog box, you should … ?

    a. Compress the appearances in a folder

    b. Delete unused appearances

    c. Combine appearances in a Group

    d. Merge appearances together

6. True or False? Appearances can only be applied to individual components/Bodies not entire assemblies.

7. Texture Map Controls are used to … ?

    a. Change the texture of a decal appearance

    b. Change the texture of the Bump Map

    c. Adjust a folder of appearances

    d. More accurately conform the decal appearance to a realistic product

8. To make the most textured material possible you would adjust which parameters?

    a. Maximize roughness, Maximize reflectiveness

    b. Maximize roughness, Minimize reflectiveness

    c. Minimize roughness, Maximize reflectiveness

    d. Minimize roughness, Minimize reflectiveness

9. True or False? Adjusting Physical Materials also adjusts the Appearance of the Component/Body.

10. Which of these choices is not a way to make parts translucent?

    a. Set the component to Transparent in the Browser

    b. Adjust the Opacity Control

    c. Set the appearance to glass

    d. Set the Physical Material to glass

CHAPTER 8
RENDERING

HOW TO MAKE YOUR PARTS LOOK
PHOTO-REALISTIC

- EDISON BULB
- A.I. VILLAIN

RENDERING

Now that you've developed your CAD modeling skills, it's time to incorporate another aspect of Autodesk Fusion into your workflow; the Render workspace. Rendering your models allows you to showcase what you've made more realistically. While you may not see many uses for it now, it helps showcase products to clients and visualize what you may eventually make in real life. Most of our students claim they'll never render their models, but after a few quick tutorials, they render their projects regularly. If you've already spent hours, days, or weeks creating a model, why not spend a few minutes making it look even better?

Below is an example of the default material, a Wood Appearance, and its render.
You can treat the Rendering workspace like a virtual photo shoot with cameras, lighting, and backdrops. You can convince people that your CAD model is a real-world object with practice.

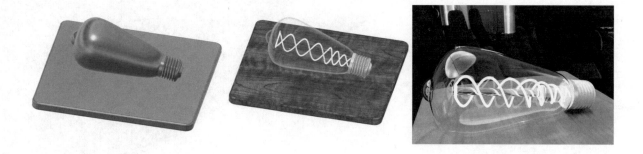

Note that the rendering terminology is the same as photography and videography. If you have any camera experience, you will understand what these terms mean. Otherwise, we encourage you to explore the terms elsewhere for a more detailed explanation.

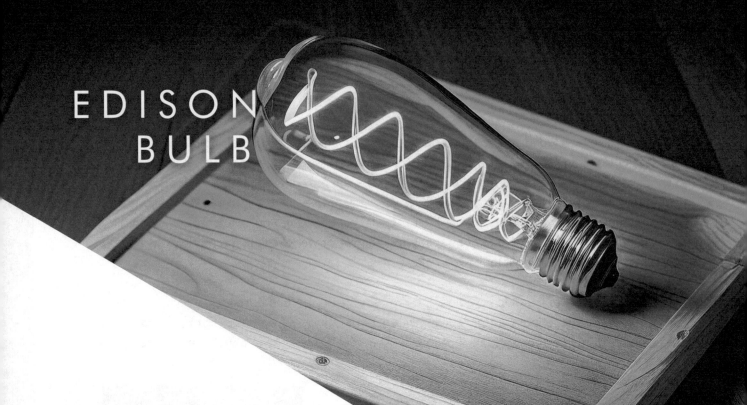

EDISON BULB

CHAPTER 8

Edison bulbs are trendy lights you may have seen in coffee shops throughout the world.

They expose the bulb's filament in a beautiful and elegant way, transfixing onlookers with their glow.

This project will give you an excellent excuse to play around with appearances to try to mimic the actual bulb.

DIFFICULTY:
★★★☆☆

TIME ESTIMATE:
2 HOURS

KEY LEARNING:
- In-depth look at the Rendering workspace
- Intersect a plane into a component and sketch on it
- Where to import HDRIs from
- Set up a virtual photoshoot

DISCORD LINK:
Discord.gg/5hbt6xDPqf

INTRODUCTION

For this project, you will recreate an Edison bulb and render it in an environment that feels more natural and fitting to the product. You'll learn a few more tips with CAD and then spend time gaining familiarity with the Render workspace.

Feel free to have more fun with this project by playing with different environments, lights, and more. After all, the best way to learn is to practice. Have fun, and as always, we'd love to see what you make.

CAD

Metal Cap

Set your Units to Millimeters (mm) and import the Edison Bulb image as a Canvas on the Front Plane. As usual, you can download this image from **CADclass.org** in the **FREE DOWNLOADS** tab.

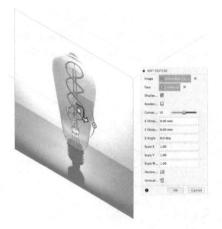

Right-click the Canvas in the Browser and Calibrate the image so the Metal Cap's top is 26 mm wide.

This is a standard E26 thread found on most lightbulbs meant for lamps.

Right-click the Canvas and click Edit Canvas. Rotate the image 1 degree so the bottom tip of the Metal Cap and the top point of the glass are vertical.

Click the square icon on the image and move the Canvas around the workspace until the Metal Cap's lowest point is on the Origin.

Since this project only contains 4 components, using Internal Components is advantageous and easier as you don't need to make a folder to house the components.

Make an Internal Component called Metal Cap.

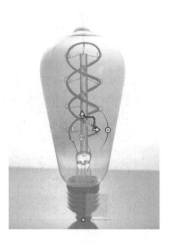

Make the following sketch on the Front Plane using the Line tool. The bottom horizontal line starts at the Origin, and the top 2 points are Horizontally Constrained.

Add a 2 mm Offset to the sketched lines. If the red lines are on the outside of the sketch, click the flip button or change the sign from + to -. Connect the end with lines to enclose the profile.

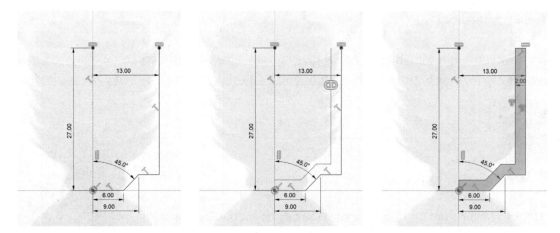

Revolve the profile about the Construction Line or the vertical Z-axis and add a 3 mm fillet to the 3 edges shown in the picture.

Lightbulb threads are not standard machining threads and, therefore, are unavailable in the Threading tool menu. Since this is meant as a visual project, simply choose the closest one visually. Select the Threading tool, click the outer curved surface, and set the Thread type to ANSI Unified Screw Threads and the designation to 1 1/16-8 UN Thread. Check Modeled, uncheck Full Length, and set the Length to 17 mm. If the thread is on the top, change your workspace viewing angle and try again.

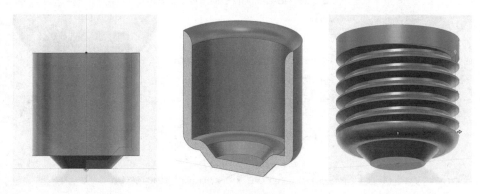

Select the 2 outer and 2 inner edges and add a 0.39 mm fillet.

Most light bulb caps are made from low-grade steel with a zinc finish, which gives them a yellowish-rainbow color. Double-click on the Steel Appearance, and enter the following RGB values: 255-250-230.

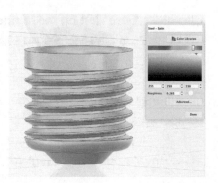

Glass Bulb

Activate the Root Component and make an Internal Component called Glass Bulb.

Start a Sketch on the Front Plane, Create >> Project/Include >> Intersect, and select all inside surfaces of the Metal Cap. Click OK and hide the Metal Cap component.

You should see a projected purple curve that intersects the Metal Cap component with the Front Plane.

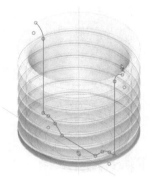

Make a vertical Construction Line from the Origin to the top of the Lightbulb Canvas and add a Fix/Unfix constraint to the top endpoint.

Make a 3-point arc that has its center coincident with the Constriction Line and add the following dimensions.

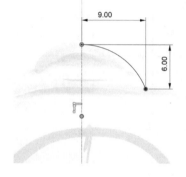

Add a Fit Point Spline to join the projected point and the arc. Adjust the spline's green vertices until it closely matches the bulb's shape.

Press O for Offset and uncheck Chain Selection. Select the arc, the spline, and the 6 projected lines on the Construction Lines right side, and the line across the Y-axis. Set the Offset to 0.8 mm. Enclose the profile with 2 small vertical lines on the Y-axis.

Using 5 lines, trace the right half of the inner glass section and connect the shape along the bottom projected line. You do not need to include the dimensions as your profile may differ slightly. This project is for aesthetic reasons, so accurate dimensions are not critical.

Note that you cannot enclose a profile with a Construction Line. The left vertical line of the inner profile must be a regular sketch line.

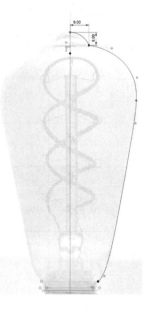
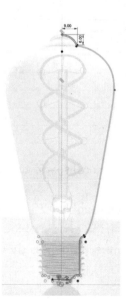

Revolve the 2 profiles around the Z-axis.

Add the Glass (Clear) Appearance to this component to finish it.

Activate the Root Component.

Filament

Make a new Internal Component called Filament. This is a metal that emits light when a current passes through it.

Make an Offset Plane 60 mm above the Top Plane to start the Coil.

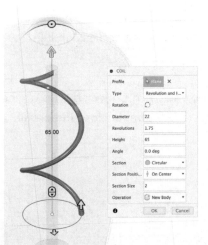

Make a 22 mm Coil on this new plane with the following dimensions:

Diameter: 22 mm
Revolutions: 1.75
Height: 65 mm
Section: Circular
Section Position: On Center
Section Size: 2 mm

Add a Circular Pattern to this Body about the Z-axis to make a second coil.

To join the 2 ends of the coils, you can Sweep a Body between the 2 ends.

Make an Offset Plane roughly 125 mm up from the Top Plane, which should put the plane through the middle of the coil. If it does not, adjust your plant until it goes through the middle, as shown.

Create a sketch on this Offset Plane and project the circular ends of the coils. Add in 2 3-point arcs that start at the middle of the projected purple lines and end at the Origin. Add a Vertical Constraint to the arc's center and the Origin.

Using the Sweep tool, select the 2 arcs as the Path and 1 of the circles (ends of the coils) as the profile.

Add 0.7 mm and 4 mm Fillets to the top and bottom edges where the coils meet the swept Body.

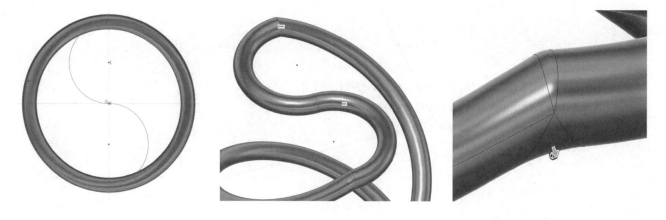

Make another coil on the first Construction Plane from the center of the workspace that is 22 mm in diameter and has a -10-degree taper.

Circularly Pattern this Coil feature around the Z-axis to make a second tapered coil. Change the Quantity to 2 and press OK.

Verify that the top set of coils lines up with the bottom set.

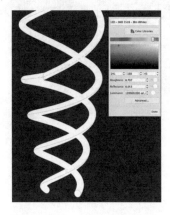

To allow the component to emit light to mimic a lightbulb's filament, open the Appearance tool and search for LED. Drag and drop any of the appearances and double-click on the appearance in the In This Design window.

Change the RGB value to 241-160-43 to add an orange glow that differentiates Edison bulbs from regular lightbulbs.

You won't be able to see the change in color due to the high Luminance value, which you will adjust in the Rendering workspace.

Activate the Root Component and add a Rigid Group to the 3 components.

Unground the Glass Metal Cap component.

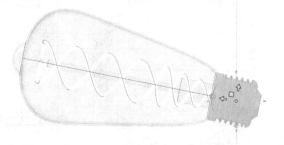

Rotate the Assembly with the Move tool by changing the Move Object to Components and rotating the Glass Bulb -79 degrees so it lies flat on the surface.

Wooden Board

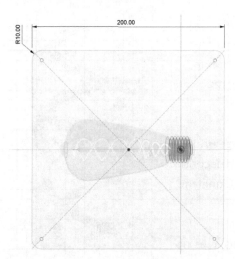

Create a new Internal Component called Wooden Board and draw a Center Rectangle on the Top Plane.

Add 10 mm fillets to all the corners and Equal constraints to the sides. Set the height of the rectangle to 200 mm.

This simple component is an excellent trick in Rendering. Adding props for the object to interact with can make the rendering more realistic.

For example, if you wanted to render a writing desk in an office, you could add pencils, lamps, rugs and wall art to the environment to "sell it".

Extrude this profile -10 mm and add 2 mm fillets to the top and bottom edges. Add a Cherry Wood Appearance to the Board and set the Scale to 48%.

Ground this component and add a Rigid As-Built Joint to the Metal Cap.

RENDERING

Navigate to the Render workspace. The tools used in this workspace act similarly to setting up a light booth for a real-life photo shoot where you need lighting in the right location and a camera with the correct exposure and focal length.

You have already used all the tools in the Setup menu except for Scene Settings. The other tools work in the same way as the Design workspace.

Open the Scene Settings tool. The settings tab defines how the image changes based on tools that affect the camera, environment, and project.

The Environment section adjusts the screen's brightness in Lux, a standard light unit commonly used when describing smartphone statistics.

The Position value rotates the background while keeping the project in the same view.

Change the solid color background by clicking the gray rectangle and adjusting the color bar.

Navigate to the Environment Library tab at the top. You are in the Sharp Highlights Environment. Adjust the Position and note how the studio lights reflect off the Glass Bulb's surface.

Check Ground Plane and Flatten Ground, which will place the project on a flat surface and add shadows. If you do not see shadows, Fusion may have added a graphic limiter that throttles your image to save on computing power.

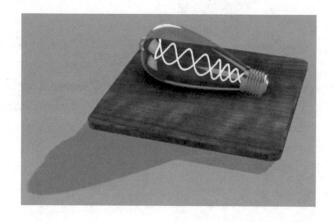

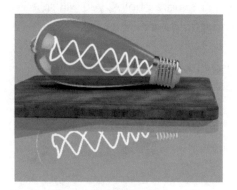

Click the Help button (? Icon) in the top right corner >> Support and Diagnostics >> Graphic Diagnostics >> and uncheck Limit Effects to Optimize Performance.

You can add a Reflection, but this is rarely used in rendering.

Move the slider to a low number, around 0.1, to get a realistically blurry reflection.

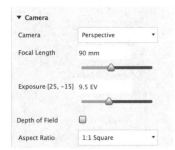

Change the Camera from Perspective to Orthographic to see the difference. Orthographic is a head-on view with parallel sights, which is suitable for the Design workspace but looks unnatural in real life.

The Perspective View uses a single viewpoint, mimicking human eyes, which looks more realistic.

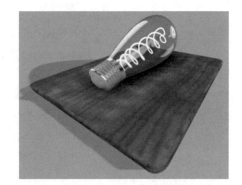

While in Perspective View, adjust the Focal Length. Focal Length is the distance from the camera's sensor to the point in the lens where the image is flipped. The human eye is about 50 mm.

Higher numbers are for further away objects like telephoto lenses for sports with a narrow view. Lower numbers give you a wider view and are often used in landscape photography.

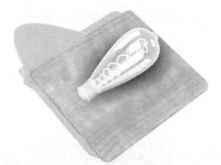

Exposure is the amount of light let into the camera's sensor. Play around with the exposure to see how your image changes.

Enabling Depth of Field will allow you to select a point on the model that will stay focused while the rest of the image will increase in blurriness with distance from the camera. Setting a value of 0.1 is a good starting point.

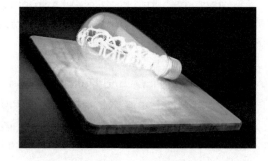

You can change the aspect ratio to save rendering time. For example, if you plan to post your render on Instagram using 1:1 square photos, you will select 1:1. This helps save rendering time and computing power.

The Environment Library tab is how you change the background. Click and drag an Environment into the background and notice what happens.

The In-Canvas Render menu is a toolset that gives you a quick live rendering preview instead of waiting for the final processor-intensive render.

The In Canvas Render tool will render the image but is computationally heavy. Every time you move your camera's view, the rendering will restart. To stop this tool, click the red stop symbol.

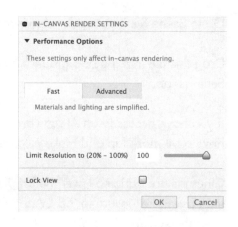

The In Canvas Render Settings tool adjusts live rendering. Leave the Fast tab enabled and lower the Resolution slider to 20% for a quick rendering. Capture Image works like a screenshot where you can adjust the aspect ratio of the final shot, and it will not render the image.

Finally, the Render tool will render your image to a final quality and size.

Rendering is computationally heavy. You have the option to render using your local machine (your personal computer) or using Autodesk Fusion's servers. Autodesk Fusion servers will require you to pay for Cloud Credit. The bigger the image, the more credits it requires. Local rendering is the faster option.

Select Local Render and enable Advanced Settings to change the render quality. Local rendering at standard quality is free. As a rule of thumb, 25% is draft quality, 50% is standard, 75% is final, and 100% is excellent quality. Once completed, select the file type. PNG is a standard option, but a TIFF file often gives you the best quality on large photos.

You can see that without changing any values, this render is a poor-quality picture.

The background is boring, the emissivity of the filament is too bright, and the angle is strange and shows more of the wooden base than the bulb itself.

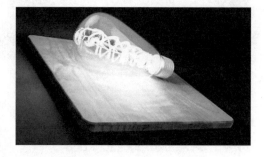

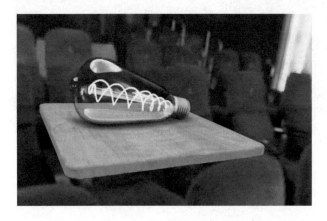

To change the background to something more fitting, search for a free HDRI Environment on a website like **PolyHaven.com**,(not affiliated with CADclass) a royalty-free page hosting hundreds of environments. Look through the categories for an environment you can imagine an Edison Bulb would fit in best.

Download the Old Cinema environment from **CADclass.org** in the **FREE DOWNLOADS** tab.

Go to Scene Settings tool >> Environment Library >> Attach Custom Environment and upload the file.

Drag this file into the background. Note you may need to change the Background to Environment in the Settings tab.

If you have access to an AI software that can produce these types of images in an HDRI file type, you can have a lot more fun and make custom backgrounds and environments.

Cinemas are dark, so lower the brightness to 3000 Lux. Increase the exposure to 9.8 EV and notice more detail from the surroundings are visible.

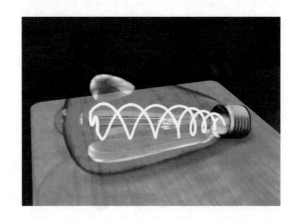

You can also position the bulb more in the frame and tilt it to show more of the attractive shape of the glass rather than the boring metal threads.

Use the position tool to rotate the background and move the view of the product to your liking.

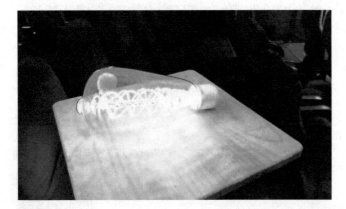

After rendering with these settings, the image looks more realistic, but the brightness of the filament is ruining the picture.

Open the Appearance tool and double-click on the LED Appearance on the filament.

By default, the brightness is over 30,000 cd/m2 (Candela or luminous power per square meter).

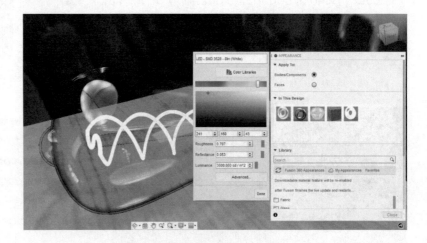

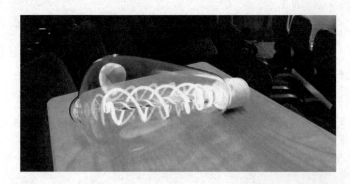

Reduce the emissivity to 3,000 cd/m2, and notice that you can now see more detail in the image. It's still slightly too bright, but heading in the right direction. Reduce it to 300 cd/m2. Now it's too low. 1500 cd/m2 is about right.

Rendering is an art, not a science. Play with the settings until the scene, angles, lights, and reflections feel right.

Set this final render to a web High-Quality Render and toggle the advanced settings to 75% quality to see the final product!

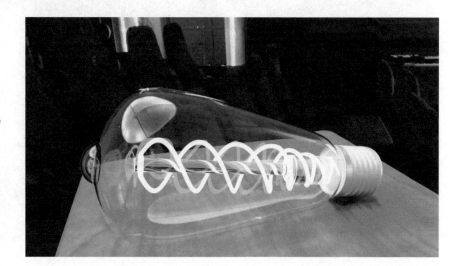

With new A.I. programs coming out every week, we wanted to highlight one that blends your CAD design with an easy-to-use UX. **Newarc.ai** (not affiliated with CADclass) is a very beginner-friendly AI tool. You can upload screenshots of your models and describe a fitting environment, and it will create an accurate image. While these new AI tools are very exciting and easy to use, they don't offer quite as much customization or control as making your own renders from scratch. Depending on your project, you may want total control on the final project, or you may be comfortable with a program doing most of the heavy lifting, the choice is yours.

CHALLENGE

Rev a colored LED with legs, the bulb, and the shape of the internal diode. Render this part with the correct luminance values to show off the detail of the part.

@Conny
User #485

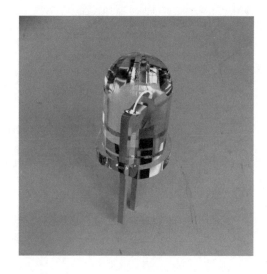

A.I. VILLAIN

CHAPTER 8

Reproducing movie props is an excellent way to get better at CAD modeling.

By recreating one of film's most unique villains, you can start to appreciate its visual impact on the art form.

DIFFICULTY:
★★★★★

TIME ESTIMATE:
3.5 HOURS

KEY LEARNING:
- Duplicate components with Joints
- Emboss text around a curved face
- How and why to add artificial colored lights to a render
- Add a named view

DISCORD LINK:
Discord.gg/5hbt6xDPqf

INTRODUCTION

For this project, you will render an artificial intelligence (A.I.) robot villain with a glowing red eye, speaker panel, camera Body, and a sleek minimalist frame. To create a replica that is both visually compelling and functional, you will render it in an environment with artificial lighting, combining the CAD and Render workspace in a unique way. This is a fun and rewarding project for those interested in AI, robotics, and 3D modeling, as it combines elements of each.

CAD

Wooden Body

Make a new Folder in the 8 - Rendering folder called A.I. Villain. This project will be made in 2 separate files that will be joined together.

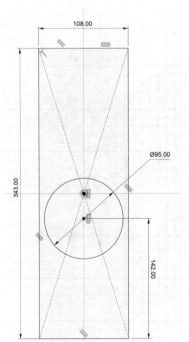

Verify your Units are set to mm (Millimeters) and make an Internal Component called Wooden Body.

Start a sketch on the Front Plane and draw a Center Rectangle and a vertically constrained circle.

Extrude this profile back 16.85 mm.

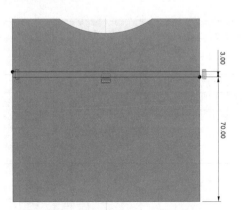

Make a new Sketch on the front face and draw a 3 mm tall rectangle.

Set the corners to be Coincident with the vertical edges of the Wooden Body.

Extrude Cut this profile -6.5 mm into the Body.

Extrude Cut the bottom face -3 mm into the Wooden Body.

This will allow the next component, the Grill, to keep the top surfaces coplanar.

Make a new Sketch on the Wooden Body's back surface and draw a 86 mm circle Concentric to the hole.

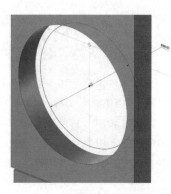

Extrude the ring profile. Change the Extent Type to To Object, select the front surface, and the Offset to 12 mm.

The Appearance of this part is jet-black wood. One option is to import an image of black stained wood, and the other option is to adjust the color of preexisting material.

Drag and drop Walnut Wood onto the Wooden Body and double-click on the icon in the In This Design window.

Change the Scale to 42% and select the Advanced section. Click on the image of the wood, not the image name below, and lower the brightness slider to 20%.

Grill

Activate the Root Component, make a new Internal Component called Grill, and Extrude the lower face of the Wooden Body 3 mm.

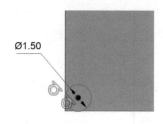

Make a new Sketch on the front surface and draw a 1.5 mm circle that is tangent to the bottom and left edges.

Extrude Cut this profile through the entire Body.

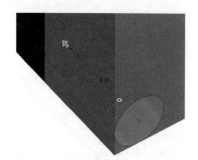

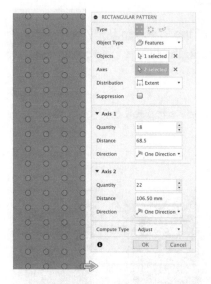

Add a Rectangular Pattern of the Extrusion Cut feature with 18 vertically and 22 horizontally that have an extent of 68.5 mm and 106.5 mm, respectively.

Add a Stainless Steel linear Brushed Appearance to this piece and verify the lines run horizontally.

Activate the Root Component and make a Rigid As-Built Joint between the Grill and the Wooden Body.

Divider Wall

Make a new Internal Component called Divider Wall.

Extrude the 3 mm tall slot in the Wooden Body outwards 8.5 mm and add a Polished Aluminum Finish to the component.

Activate the Root Component and add a Rigid As-Built Joint to the Divider Wall and the Wooden Body.

Side Walls

Make a new Internal Component called Side Walls.

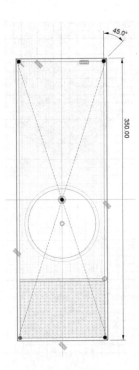

Start a new Sketch on the back face of the Wooden Body.

Make a Center Rectangle from the Origin that is 350 mm tall.

Sketch a diagonal line from the top right corner of the Wooden Body to the top right corner of the Center Rectangle, and dimension the line to be 45 degrees from a vertical line.

Sketch 2 more diagonal lines from the Wooden Body's top left and bottom right corner to the Center Rectangle's corners.

Extrude the right profile 19 mm towards your view, Show Sketch 1 again, and extrude the top profile to the same height with the Operation set to New Body.

Hide Sketch 1 and set the Appearance to Polished Aluminum.

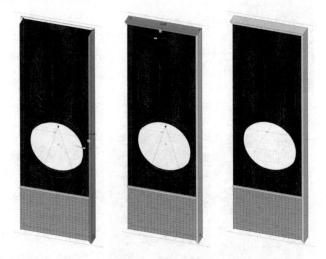

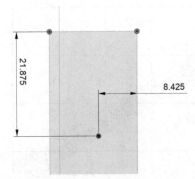

Make a new Sketch on the right face of the right Wall, add a Point to the top of the face, dimension it 16.85 / 2 mm from the right edge, and 350 / 16 mm from the top edge.

This will give you evenly spaced points for 8 countersunk holes down the length of the component.

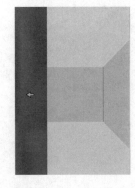

Add a Countersunk hole to this point, 4 mm in depth, 4.5 mm Countersink diameter, and 2.25 mm drill diameter.

Rectangularly pattern this feature downwards. Change the Quantity to 8 and even spacing of 350/8 mm.

Add a Polished Aluminum Appearance to this part.

Finish Editing in Place and activate the Root Component.

Top/Bottom Walls

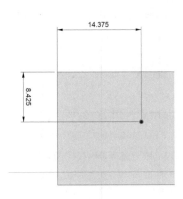

Make a new Internal Component called Top/Bottom Wall which will be identical in construction to the Side Walls but will have 4 holes instead of 8. This component has been left empty as an exercise for the reader. Note that the total width of the part should be 115 mm, 3.5 mm thick, and 19 mm deep. The first hole is 115 / 8 mm from the edge, and the hole spacing is 115 / 4 mm.

Activate the Root Component, add a Rigid As-Built Joint between both Side Walls and the Wooden Body, and open the McMaster Carr tool.

Download a flathead countersunk screw, 91781A081.

The threads will be inside the Wooden Body and not visible, so download it as a 3-D STEP no threads file to save data space.

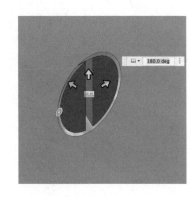

Rotate the part 180 degrees in the Y Angle and add a Rigid joint to the top hole on the right Wall by clicking the outer edge of the bolt head and the countersink's outer hole.

Click the house icon on the View Cube, navigate to Assemble >> Duplicate With Joints, select the countersink screw, and click the outer chamfer edges on all 7 holes of the right Wall and the top 4 holes on the top Wall.

This new Fusion tool duplicates the component and the joint at the same time.

Create >> Circular Pattern, set the Object Type to Components, hold down Shift, click the Walls component, click the bottom screw component, and pattern all 13 components 2 times about the Y-axis. This is the advantage of designing symmetrically and about the Origin and using the Center Rectangle.

Add a Rigid Group to the Wall components and the Wooden Body.

Activate the Root Component and make an Internal Component called Screws. Highlight all the screw components and drag and drop them into this new component to act as a folder for all the screws. Highlight all actions in the Timeline pertaining to the screws, right-click, and Create a Group.

Nameplate

Make a new Internal Component called Nameplate. Draw a 17.75 mm by 90 mm Center Rectangle on the front of the Wooden Body that is and 8 mm below its top edge.

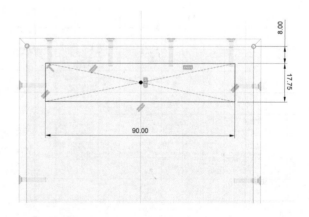

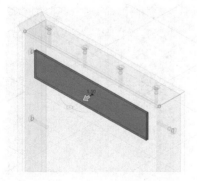

Extrude this profile 1.5 mm outwards and add the Stainless Steel - Brushed Linear Long appearance to it.

Activate the Root Component and add a Rigid As-Built Joint to this component and the Wooden Body.

Click the (+) symbol to open a new Tab and save this blank file to the A.I. Villain Folder as Camera Subassembly.

This new file will house the several components that make up the camera. Because of its complexity, it makes more sense to model this part about a new Origin in a blank workspace and then import the subassembly into the main assembly as External Components.

Camera Ring

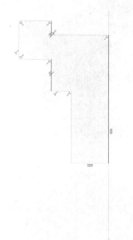

Make a new Internal Component called Camera Ring and make the following Profile on the Right Plane and a horizontal Construction line from the Origin.

Make the right vertical line Coincident with the Origin and the 2 highlighted lines Collinear.

Add the following dimensions and note that the 47.5 mm is from the top right point to the Construction line.

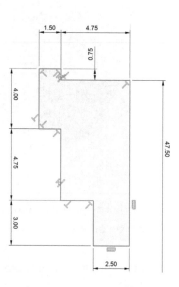

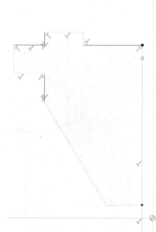

Revolve this Profile about the Y-axis and add a Polished Aluminum Appearance to it.

Camera Body

Activate the Root Component and make a new Internal Component called Camera Body.

Start a new Sketch on the Right Plane, Project the inner stepped face of the Camera Ring, and Hide the Camera Ring.

Set the 4 highlighted lines to be Collinear and add the following dimensions.

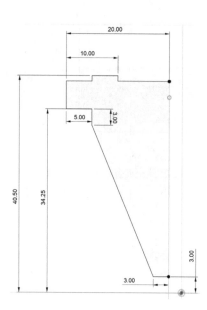

Revolve the profile about the Y-axis and add a Paint-Metallic (Black) Appearance to it.

Make a new Sketch on the front-most face and project its outer edge. Make a right triangle with equal left and right edges, its lowest point Vertically constrained to the Origin, and a Tangent coincident to the projected edge.

Extrude Cut this profile through the entire Body.

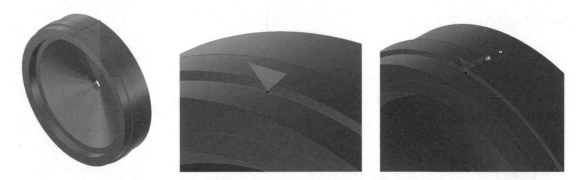

Circularly Pattern this feature about the Y-axis 100 times to mimic the focus grip on a camera.

If your computer has trouble calculating this many features, reduce the number by half and try again. Remember, these details are purely aesthetic and don't need to be exact.

To add the text around the Camera Body, make an Offset Plane 50 mm above the Top Plane and start a Sketch on this plane.

Make a text box with "Fish - eye - NIKKOR 1:8 f=8mm" inside using the Text tool. The text has 9 spaces between NIKKOR and 1:8, and 5 spaces between 8 and f=8.

Make the font Arial and **bold**; Make the height of the text 2.75 mm and the text with a middle alignment. Click OK.

Add Coincident constraints to the text box's left edge and the Origin and the text box's top edge Collinear with the front of the Camera Body.

Navigate to Create >> Emboss and deboss this text into the curved top face with a -0.25 mm cut.

Add a White Paint Appearance to the text faces to make them more visible. Set the "Apply To" to Faces and note that you can highlight the letters 1 word at a time and apply the White Paint Appearance.

Activate the Root Component and add a Rigid As-Built Joint to the two components.

Red Eye

Make a new Internal Component called Red Eye, make a cylinder on the back face of the Camera Body that is 6 mm in diameter and 3 mm deep, and add the red LED Appearance to the component.

Set the LED (Red) Appearance's Luminance to 20,000 cd/m2.

Activate the Root Component and add a Rigid As-Built Joint to either of the parts.

Lens

Make an Internal Component called Lens, make a new Sketch on the Right Plane, and project the highlighted face on the Camera Body.

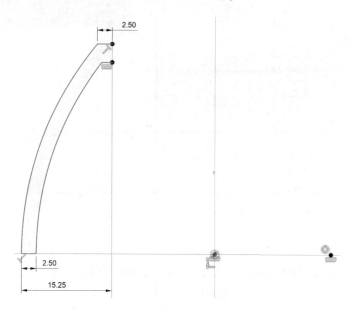

Make the following sketch from a horizontal line that is coincident to the Origin, 2 Concentric 3-point arcs, and two horizontal lines.

Add a Horizontal Constraint to the Origin and the 2 3-point arc's center and add the following dimensions.

Revolve this profile about the Y-axis and add a Glass-Clear Appearance to it.

Activate the Root Component and add a Rigid As-Built Joint to the Camera Body.

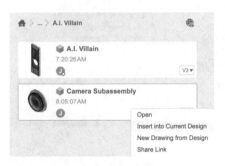

Save the Subassembly file, open the A.I. Villain Assembly File, right-click the Subassembly file in the Data Panel, and click Insert Into Current Design.

Note how the Subassembly file has a chain link icon in the Browser denoting it is a linked External Component; external because the file's data is stored outside the Assembly file.

Pull the Subassembly away from the Assembly and add a Rigid joint from the back edge of the Camera Ring and the inner edge of the Wooden Body's step.

RENDERING

You can add studio lighting within the Design workspace to accent the project you are rendering.

Make 2 new Internal Components on the Top Plane that are Cylinders, 75 mm in diameter and 360 mm tall.

Drop on LED Appearance to each cylinder. Make each one a different color. Red and Blue is a classic approach in photography. Increase the LED's luminance values to 1500 cd/m2.

Make another Internal Component called Light Box that is simply a 20x400x400 mm Box with a LED (white) Appearance added to it.

Lower the Luminance to 100 c/m2 to act as a soft light illuminating the front face of the prop instead of angled lights, which will cast strange shadows and hides detail.

There is no need to Ground or join any of the 3 lights, so you have the opportunity to reposition them if necessary.

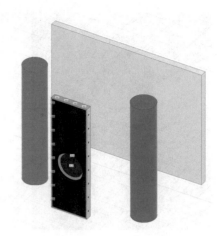

Navigate to the Render workspace and open the Scene Settings tool. Change the aspect ratio to 1:1 for less rendering time. This will also hide the accent-colored lights from view.

Move the camera to a bottom-up view called the "Larger than Life" shot by some photographers.

Change the camera to perspective for a more realistic view, and adjust the focal length to your liking. 23 mm will give a fish-eye lens effect.

Once you get a viewing angle that suits you, right-click Named Views in the Browser, and click New Named View.

This will save the angle and zoom from that view. Now, if you move your camera, you can click this new view to return to it, similar to the View Cube.

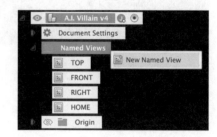

Reduce the brightness to 400 lx, as the scene will be lit with the accent lights you created earlier in the Design workspace.

Change the Background from Solid Color to Environment, open the Environment tab, and drag the Grid Lights to the Background.

Use the Position tool to rotate the background to your liking.

Return to the saved view and click the In-Canvas Render tool to preview what the final Render will look like.

Move the blue and red cylinders outside the frame, and start the render.

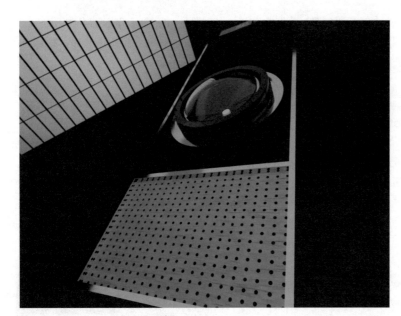

Click the Render tool and set the Custom image size to 1600x1200, 1.9 MP, to capture as much detail as possible.

Render the image using Fusion's Cloud servers or using your local machine. Enable the Advanced Settings and adjust them to a high quality, about 75%.

Depending on your computer's capabilities, rendering may take 10 or more minutes.
Once done, you will have a fantastic photo of the villain from a great film!

CHALLENGE

Recreate a prop from your favorite movie and render it in an environment that suits the film.

@Dairy Air
User #569

CHAPTER 8 QUESTIONS

1. True or false? There is no difference between the Appearance tool in the Design workspace and the Rendering workspace.

2. What does the Position tool move?

    a. Linearly moves the background

    b. Rotationally moves the background

    c. Linearly moves the project

    d. Rotationally moves the project

3. What does the Flatten Ground tool do?

    a. Converts the curve HDRI into a flat environment

    b. Removes rough textures from the environment

    c. Moves the project to the ground of the environment

    d. Removes the Ground from the grounded component

4. True or False? Rendering at a draft quality will make for a clearer picture ready for high quality printing.

5. Which tool should you use to save a specific a certain view and zoom?

    a. Named View

    b. New Detail View

    c. Detail View

    d. New Named View

6. If you do not see certain high quality rendering elements you should … ?

    a. Consider upgrading your computer

    b. Delete and re-download Autodesk Fusion

    c. Navigate to Graphics and Diagnostic

    d. None of the above

7. How can you make a scene brighter?

    a. Adding extra lights

    b. Increasing brightness

    c. Change to a brighter environment

    d. All of the above

8. Which is faster, Local or Cloud rendering?

    a. Local

    b. Cloud

9. Which is a more realistic camera view?

    a. Perspective

    b. Orthogonal

10. To place a company logo on a product rendering, which tool would you use?

    a. Canvases

    b. Decals

    c. Neither

    d. Both

CHAPTER 9
ENGINEERING DRAWINGS

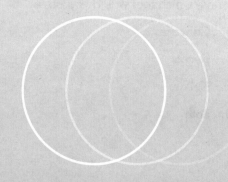

HOW TO MAKE YOUR OWN
BLUEPRINTS

- DRUMSTICKS
- SPACE PROP EMITTER

ENGINEERING DRAWINGS

Engineering Drawings are blueprints to aid in the manufacturing of products and parts by individuals and teams. Parts often require plans that give information about dimensions, thread specifications, surface quality, and more. If a manufacturer is only given a 3D file, they will know the dimensions but may miss other important manufacturing details.

Engineering Drawings are a communication tool with strict formats and guidelines. Here are some of the things often included in Engineering Drawings:

- Who made and verified the drawing
- Revision history
- Welding specifications
- Exploded Diagrams for disassembly and reassembly
- Product weight and material
- Detailed and Section Views
- Quality control standards

This chapter exposes you to a New Drawings workspace in Autodesk Fusion. Each separate workspace has new tools and new functionality and is almost like learning a new program. Each workspace will become another tool in your toolbox as you advance your CAD modeling skills. You will return to this workspace later in the program with Exploded Diagrams.

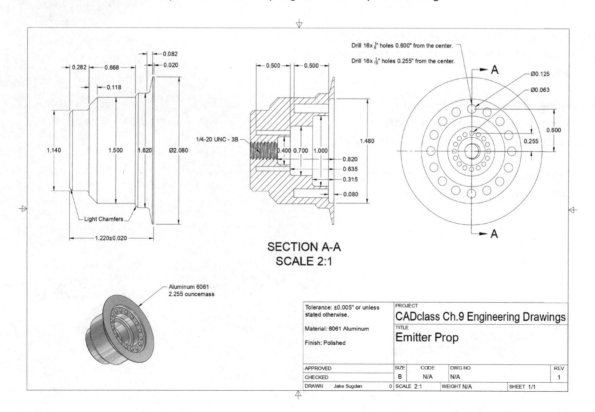

DRUMSTICKS

CHAPTER 9

Learning CAD allows you to communicate your 3-dimensional ideas to people and machines.

Engineering drawings help you communicate specific design features, such as material and size, to other people.

Drumsticks offer an excellent opportunity to explore engineering drawings.

DIFFICULTY:
★★☆☆☆

TIME ESTIMATE:
2 HOURS

KEY LEARNING:
- Set up an engineering drawing
- Add multiple views
- Make a detail view of a body
- Importance of material choices and finishes

DISCORD LINK:
Discord.gg/5hbt6xDPqf

INTRODUCTION

Drumsticks are relatively simple objects to model and make in real life. They are made of flexible woods on a wood lathe, and need to be manufactured to exact specifications and dimensions. In this project, you will model and then create an Engineering Drawing for a drumstick as if you were going to give it to a manufacturer in real life.

CAD

Set the Units to Inches since most lumber sold in the USA is listed in imperial units at quarters.

Make a new Sketch on the Front Plane of a 3-point arc, an ellipse, a Centerline that extends to the right side of the Ellipse, and two lines. Horizontally/Vertically Constraint the arc's endpoints to its center.

Add the following dimensions:

Revolve this shape by selecting the top two Profiles and the bottom horizontal line as the Axis. Click OK.

Add a Pine Wood Appearance, set the Scale to 48%, and the Rotation to 90 degrees to match the correct grain direction for a Drumstick. This mockup of a drumstick is all you need for the Engineering Drawing.

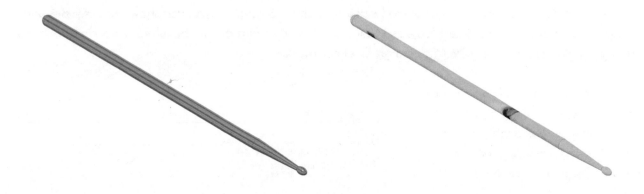

To open the Drawing workspace, navigate to File >> New Drawing >> and select From Design.

This will open up a pop-up showing which Standard you are using, ISO (International Organization for Standardization) or ASME (American Society of Mechanical Engineers). Choose ASME, Sheet Size B.

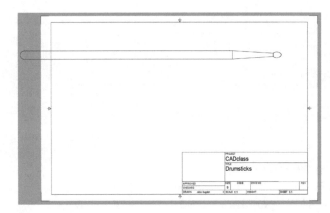

Click the new screen to place the Base View anywhere on the screen and set it as a 1:1 ratio. You will notice it no longer fits on the page when you do this.

There are a few ways to fix the problem of the drumstick not fitting on the page. You can reduce the Scale or add a Section Break. Since this drawing has repeating information, you will add a Break.

Navigate to Create >> and select Break View. Click 2 locations in the middle of the drumstick as shown in the photo. Notice this shortened view has symbols denoting that the part has been cut at these points.

The manufacturer will be able to tell that the information in the middle is an extension of what's on either side of the cut. If you do this to a part, you should not cut out any important information such as drilled holes, decals, grooves, or other geometries.

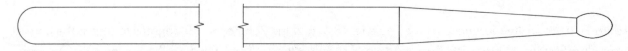

You also want to see a head-on view of the back end of the drumstick so you can show the outer diameter. Navigate to Create >> and select Projected View. Click the part and pull to the left to see a circle with the same diameter as the Base view. Click the green check mark.

Having at least 3 views is a standard minimum when making a part. An isometric view is almost always helpful since it conveys an overall picture of what is being made.

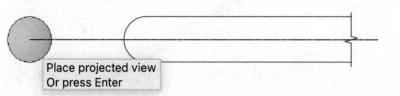

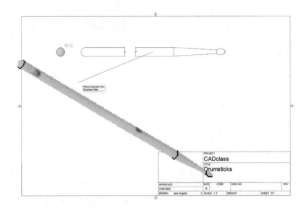

Navigate to Create >> and select Detail View. Make a circle around the drumstick's tip by clicking the center, pulling away, and clicking again. Click somewhere else on the workspace to place the view.

Change the Scale to a 3:1 ratio. If your Detail View shows a break, simply remake it until the break disappears.

Use the Projected View tool, click the Base view, pull diagonally down to the right, and click the green check mark. Double-click this view, change the Scale to 1:2, and the Style to Shaded.

Now, you can click and move the Views around to organize the workspace. It is good practice to keep a space in the middle to add notes about the final product.

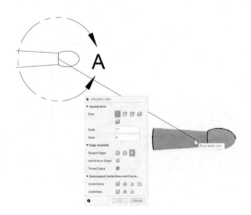

Navigate to Create >> Detail View, click at the Drumstick's head's center, pulling away, and clicking again to make a circle. Click below and to the right to place a zoomed in Detail View of the head.

Change the Scale to a 3:1 ratio and click OK. This Detail View makes some of the smaller details in the model large enough to add dimensions to.

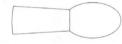

DETAIL A
SCALE 3:1

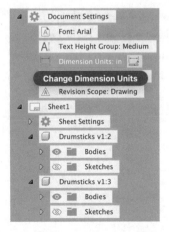

First, you need to define your Linear Precision, or how many digits after the decimal you need for accuracy. To verify this precision, navigate to the Browser, expand Document Settings, and click on Change Dimension Units.

This will open a Dialog Box where you can verify that the Linear Precision is 0.12".

Click the first 2 boxes in Zeros/Units to add Leading and Trailing Zeroes.

DOCUMENT SETTINGS

Standard	ASME
Units	in
Projection Angle	Third Angle
▶ Text	
▼ Units	
Units	in
Format	Decimal
Linear Precision	0.12
Angular Precision	0.12
Zeros/Units	in

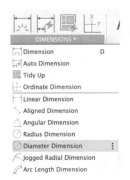

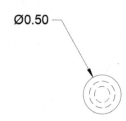

Expand the dimensions menu and notice the different types of dimensions. Select the Diameter Dimension, click the circle's circumference, move your mouse away, and click again to set it.

Note, you aren't going to deal with tolerances in this project, as this tutorial will just be covering the basics.

Type D for Dimensions and make the following on the Detail View. Note that the dimension lines cross over each other which is bad practice in Engineering Drawings as the reader can't be sure it isn't a 90 degree corner of a sketch.

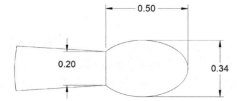

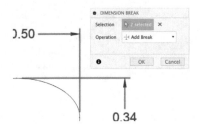

Navigate to Dimension >> Dimension Break, select both dimension lines, and click OK.

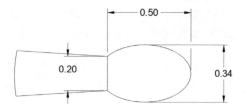

Navigate back to the Front View and select and dimension the angled line length. It will default to dimensioning the hypotenuse, but you want its horizontal length.

Pull the dimension up and move your cursor to the left, which will measure the horizontal dimension.

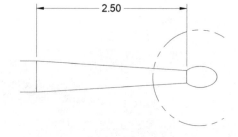

You will encounter some issues when you try to add the drumstick length. If you just click on the arc on the left side, it will snap to the arc's center.

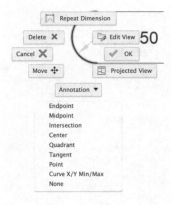

To resolve this issue, press D, hover your mouse over the semicircle, right-click, and select Quadrant. This will add clickable points on 4 circle quadrants (top, bottom, left, right). Now you can hover your mouse over the right end of the drumstick, click it, and dimension the entire part length.

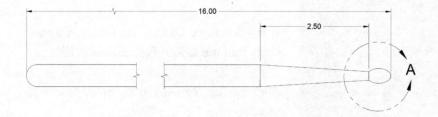

Notes are a critical part of drawings as they can transmit information about the part that isn't dimensional. You can add notes by typing in a simple text box or making a leader note with text pointing to a specific part of the model. Add the notes and anything else you think might be relevant to a manufacturer.

Finally, you will edit the Title Block in the bottom right corner of the sheet. The Title Block houses information about the file, who made it, who approved it, tolerances, and physical properties such as weight or volume. Make this Title Block as accurate as possible, and pretend you are handing your model to a manufacturer. Double-click the Title Block and add the information shown. Some parts will require a text box.

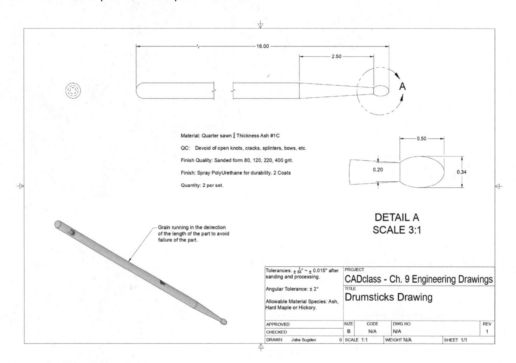

DISCUSSION

Material Tolerances

Some projects require extreme precision, such as aerospace manufacturing, where material tolerances are often 0.001" (1 thou) or less. Other projects, such as carpentry, do not require such high precision since wood expands and contracts.

CHALLENGE

Make an Engineering Drawing for the Tensegrity Tower from Chapter 1.

SPACE PROP EMITTER

CHAPTER 9

If you look closely, you can spot this prop in the hands of a powerful wizard in your favorite Space Opera movie!

For this project, you will create an engineering drawing of a space prop emitter, one component of a space prop you will make later.

DIFFICULTY:
★★★☆☆

TIME ESTIMATE:
2.5 HOURS

KEY LEARNING:
- Make multiple projected views
- Split a body and view its cross-section
- What a leader note is and what information goes in it

DISCORD LINK:
Discord.gg/5hbt6xDPqf

INTRODUCTION

Prop replication is an art. When a prop is needed, pre-made parts are often cobbled together instead of manufacturing them from scratch. Some films in the 1950s, 60's and '70s were famous for making futuristic-looking weapons from junk car parts, bathroom fittings, and even World War II weapons, making them feel "lived in" and "in universe."

For this project, you will recreate an iconic end of a space film prop known as the Emitter, and make an Engineering Drawing stating exactly how to build it.

CAD

Change your Units to Inches since many USA-based manufacturers work in inches.

Start a Sketch on the Front Plane. It is critical to select the correct plane for this project. You won't be able to change it in the Drawings workspace.

Draw a horizontal line on the X-axis and dimension to 1.22" as shown.

Draw the shape in the picture. Ensure the left vertical line is on the Y-axis, and the bottom horizontal line is on the X-axis. Add all the dimensions as shown.

Click Finish Sketch.

Navigate to Create >> Revolve and revolve the profile about the bottom horizontal line.

Navigate to Modify >> Physical Material and set the component as Aluminum 6061, a common subtype of Aluminum used in machining.

Navigate to the Browser, turn off the Body, and turn on Sketch1 by clicking the Eye Icon next to each.

Create a new Sketch on the Front Plane. Press P for Project and click the left, right, and bottom lines. Press OK. Draw the new lines shown in the picture that has 5 horizontal lines.

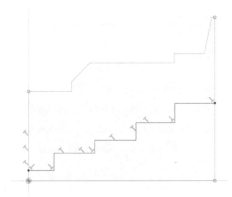

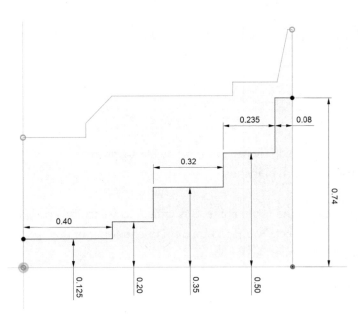

Add the dimensions shown in the picture.

The bottom sketch will appear darker blue than the top sketch since there is a sketch inside of another sketch.

Click Finish Sketch.

Revolve the lower, darker blue profile about the bottom horizontal line and turn the Body back on to make the cut.

Add a 0.04" chamfer to the 2 sharp external edges.

Add a 1/4" - 20 Modeled Thread to the back hole.

Add 0.04" fillets to the internal corners on the inner cavity.

These fillets mimic the radius of the cutter that would make this part on a metal lathe. By not specifying this radius on the part, the cost to make this component would increase exponentially.

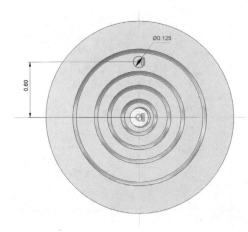

Create a new Sketch on the second face and draw a circle on this surface. Vertically Constrain the circle to the Origin. Dimension the diameter to be 1/8″ and the center-to-Origin distance to be 0.60″.

Extrude Cut this circle into the part -0.50″.

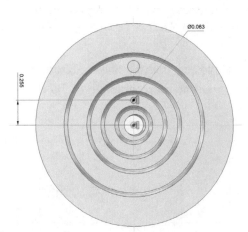

Create a new Sketch on the 2nd from the inner face. Draw a 1/16″ circle with a center-to-Origin distance of 0.255″, and Vertically Constrain it to the Origin.

Click Finish Sketch and extrude cut this circle to -0.50″.

Navigate to Create >> Pattern >> and select Circular Pattern. Change the Object Type to Features and select the 2 most recent extrusions on the Timeline.

Select the Axis of Revolution as the X-axis, set the Quantity to 16, and click OK.

Navigate to File >> New Drawing >> and select From Design.

Select ASME for Standard, Size B for Format, and click OK.

Click anywhere to place your Emitter on the screen. Change the Scale to 2:1 and click OK.

Double-click the Emitter and change the Style to Visible Edges. Click OK.

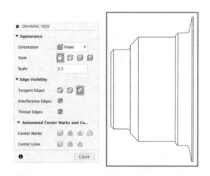

Navigate to Create >> and select Projected View.

Click the emitter, drag your cursor around the screen, and click again when your part is in the orientation shown.

Double-click the new view. Change the Scale to 1:1 and the Style to Shaded. The Isometric View should often be a close, realistic representation of the final product.

Add another Projected View to the right as shown.

You may need to drag your mouse around the screen for the correct orientation.

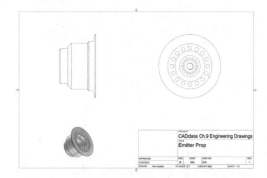

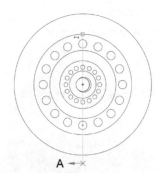

To get an internal view, navigate to Create >> and click Section View. Click the right drawing.

Move your cursor to the Origin and then down. You should see a green dashed line. Click outside the outermost circle as shown.

Move your cursor up above your part, click outside the circle, and select the check mark that appears. Click OK.

Now, you should have a dashed line that is perfectly vertical and intersects with the center of the part.

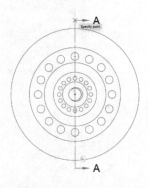

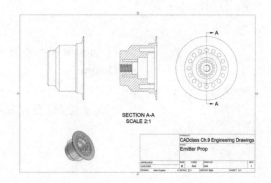

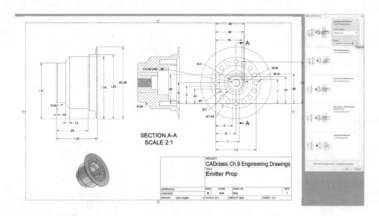

A new tool to Fusion in the Drawing workspace is the Auto Dimension tool.

After enabling it, Fusion offers several formats for dimensioning parts.

Some of these automatically created dimensions are helpful and need only minor adjustments, some are over complicated.

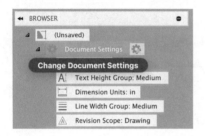

Navigate to the Document Settings and click its gear icon.

Because this is a metal part, set the Linear Precision to 0.123 and enable the first 2 Zeros/Units settings.

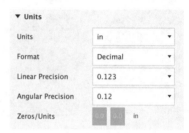

If you need to move a part connected to the Base view, hold Shift, and you can now drag the part wherever you want.

Press D for Dimension and add the following dimensions. Note, you can click on points and lines and will sometimes need to move your mouse around the screen to get the correct dimension.

Press Esc to exit the Dimension tool.

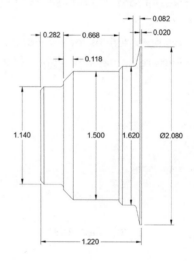

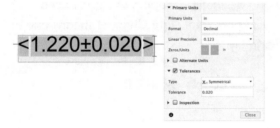

Double-click the 1.22" dimension, check the Tolerances box, expand the Tolerances pull-down, and enter 0.02" for Tolerance.

Add the following dimensions to the Section View.

Add a Dimension Break for any lines intersecting using the Dimensions >> and select the Dimension Break tool. You can also right-click a dimension and select Add Dimension Break.

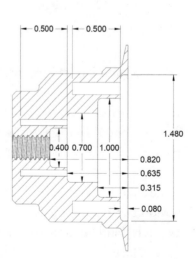

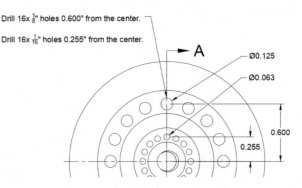

Add a Note denoting the drilled holes in the Projected View and their Quantity.

Add the following dimensions to this Projected View too.

Add a Note to the Isometric View and check Properties in the Dialog Box.

Set the Type to General, the Property to Material and click the (+) symbol. Set the Type to Physical, the Property to Mass and click the (+) symbol.

Press N for Note and select the threaded face on the section view.

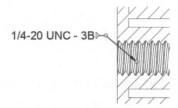

This note defines the threaded hole as a 1/4"-20 Thread cut to a class 3B, which regulates how tight a fit it is.

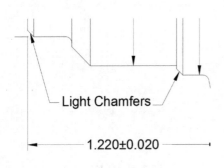

Add another note for a light chamfer on the edges shown by clicking 1 edge, typing "Light Chamfer", and clicking OK.

Click the other edge and drag the line down until it meets the word Light Chamfer. Click OK.

These chamfers are small and aesthetic, meaning you don't need high accuracy. Machinists will know what Light Chamfer means and will file these edges appropriately.

Add the following information to the Title Block in the bottom right by double-clicking it.

To add the text in the top left, navigate to Text >> and select Text. Make a text box in the blank box of the Title Block.

To add the (±) symbol for tolerance, navigate to the Dialog Box, and select Symbols. Find the appropriate symbol and press Close.

Tolerance: ±0.005" or unless stated otherwise.	PROJECT CADclass Ch.9 Engineering Drawings				
Material: 6061 Aluminum	TITLE Emitter Prop				
Finish: Polished					
APPROVED	SIZE	CODE	DWG NO		REV
CHECKED	B	N/A	N/A		1
DRAWN Jake Sugden 0	SCALE 2:1	WEIGHT N/A		SHEET 1/1	

Now you can pass this information off to a manufacturer and have them make a perfect Emitter for you!

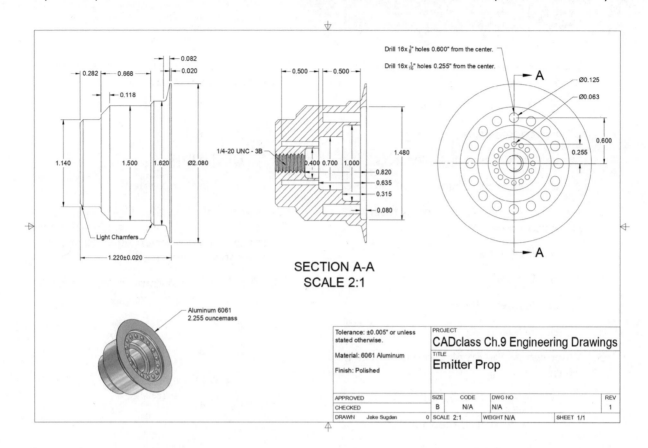

DISCUSSION

A good ethos about Engineering Drawings is that you want to display all the information you need and no more. Avoid duplicating the same dimension, and ensure everything is as neat as possible.

CHALLENGE

Make an Engineering Drawing of the Plastic Building Brick from Chapter 2.

@Conny
User #485

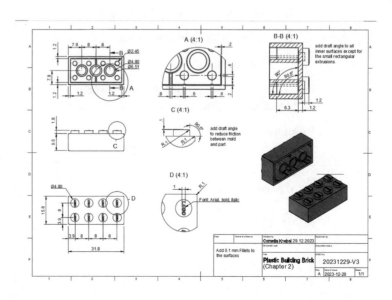

CHAPTER 9 QUESTIONS

1. Engineering Drawings are traditionally used between _____ and _____ ?

    a. Proprietor, Distributors

    b. Engineers, Manufacturers

    c. Manufacturers, Distributors

    d. Engineers, Distributors

2. A colored version is most often reserved for which view?

    a. Detail View

    b. Base View

    c. Isometric View

    d. Break View

3. When would the Break Dimension tool be used?

    a. To cut a view in half

    b. To delete a dimension

    c. To intersect dimension lines

    d. It isn't used in the Drawing workspace

4. True or False? You can pattern multiple features at the same time.

5. What is the most likely element to find in the Title Block?

    a. Name of the project

    b. Tolerance of a specific dimension

    c. Location of light chamfers

    d. The isometric view

6. True or False? You cannot draw a sketch on top of an engineering drawing.

7. To make 4 clickable points on an ellipse, you would right-click the geometry and select?

    a. Midpoint

    b. Endpoint

    c. Quadrant

    d. Corners

8. A common Linear Precision for metal products would be … ?

    a. 0.01"

    b. 0.001"

    c. 0.0001"

    d. 1/64" increments

9. True or False? Leader Notes have "smart qualities" and can identify thread specifications without requiring you to enter them in manually.

10. What is the most common export file type for engineering drawings?

    a. PDF

    b. JPG

    c. STEP

    d. DXF

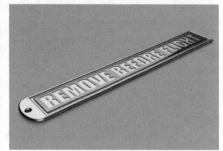

CHAPTER 10
EXPLODED DIAGRAMS

HOW TO EXPLODE YOUR PROJECT
AND REBUILD THEM

- JAPANESE PULL SAW
- MACHINIST HAMMER

EXPLODED DIAGRAM

Exploded Diagrams show expanded drawings of individual components. To make them, you must first understand how to make exploded animations. Since you learned how to make animations in the previous chapter, now is the perfect time to make exploded animations.

Exploded Diagrams often display information about the reassembly order and match each component with a number and a code, so consumers can order a replacement part to fix something themselves. Below is an example you will make:

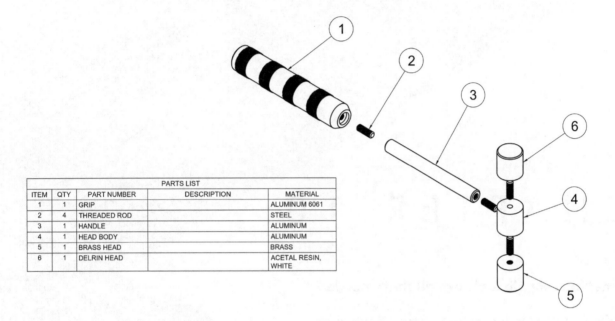

PARTS LIST				
ITEM	QTY	PART NUMBER	DESCRIPTION	MATERIAL
1	1	GRIP		ALUMINUM 6061
2	4	THREADED ROD		STEEL
3	1	HANDLE		ALUMINUM
4	1	HEAD BODY		ALUMINUM
5	1	BRASS HEAD		BRASS
6	1	DELRIN HEAD		ACETAL RESIN, WHITE

This requires entering the Animation workspace, where an Assembly can be manipulated and moved sequentially. Additionally, it can be used to animate the Joint movements in a final product. For example, animating a helicopter's blades spinning and propelling it up and out of frame.

JAPANESE PULL SAW

CHAPTER 10

Sometimes simple tools are all that's needed.

While a pull-saw lacks complexity, it provides an excellent opportunity to create an illustration that "explodes it" and puts it back together.

Exploded diagrams show how unique components fit together.

DIFFICULTY:
★★★★☆

TIME ESTIMATE:
2.5 HOURS

KEY LEARNING:
- In-depth look at the animation workspace
- View and move blocks
- Reversing a storyboard
- Publishing a video

DISCORD LINK:
Discord.gg/5hbt6xDPqf

INTRODUCTION

Japanese Carpentry is known to be one of the most precise and intricate forms of woodworking and requires a lifetime of skills to master. A pull saw is an essential tool in the trade.

In this lesson, you will learn how to make an exploded diagram of a Japanese Pull Saw. Exploded Diagrams are a powerful communication tool that allows you to quickly communicate Construction and Assembly ideas.

CAD

Blade

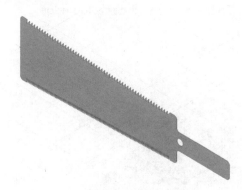

Save an Assembly file as Japanese Pull Saw Assembly and set your Units to Millimeters (mm).

Make an Internal Component called Blade and start a new Sketch on the Front Plane.

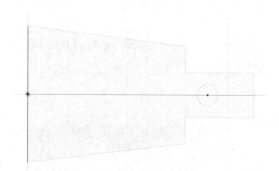

Draw this shape and make it symmetric about the X-axis.

Horizontally Constrain the circle to the Origin.

Add the following dimensions to the sketch.

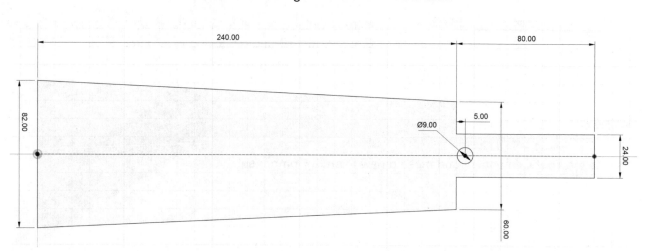

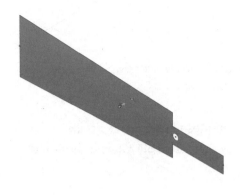

Symmetrically Extrude this profile to a Whole Length of 0.5 mm and add 8 mm fillets to all 8 internal and external corners.

Add a Brushed Stainless-Steel Appearance, rotate the image 90 degrees, and 50% Scale.

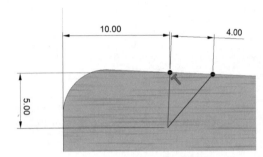

Make a new Sketch on the Blade face and Sketch a right triangle with its top edge Collinear to the Blade's top edge.

Extrude Cut this through the part.

Rectangular Pattern the extrusion 55 times with a 4 mm Spacing along the Blade's top edge.

An error may pop up about the large number. Ignore it.

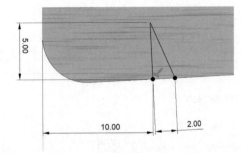

Make a new Sketch on the Blade's front face and draw another right triangle with its bottom line Collinear to the Blade's bottom edge.

Extrude Cut this profile through the Body and pattern it to a Quantity of 110 and a Spacing of -2 mm.

Arms

Activate the Root Component and make a new Internal Component called Arms.

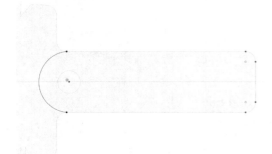

Start a new Sketch on the Blade's front face.

Project the Blade's right-most geometries and join the ends with a 3-point arc tangent to the top and bottom projected lines.

Extrude this profile outwards 1.5 mm and add a Brushed Stainless-Steel Appearance.

Activate the Root Component.

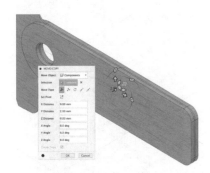

Move the Arm component and check Create Copy. Move the second Arm 2 mm to the other side of the Blade.

You should now see Arm 1 and Arm 2 in the Browser.

Ground the Blade and add a Rigid Group to the 3 components.

Nut

Activate the Root Component and make a new Internal Component called Nut.

Make a new Sketch on the front Arm. Project the hole and make a 5 mm circle in the middle.

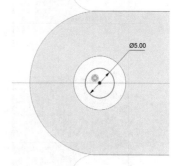

Extrude the ring profile -3 mm into the Saw.

Add an M5 thread to the inside of this tube.

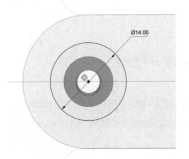

Make a new Sketch on the cylinder's front face of and draw a 14 mm Concentric circle.

Extrude the profiles 4 mm outward and add a 4 mm fillet to the outer edge to make a dome.

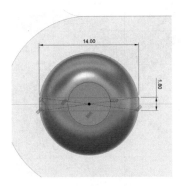

Make a new Sketch on the front face of the Nut and draw a 1.8 mm x 14 mm center rectangle at the circle's center. Project the fillet's surface.

Extrude Cut this profile into the Nut -3 mm to make a flathead screwdriver slot.

Move your view to the back side, type E, select the inside face of the hole, and extrude it through the Nut.

Add a Polished Stainless-Steel Appearance to the Nut, activate the Root Component, and add a Rigid As-Built Joint.

Import the McMaster Carr tool bolt, 92095A308, and rigidly join it to the back of Arm 2.

Handle

Activate the Root Component and make a new Internal Component called Handle.

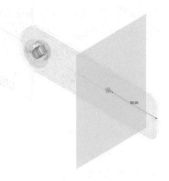

Create an Offset Plane 30 mm from the end of the Blade.

If you accidentally select either Arm, your Origin won't be in the middle.

Make a new Sketch on the Offset Plane, draw a Center Point Slot from the Origin, and dimension the slot.

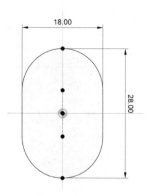

Extrude this profile to the 300 mm and add a 2 mm chamfer to the outer edges.

Select the Combine tool, change the Operation to Cut, set the Handle as the Target Body, and the other components as the Tool Bodies. Check Keep Tools.

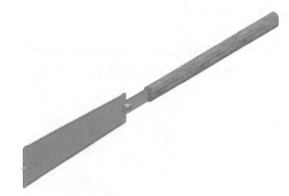

Add an Oak Appearance to the Handle, rotate the wood grain 90 degrees, and Scale it to 40%. Activate the Root Component and show all the components.

Add Rigid joints to the rest of the components, and this model is done!

EXPLODED ANIMATION

Navigate to the Animation workspace, where you can animate the movement of individual components and how they exploded away from each other.

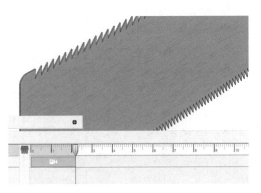

Move the play head to the Scratch Zone (to the left of time-point 0) and click the View Cube's top right corner. This will set the Original viewing angle of the project. Move the play head to 2 seconds, rotate your view, and zoom into where the Handle and the Arms meet.

Note that a blue Camera View block will appear in the Timeline, noting a change in the camera's view while the camera is recording. Press the spacebar to play this action and notice that it doesn't show the final product for long.

Click the Camera View block and move it to the right so it starts at 1.50 seconds. This value does not have to be accurate; if it reads 1.52 seconds, that is fine.

Play the video again and notice how the full model stays in the frame for longer and then zooms in quickly.

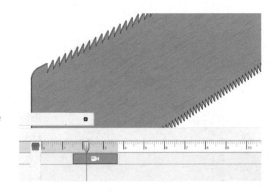

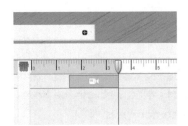

Right-click the Camera View block and select Duration. Press the up arrow to 3.0 seconds and click the green check mark.

Replay it a notice it's a more fluid motion. You could have also selected Edit Start/End and set the block to 1.5 and 4.5 seconds to achieve the same result.

Move the play head to 7 seconds and click the View tool to turn off the recording. Zoom out, select the Transform Component tool, and click the Handle Component. Pull the arrow to slide the Handle out of the Saw 60 mm. Click OK.

Set the new Move block to start at 5 seconds and end at 7 seconds by right-clicking and selecting Edit Start/End. Turn the View back on.

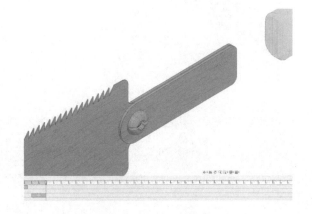

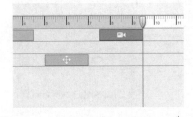

Move the play head to 9.5 seconds and move the camera's view, so the Nut and Bolt are in the screen's center. Move your cursor to the View block's left side and drag the arrow to 7.5 seconds.

Move the play head to 13 seconds and Transform the nut -25 mm in the Y Distance and Rotate 360*31.25 degrees about the Y Angle. The thread of the nut is an M5x0.8 that moves 25 mm (25mm / 0.8 pitch = 31.25 revolutions) for a more realistic disassembly.

Enable Trail Line Visibility to show where the Nut component's starting location was, and click OK. Set the Move block to start at 10 seconds.

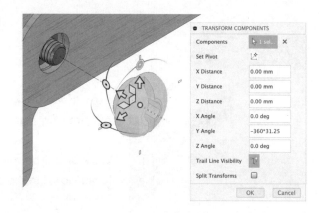

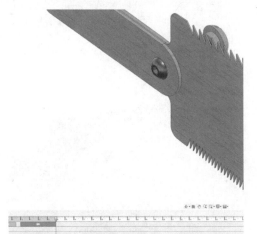

Move the play head to 14 seconds, move the camera to the other side of the Saw, and centralize the Bolt on the screen. Set the View block to start at 10 seconds.

Note that a camera movement and component movement are happening simultaneously. This complexity is a hallmark of an elevated Exploded Diagram video.

Move the play head to 14.5 seconds and Transform the nut 25 mm in the Y Distance and Rotate 360*31.25 degrees about the Y Angle with Trail Lines Enabled.

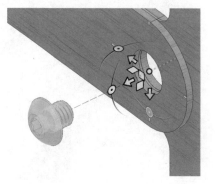

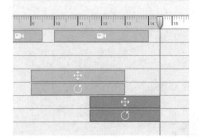

Hold down Ctrl and select both the Move and Rotate block in the Timeline, move your cursor to the left side of the block, and move to 11.5 seconds.

Move the play head to 17 seconds and change the view so the Arms are centered and lower in the frame. Start this View block at 15 seconds.

Note the 0.5 seconds between the end of 1 View block and the start of another. This avoids the "jerkiness" of camera movements and makes for a more comfortable viewing experience.

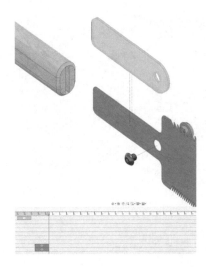

Expand the Browser, select Arm 1 and Arm 2, and Transform them up 60 mm with Trail lines from 17.5 to 19.5 seconds.

Click and drag the storyboard upwards since the 2 components will be lower down in the component list.

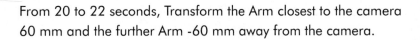

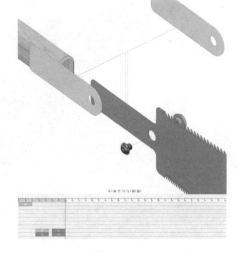

From 20 to 22 seconds, Transform the Arm closest to the camera 60 mm and the further Arm -60 mm away from the camera.

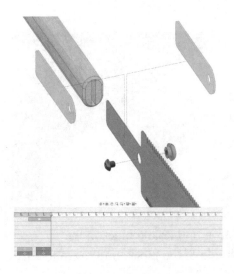

With the play head still at 22 seconds, move the camera's view to show the Arms fully Transformed away from each other like in the picture. Leave this View block to start at 19 seconds.

Move the play head to 25.5 seconds, click the View Cube's top right front corner, like in the first view, and try to match the amount of zoom from the first shot.

Set this view to be from 22.5 to 25.5 seconds.

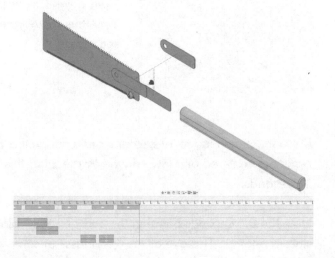

Right-click Storyboard 1 in the bottom left corner of the Timeline and select Copy.

Ctrl+V paste this, and you will see Storyboard1-copy next to it.

Right-click this new storyboard and click Reverse, which will flip the order of Operations of the Timeline, showing an Assembly instead of a disassembly.

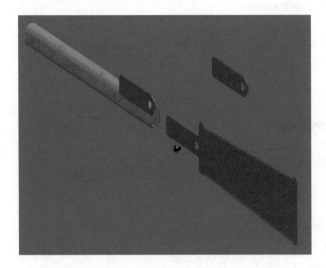

Change the Visual Style of the Saw and the environment to make it look more visually aesthetic.

Navigation bar >> Visual Style >> Shaded, and Environment >> Tranquility Blue or Infinity Pool.

Click the Publish tool and change the Video Scope from Current Storyboard to All Storyboards. This will stitch both of them together.

Set the Resolution to the highest you can, 16:9 1920x1080, and save it to your computer.

DISCUSSION

New Storyboard - The first tool in the toolbar is New Storyboard; a storyboard is a Timeline of components and camera movements. You can make multiple storyboards to show different parts of Exploded Diagrams.

Transform - The Transform menu is where the most useful tools are. Like the Move tool, the Transform Components tool allows you to move Components manually.

Restore Home - Moves components back to their Original location.

Auto Explode - One Level and All Levels are both rarely used tools that will do all the work for you. Unfortunately, as of the publishing of this book, these automatic Operations fail to make functional Exploded Diagrams.

Manual Explode - Similar to the Transform Components tool, this tool only allows components to move linearly but is easier for sequential movements.

Show/Hide - Allows components to fade slowly, reducing workspace clutter.

Annotation/Create Callout - This tool allows notes to be pinned to components and is often used to transfer information across teams about assembly. They will show up in the final video if not removed.

View - allows a virtual camera to record camera movements while panning, orbiting, or zooming.

Publish - Exports the exploded diagram as a video at a set resolution and quality.

Animation Timeline – Found at the bottom of the screen and consists of an empty Timeline, a play head to scrub through the video, the Scratch Zone at 0 seconds where the camera is not recording, and a list of components that have been moved on the left.

CHALLENGE

Animate the exploded Assembly of the 3DP Hot End in Chapter 4. Avoid exploding the project in one long line.

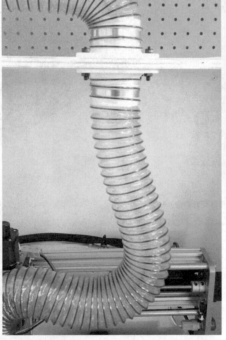

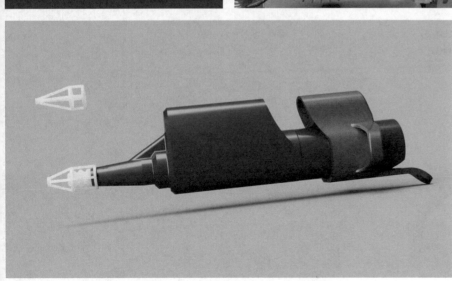

MACHINIST HAMMER

CHAPTER 10

We've come a long way since hammers were made from sticks and rocks millions of years ago.

And yet, the hammer remains a staple in toolkits across the world.

For this project, you will model and then create an exploded diagram for a machinist hammer, one of the most useful tools in a machinists toolkit.

DIFFICULTY:
★★★★☆

TIME ESTIMATE:
3 HOURS

KEY LEARNING:
- Make a parts list on an exploded diagram drawing
- Animate a movement
- Add balloons to a drawing
- How to design an exploded diagram

DISCORD LINK:
Discord.gg/5hbt6xDPqf

INTRODUCTION

Machining is a subset of metalworking that uses machines, such as lathes, mills, and CNCs, to accurately and repeatedly make precise parts. Machinists often read Engineering Drawings to gather the necessary information to produce those parts or to repair whole machines.

In this lesson, you will use an Engineering Drawing to make a CAD model of a machinist hammer. You will then create an exploded animation, and an exploded Engineering Drawing from that model.

All the steps to make this hammer have been used several times in previous projects, and it will be up to you to figure out how to make these parts based on the drawings.

CAD

Save an Assembly file called 000 Machinist Hammer Assembly to a new folder and set the Units to Inches.

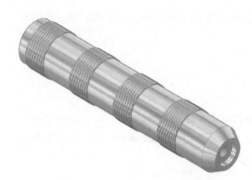

Grip

Make a new Internal or External Component called Grip and make the following part with the dimensions found in the Engineering Drawing on this page or the next one.

Make the Sketches for this part on the Front Plane and set your Units to Inches.

We created this in 10 features, but you may use a different number depending on how you create yours.

1. Sketch on Front Plane
2. Revolve about X-axis
3. Knurl Sketch on Front Plane
4. Revolve about X-axis
5. Coil Cut
6. Mirror Coil Cut about Front Plane
7. Circular Pattern Coil Cut and Mirror features
8. Rectangular Pattern to make 4 knurled sections
9. Chamfer on the back edge
10. ¼-20 Threaded Hole

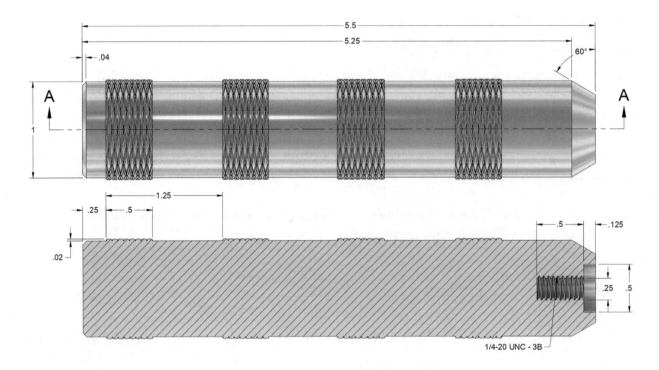

The knurled section of the Grip can be made using a revolved rectangle that sits proud 0.02" from the main cylinder's Body.

Follow the same steps as the Geocache Hide knurls from Chapter 2.

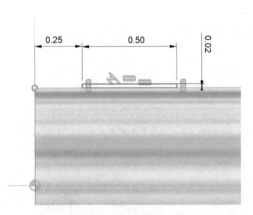

Note, you will revolve this profile and create a triangular coil on its edge. You will then use a combination of mirror, circular, and Rectangular Patterns.

Specific values for the coil are not necessary. Give it your own Style.

Set the Physical Material to 6061 Aluminum.

Finish this component and activate the Root Component.

Threaded Rod

Make a New Component called Threaded Rod. This is a threaded cylinder with chamfered ends, and it can be made into a stand-alone file in a new tab or inside the Assembly file.

The Threaded Rod is 0.75" long and is positioned 0.125" from the bottom of the 0.25" hole on the Grip.

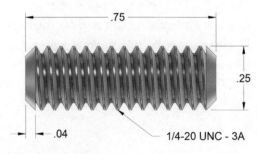

Material: Steel

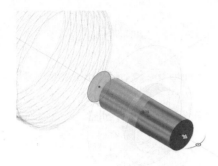

This part can be made in 4 features:

1. Circular Sketch on an inside face in the Grip
2. An Offset Extrusion
3. 2x Chamfers
4. ¼-20 Modeled Thread

Keep the Physical Material as the default Steel and Activate the Root Component.

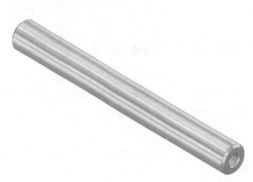

Handle

Make a New Component called Handle.

This component can also be made in the Assembly file by extruding the 0.5" hole inside the Grip.
This component can be made in 6 features:

1. Circular Sketch inside the Grip
2. Circular Extrusion
3. Countersunk, ¼-20 Tapped Hole
4. Outer Edge Chamfer
5. Midplane of flat faces
6. Mirror Hole and Chamfer features

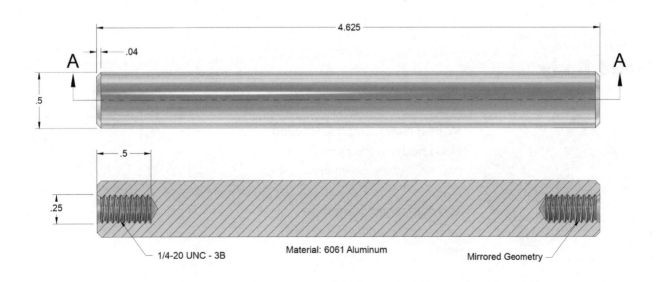

4.625

.04

A A

A A

.5

.5

.25

1/4-20 UNC - 3B

Material: 6061 Aluminum

Mirrored Geometry

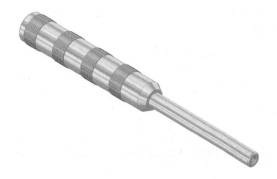

Give this part a Physical Material of 6061 Aluminum.

Finish this component and activate the Root Component.

Ground the Grip and add a Rigid Group to all 3 components.

Threaded Rod: 2

Copy and paste the Threaded Rod, and move the new component to the Handle's front.

This will show up as Threaded Rod: 2 in the Browser.

Add a Rigid joint to the Threaded Rod's outer edge and the Handle's outer edge and set a -0.375" Offset so the Threaded Rod: 2 sticks out halfway from Handle.

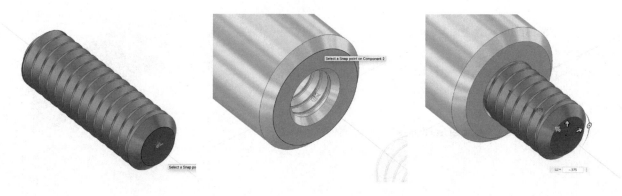

Head Body

Make a New Component called Head Body on the Front Plane and project the geometry shown.

This component is a simple cylinder with an axial threaded hole.

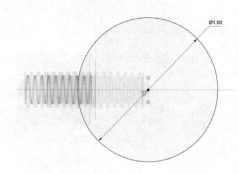

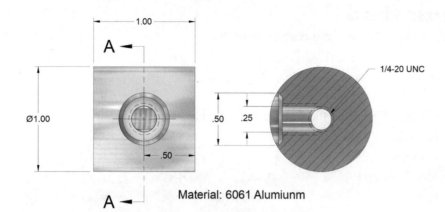

Material: 6061 Alumiunm

This component can be made in 4 features:

1. Circular Sketch on the Front Plane
2. Symmetric Extrusion
3. Combine Cut
4. ¼-20 Threaded Hole

Add a Physical Material of 6061 Aluminum to the component and finish the component.

Activate the Root Component and add a Rigid As-Built Joint to the Head Body and the Handle.

Threaded Rod: 3 & 4

Use the Rectangular Pattern tool to make 2 more Threaded Rods anywhere in the workspace.

Rigidly Join both the Threaded Rods to the ends of the Head Body by selecting the outer edge of the Threaded Rod and the outer edge of the Head Body and Offsetting them -0.375" into the Head Body.

Open the Section Analysis tool on the Top Plane, and note how the Threaded Rods don't interfere with each other.

Cancel the tool.

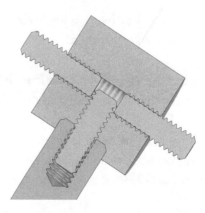

Brass Head

Make a New Component called Brass Head.

This component can be made in 4 features:

1. Circular Sketch on the front face of the Head Body
2. Extrusion
3. Chamfer
4. ¼-20 Tapped Hole

Add a Brass Physical Material to the component, finish the component, and Activate the Root Component.

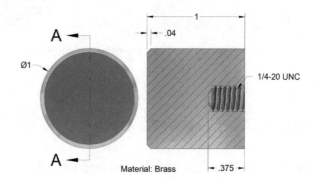

Delrin Head

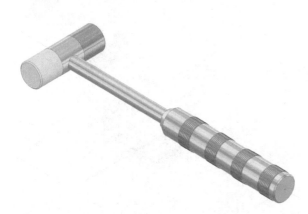

Mirror the Brass Head component about the Front Plane and rename the new component in the Browser, Delrin Head.

Add the Physical Material Acetal Resin White to the new component. Acetal is another name for Delrin, a common plastic used in machining known for its easy cutting.

Add a Rigid Group to the rest of the components to lock them in place.

EXPLODED ANIMATION

Navigate to the Animation workspace and start a new Storyboard.

Move the play head in the Scratch Zone where the camera isn't recording.

Select the View Cube's top front left corner and move the Machinist Hammer into the middle of the frame.

Move the play head to the 4 second mark and expand the components in the Browser to show the 000 Machinist Hammer Assembly file.

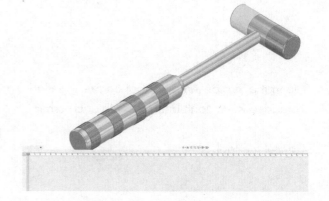

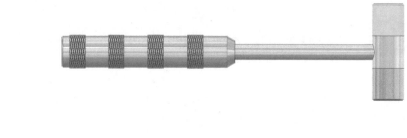

Using the Transform tool, select the Assembly file and rotate it 90 degrees about the X-axis. Move the camera's view to a Front View and zoom in appropriately.

Click OK and shorten both the View and Move Blocks to start at 1 second.

Move the play head to 5.50 seconds, open the Transform tool, and select the assembly.

Rotate the Hammer 25 degrees upward, mimicking a hammer hit, and set this to start at 4.5 seconds.

Move the play head to 6.5 seconds and rotate the hammer back down to horizontal. Start the rotate block at 5.5 seconds.

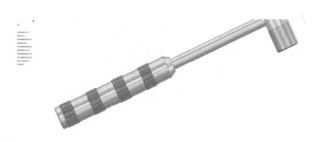

Zoom where the Grip meets the Handle to make a View Block from 4.5 to 6.5 seconds. Set the view block to start at 4.5 seconds.

In this project, the Handle will be the "grounded" component, and the other components will explode away from it.

Move the play head to 10 seconds and Transform the Grip -2.5" to the left. Click OK and start this Move block at 7 seconds.

Without moving the play head, Transform the Threaded Rod -1.25" to the left. Click OK.

Move the left side of this Move Block to line up with the start of the previous Move Block.

Move the play head to 13.5 seconds and rotate the View Cube so the Hammer's head is in the middle of the screen. Set the start of this View Block to 10.5 seconds.

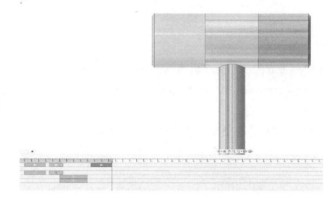

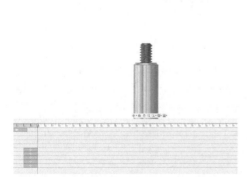

Move the play head to 15 seconds and expand the Assembly in the Browser.

Open the Transform tool, select the Head Body, hold down Shift, select the Delrin Head, and move all 5 components upwards 1.50". Click OK.

Scroll down in the Storyboard to select all 5 Move Blocks at the bottom and set them to start at 12 seconds.

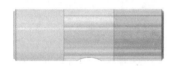

With the play head still at the 15 second mark, Transform the Threaded Rod: 2 upwards 0.75". Click OK.

Edit this new move block to start at 12 seconds.

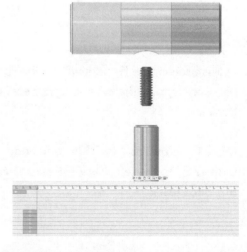

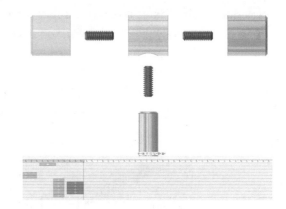

Move the play head to 18.5 seconds, and in 4 individual steps, move the Delrin Head and the Brass Head 1.5" away from the Head Body, and move the Threaded Rods: 3 & 4 0.75" away from the Head Body.

Set these 4 Move blocks to start at 15.5 seconds.

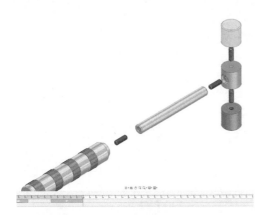

Finally, move the play head to 22 seconds, move the camera to the Top Front Left corner of the View Cube, and zoom in appropriately to view the entire disassembled hammer starting at 17 seconds.

Publish this Storyboard at the highest resolution and save it to your computer.

EXPLODED DIAGRAM

With the play head still at 22 seconds, navigate to Drawing >> and select From Animation workspace.

Make a new ASME Size B Drawing.

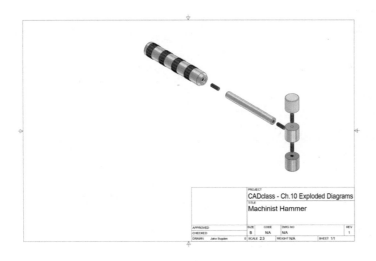

Click on the page's right side to place the exploded diagram and keep the Style as Visible Edges. This Style is also commonly known as the Wireframe View in other CAD software.

Change the Scale to 2:3 and click OK.

Navigate to the Tables menu and select the Parts List tool. Click on the left side of the page to open a table automatically filled with information about the components inside the assembly.

This will reference their name, Quantity, material, and a blank box under the description for additional information, like a Vendor ID. Click and drag the balloons to shorten their lines and organize the space. Navigate to the Tables menu and select the Balloon tool.

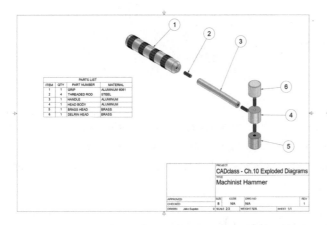
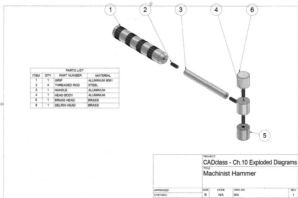

Click the other 3 Threaded Rods and place their balloons in an appropriate location.

Note that they don't get their own individually numbered balloon, as the first Threaded Rod has a Quantity of 4, so all 4 components will receive a #2 balloon.

As you can see, this is a powerful tool that can assist you in your next big manufacturing project!

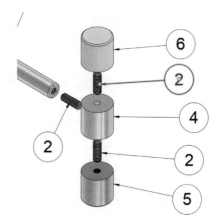

CHALLENGE

Animate the Pizza Cutter project from Chapter 5 and make exploded diagram with the correct Physical Materials.

@Vasile
User #498

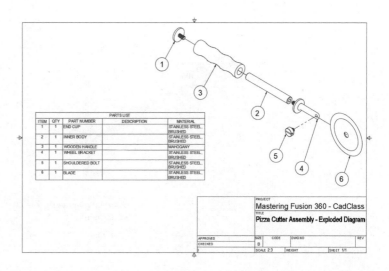

CHAPTER 10 QUESTIONS

1. Where is the Scratch Zone?

   a. Timeline

   b. Browser

   c. Animation Toolbar

   d. Export dialog box

2. View Blocks will show … ?

   a. Zoom

   b. Camera movement

   c. Panning

   d. All of the above

3. How would you change the length of a Block?

   a. Edit the duration

   b. Drag edges of the Block

   c. Set Start and End time

   d. All of the above

4. True or False? View Blocks, Rotate Blocks and Move Blocks can exist all the same time.

5. What is a Trail Line?

   a. A linear move Block

   b. A path of movement

   c. An arc movement Block

   d. A setting not in the Animation workspace

6. To reverse the order of the exploded animation you would first need to … ?

   a. Make a new Story Board

   b. Right-click Story Board

   c. Select the reverse tool in the View menu

   d. It is automatically created for you in the export dialog box

7. What is the highest exporting resolution?

   a. 1080p

   b. 720p

   c. 4K

   d. 480p

8. True of False. After exporting, annotations will not be visible in the final video.

9. What is a balloon?

   a. This is not a real term in CAD

   b. Annotations that point to steps in the storyboard

   c. Circles that point to components

   d. Another word for the Detail View in a Drawing

10. Tables in drawings are often used to chart information about each component. Which of the following would you least expect to find in a table?

    a. Cost

    b. Material

    c. Surface Quality

    d. If part was likely to break in shipping

CHAPTER 11
CAM

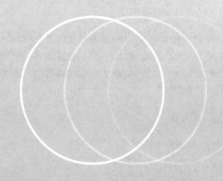

HOW TO MANUFACTURE PARTS ON A CNC
WITH COMPUTER-AIDED MANUFACTURING

- WOODEN LONGBOARD
- ELECTRIC GUITAR

CAM

In this chapter, you will learn how to use the Computer Aided Manufacturing (CAM) workspace inside Autodesk Fusion. You will model and then design a manufacturing process (called a toolpath) for making a longboard skateboard and an electric guitar.

Computer Numerical Control (CNC) is automated machining that feeds information from a 2D or 3D model into a machine such as a mill, router, or lathe that cuts it out. These machines are increasingly used in all types of manufacturing and will likely only increase in popularity over the following decades.

CNC is a general term that can be applied to several different types of machines that yo wouldn't normally call a CNC such as 3D Printers, Plasma Cutters, and Laser Etchers. The difference is that 3D Printers are additive machines, and CNC Routers or Mills are subtractive as they remove material.

It is important to note that this book focuses on teaching CAD modeling to beginners rather than teaching advanced manufacturing techniques. Therefore, we will show you how to navigate the Autodesk Fusion CAM workspace but will not go in-depth about the machining process. If you want to learn more about CNC machining, there are many excellent books, courses, and YouTube videos.

Lastly, while these projects can be manufactured in real life, we recommend consulting with an experienced machinist before attempting to do so. If you decide to make them, proceed at your own risk and know that these designs may not be sufficient or safe, depending on your machine or setup.

LONGBOARD

CHAPTER 11

Few toys inspire as much nostalgia as the skateboard.

The simplicity-to-fun ratio is tough to beat.

In this project, you will learn how to program a CNC machine to make a longboard skateboard repeatedly, making it possible to reproduce many more than you could by making them by hand.

DIFFICULTY:
★★★☆☆

TIME ESTIMATE:
2 HOURS

KEY LEARNING:
* Exploring the basics of the CAM/manufacturing workspace
* A stock box and how it relates to the real-world material
* Make a custom tool
* Simulate a toolpath

DISCORD LINK:
Discord.gg/5hbt6xDPqf

INTRODUCTION

Computer-controlled machining (CNC) has revolutionized the manufacturing world and is expected to grow in popularity over the next decades. Although skateboards can be made by hand, an automated machine allows for near-perfect replication of drilled holes, board shapes, and manufacturing processes. In addition, the process can be scaled and replicated without using dangerous woodworking machinery such as table saws, ultimately reducing the risk of injury.

The longboard skateboard makes for an excellent introduction to the manufacturing workspace since it is a relatively simple object that does not require machining on both sides and requires a limited number of tools. In addition, this project can be made and used in real life if you have access to a CNC.

CAD

Set your Units to Inches and start a Sketch on the Top Plane.

Some CNC machines accept metric Units, and others imperial. You will design this skateboard in Inches but can export it in Inches or Millimeters later.

Make a 4" x 33" Construction Rectangle with its bottom left corner Coincident with the Origin. This is a symmetric design, so the left vertical line will be used as a Mirror Line.

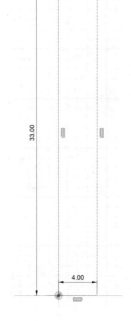

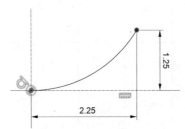

Draw a 3-point arc from the Origin. Add a Coincident constraint between the arc's center and the left vertical Construction Line (this may be automatically applied). Add the dimensions shown.

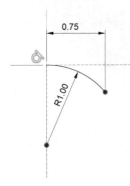

Make another 3-point arc that starts at the Construction Rectangle's top left corner, is constrained in the same way as the bottom arc, and add the dimensions shown.

Draw a line from the bottom 3-point arc's end that is 12" up and 3.625" to the right of the Origin.

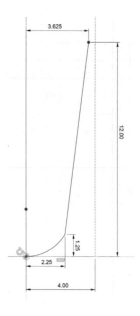

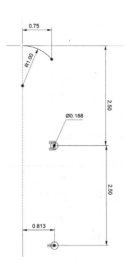

Draw 4 Vertically and Equally constrained circles.

Dimension them to be 0.8125" to the right of the centerline and 3/16" in diameter. Set the circles 2.5" apart and 2.5" from the top and the bottom.

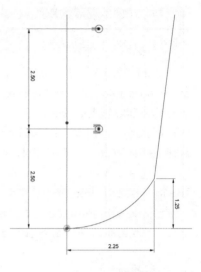

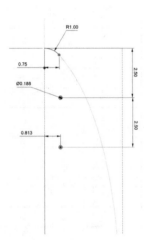

Join the 2 arcs with a Fit Point Spline and click the green check mark by only clicking on the 2 endpoints with no extra points in between.

Add Tangent constraints to both ends and adjust the spline's vertices to make a longboard shape that doesn't extend outside the Construction Rectangle. Fix the Spline.

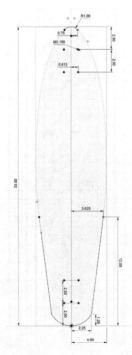

Mirror the sketch across the rectangle's left vertical line and Finish the Sketch.

Extrude the Profile 0.71" if you are planning on making this longboard out of plywood or 0.54" for hardwood like oak or birch.

0.54" is a suitable thickness for longboards as it is thin enough to flex for a comfortable ride but not too thin so it will break.

Add a Bamboo appearance to the part and add a 1" fillet to the 2 edges at the back of the board as shown. Add 0.125" chamfers to all 8 top holes, make a new Sketch on the top face, type O for Offset, click the top edge, and set the Offset to -0.50".

Using the Text tool, write words of your choice, set the Height to 1.5", and change the Font to American Typewriter or an equivalent Font.

Extrude this text down -0.125" and click OK. If this feature doesn't work and gives you an error, choose a different Font.

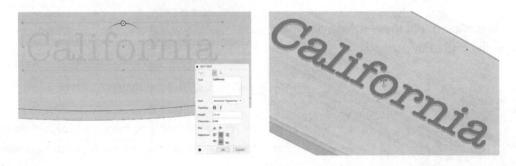

CAM

Navigate from the Design workspace to the Manufacture workspace, where the CAM portion of this chapter will take place.

The new workspace and terminologies may seem intimidating at first, but this chapter will cover simple processes to inspire you to dig deeper into this topic.

You will learn how to:
* Set up stock material and define a home position
* Create new tools
* Drill and Countersink the holes
* Cut the outer profile with tabs
* Simulate the Operations
* Posting process the result to prepare for CNC cutting

Verify your Units are set to Inches.

Navigate to Setup >> and select New Setup.

This will make a yellow box around the model known as a Bounding Box. This represents the block of wood you will cut your skateboard from. You can adjust its size depending on the material you use for your projects.

Click the Stock tab and change the Mode to Fixed Size Box. This is where you can adjust the size of the Bounding Box to match the piece of wood you will cut.

Change the X, Y, and Z dimensions to 9", 36", and 0.71".

For more information about these values, see the Discussion at the end of this chapter.

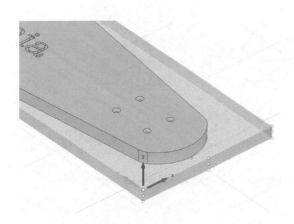

Navigate back to the Setup tab.

Notice white dots on all corners and midpoints of the Bounding Box. Select the front left bottom corner.

Verify the X is pointing down the width, the Y is pointing down the length, and the Z is pointing upwards.

If, for some reason, yours are not, you may need to play around with the Orientation dropdown menu and click the colored axes arrows to reorient them.

These white dots are Stock Points (AKA Datum Points) and act as a home location for referencing the geometry. It can be thought of as the Origin of the CNC where all locations are measured from. Click OK.

Navigate to your profile in the top right corner of the screen >> Preferences >> Manufacture >> Enable Cloud Libraries. Click Apply and OK.

Now any tools you make will be accessible on any computer.

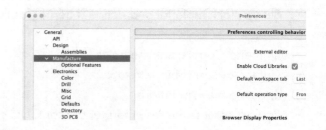

This project requires 3 tools: a drill bit, a countersink bit, and an end mill. The countersink bit can be imported from Fusion's tool Library, but you will custom-make the drill bit and end mill.

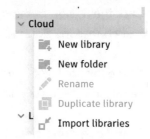

Navigate to Manage >> and select tool Library. Right-click Cloud, click New Library and name it CADclass CNC Tools. This Library will be filled with cutting tools for your projects. Because Autodesk Fusion is a Cloud-based software, you can sign in on any computer in the world and see all your files. Many CNCs in workshops have dedicated computers or shop laptops available for use that are provided so they can get covered in sawdust instead of your nice personal computer.

Click the (+) symbol at the top of the screen to make the first tool.

Navigate to Hole Making and select Drill.

Describe this tool as a 3/16" Custom Drill Bit.

Click the Cutter tab, where you can enter the dimensions of your drill bit. This drill has 2 flutes and is made of high-speed steel (HSS), standard hard steel.

Enter the cutter information from the picture.

Navigate to the Cutting Data tab where you will input values known as feeds and speeds.

Set the spindle speed to 5000 rpm, a relatively slow speed appropriate for the small diameter drill bit.

Set the plunge speed to 40 in/min and click accept.

These values are typical for an industrial-size CNC but will differ for a hobby-level CNC with less power.

An in-depth discussion of feeds and speeds is outside the scope of this chapter but can be found easily online.

Click the + sign at the top of the screen to add a new tool and choose the flat-end mill.

Name this tool 1/4" End Mill and enter the following details in the Cutter and Cutting Data tabs.

Click Accept and close the window.

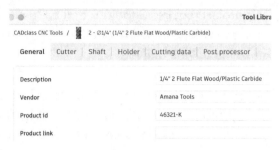

You can use a premade tool to add the countersink to the hole. Select Tutorial Tool (Inch) on the left side column, scroll down the list, right-click 19- ½" 45deg (Engrave/Chamfer mill), Copy Tool, navigate to your CADclass CNC Tools Folder, Ctrl/Cmd + V (Paste), to add the tool to your tool list.

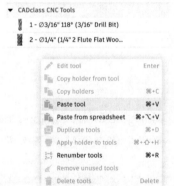

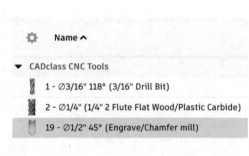

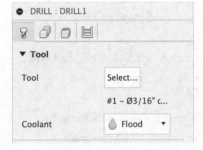

Navigate to Drilling >> and select Drill.

Select the tool, which will bring up the tool Library, and select the 3/16" drill bit you created.

Select the Geometry tab in the Dialog Box, check "Select Same Diameter", click Select next to Hole faces, and click any hole's face and it will automatically select all holes.

The yellow lines are the travel paths, the red downward arrow denotes where the drill will first enter, and the green up arrow denotes where the last hole will be drilled.

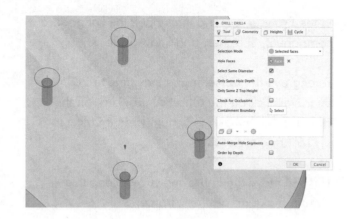

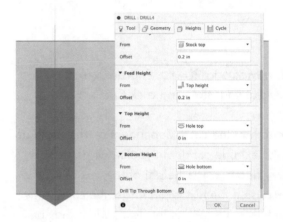

Select the Heights tab. Click the check box next to Drill Tip Through Bottom, which lets the drill bit's tip pass through the longboard. Click OK.

To drill the countersinks, select the Drill tool again, click Select next to Tool, click on the CADclass CNC Tools Folder, click Milling under the Tool category on the right side, and select the Engraving tool.

Click on the Geometry tab, select all 8 of the countersink surfaces, and click OK.

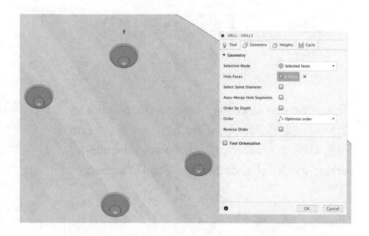

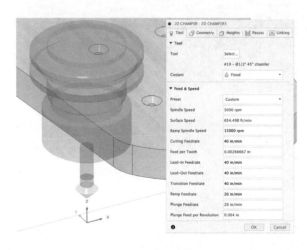

To chamfer the top outer surface, navigate to 2D >> 2D Chamfer, click the top edge of the Longboard, click on the Tool Tab, change the Ramp Spindle Speed to 15,000 rpm, the Cutting Feedrate to 40 in/min, the Ramp Feedrate to 20 in/min.

Click on the Passes Tab and set the Chamfer Width to 0.125".

Click OK.

▼ Chamfer	
Chamfer Width	0.125 in
Chamfer Tip Offset	0 in
Chamfer Clearance	0 in

In the Browser, expand the Model, the Longboard component, Sketches, and Show Sketch2.

To engrave the Offset frame, navigate to 2D >> Engrave, click on the Offset curves, click on the Height Tab, change the Bottom Height Offset to -1/16", and click OK.

This will move the Engraving cutter along this path to make an aesthetic frame.

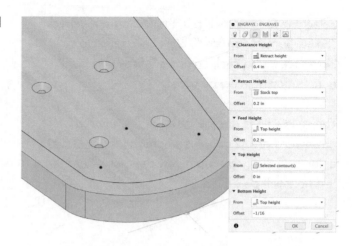

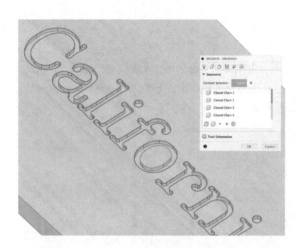

Hide Sketch2, navigate to 2D >> Engrave, select the top edge of all parts of your text, and click OK.

Because the depth of the cut is dependent on the width of the lettering, the extrude cut depth you set of -0.125" is just an arbitrary number. The height of the Text of 1.5" is important, because if the text is too large, the cutter may not be able to fully cut it out, as the Text's width may be larger than the diameter of the cutter.

To cut the profile of the Longboard, navigate to 2D >> 2D Contour, set the Tool as the ¼" End mill, click the Geometry Tab, select the bottom edge, check Tabs, and set the Tab Distance to 8".

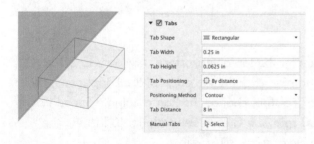

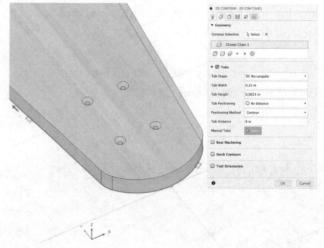

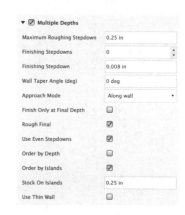

Click on the Passes tab to verify the Sideways Compensation is set to Left, check Multiple Passes, verify the Maximum Roughing Stepdown is set to 0.25", and check Use Even Stepdowns.

Note that the Finishing Stepdown is set to 0.008", which continues to cut 0.008" below the bottom surface of the wood to ensure that the profile is cut all the way through.

Most CNC Router projects are cut on a surface known as a Spoil Board, a sacrificial sheet of material that is okay to cut into, but only lightly, hence 0.008".

Click on the Linking Tab, set the Ramping Angle to 10 degrees, and set the Maximum Ramp Stepdown to 0".

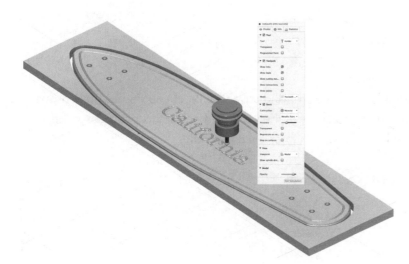

Right-click Setup in the Browser and click Simulate. Click the play button at the bottom of the screen.

For safety and quality purposes, it is always a good idea to watch and analyze each simulation before sending it to a CNC machine.

This is one way to find and correct many mistakes.

The Dialog Box houses lots of good information about how you can view the simulation.

At the top, you can set whether to see the tool or the holder, or whether the tool is transparent or has a point on the end. Like all new menus, it helps to take extra time to review the functionality before moving on.

Click on the Statistics Tab to see the estimated CNC cutting time. The real life time will be about 10-20% longer because most CNC simulations ignore the time of the tool retracting. You can also right-click each of the operations in the Browser to see its individual Machining Time.

As you get more experience in CNC'ing, you'll be able to build a skill to estimate how much time is needed for each operation to identify a problem if the machining time is too long. It is a common experience in beginner CNC'ing to accidentally set the depth of a Contour cut to 0.025" instead of 0.25" leading to a cutting time 10 times longer than needed.

Select the Drilling operation in the Browser. You will export the operations using the Post Process tool in the Actions menu.

Each CNC machine has a dedicated file called a Post which is how Autodesk Fusion saves commands that the CNC can read. This section can be left empty if you do not have access to a CNC.

Note that each CNC has its own post processor and it can be dangerous to start a file on a CNC that was designed for another.

If you have CNC access, now is an excellent time to locate the post-processor on the manufacturer's website or in the Fusion library under Manage >> Post Library.

Name the file 3/16 Drill, select a folder, set the Units to mm, and save the file. If you do not have a post processor selected, you cannot save this file, and you can exit the window. Repeat this process for the other 2 Operations. These files will be saved as .NC or a numerical control file.

Now it's time to take your skateboard to a CNC and make it!

DISCUSSION

CNC or hand tools?

It is easy to assume that a CNC will magically make an entire project with minimal work on your part, but it is often more efficient to perform some of the manufacturing steps by hand, and the rest can be done on the CNC. Match the complexity of the job to the complexity of the tool.

In other words, CNCs are great for repetitive tasks or tasks that require high precision, but simple Operations like routing a radius on the outer edges are sometimes better done by hand.

How Large does the Bounding Box need to be?

A rule of thumb for wood is to add twice the diameter of the cutter to all sides and a 1/4" frame. For example, 8 + 4*0.25" = 9". You need areas in the wood to drive screws into the CNC's spoil board, so placing those screw holes at the ends of the wood saves material. Finally, you are assuming that the board has been planed down to the final thickness before the CNC Operations. If this is not the case, you must adjust the height accordingly.

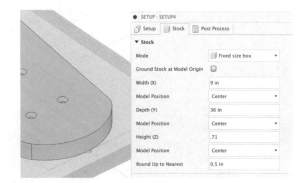

Drill Bit RPM

Usually, this value is higher with smaller diameter bits since higher speeds eject more wood chips and dissipate heat. But in this case, the drill bit is held in place by a heavy tool called a Jacob's chuck which adds considerable weight relative to the bit. For that reason, most CNCs Discourage speeds over 5000 rpm when using these drill chucks.

Tabs

Tabs prevent the project from being picked up by the cutter. The more tabs, the more work to clean up. The fewer tabs, the more likely they will break off and your part moves.

Datum Point

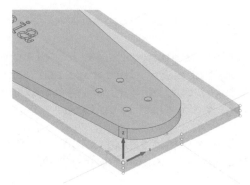

When cutting through stock, selecting the lowest datum point is generally advisable. When engraving on the top or cutting to a specific depth, it is generally advisable to select the top.

CHALLENGE

Make a custom wooden sign with engraved letters and a decorative border. Download an SVG online and use the Engrave tool with a 90-degree V bit to cut out the letters and a 1/4" end mill to carve out the profile.

@Conny
User #485

ELECTRIC GUITAR

CHAPTER 11

Rock on!

Electric guitars take a ton of time to make by hand. But what if we use a machine? It turns out, machines are an excellent way to make electric guitars.

This project explores the computer-assisted manufacturing (CAM) workspace.

DIFFICULTY:
★★★★☆

TIME ESTIMATE:
3.5 HOURS

KEY LEARNING:
- Roughing and Finishing passes and their differences
- Calculate feeds and speeds
- Make non-45-degree chamfers
- Double-sided CNC projects

DISCORD LINK:
Discord.gg/5hbt6xDPqf

INTRODUCTION

Designing and creating a toolpath for an electric guitar is a great intermediate Computer Aided Manufacturing (CAM) project. It has an adaptable shape, standard cavities that are difficult to make by hand, and features on both the top and bottom, meaning you must flip the workpiece over and machine the other side. In this lesson, you will continue to explore the CAM workspace as you model and design the toolpath for an electric guitar. Rock on!

CAD

Set your Units to Inches. Download the guitar image found at **CADclass.org** in the **FREE DOWNLOADS** tab.

Navigate to Insert >> and select Canvas. Select the guitar picture, and click the Top Plane. Rotate the image to -8.5 degrees so the strings are vertical. Click OK.

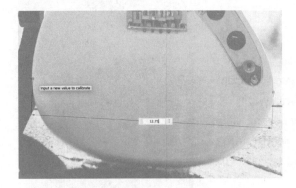

Expand the Canvas in the Browser, right-click the picture, and select Calibrate. Select the 2 widest points of the guitar and set it to 12.75".

Make a new Sketch on the Top Plane and add points at each curve's highest and lowest points.

In general, the fewer points you place on the profile, the better the Fit Point Spline will work. Highlight them all and apply a Fix/Unfix constraint so they don't move.

Make an "L" shape to join the top of the guitar Body to the neck.

Use the Fit Point Spline tool and click on the points shown to make an enclosed profile. Click the green check mark.

Work your way around the Spline and adjust each green vertex until the Spline matches the shape of the guitar. This is an iterative process, so you may need to adjust each point a few times to get it right. Once done, Fix the Spline profile in place.

Extrude this profile upwards 1.75".

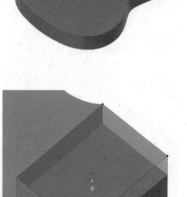

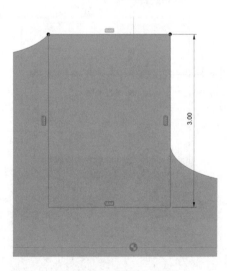

Start a Sketch on the top face of the Guitar and sketch a rectangle from the top left point. Coincidentally Constrain the top right corner to the other top Spline point, dimension its height to 3.00", and extrude cut it down 0.75".

Make a new Sketch on the newly extruded face of a vertical constriction line at the midpoint of the horizontal line, 2 Vertically Constrained 3/16" circles, dimension the circles, and mirror about the vertical Construction Line.

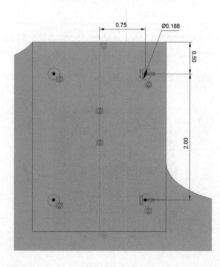

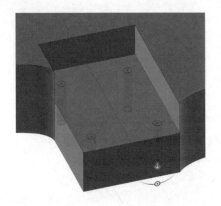

Extrude cut the 4 circles through the entire component and add 0.375″ fillets to the vertical corners.

If an error message pops up incrementally reduce the fillet size by 0.005″ until it works.

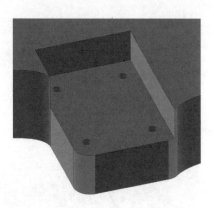

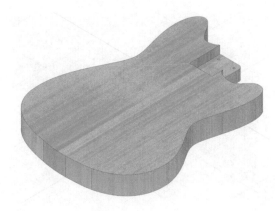

Drag a Bamboo Appearance, or any light-colored wood of your choosing onto the guitar Body.

Make a new Sketch on the guitar's top and draw a vertical Construction Centerline from the midpoint of the neck extrusion.

Draw the right side of the sketch using the Line tool.

Add an Equal and Collinear constraint to the 2 vertical Sketch lines.

Dimension the sketch and mirror it to the left side.

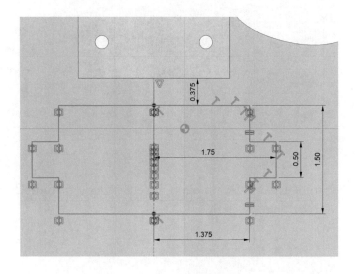

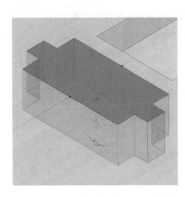

Finish the Sketch and extrude cut this profile -1″ into the guitar Body.

Add 0.125″ fillets to the internal and external corners of the Cut profile.

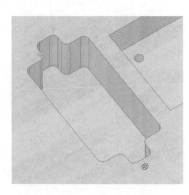

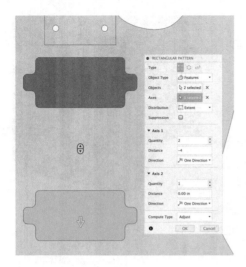

Navigate to the Rectangular Pattern tool, change the Object Type to Features, and select the Fillet and Extrusion to pattern in the direction of the Y-axis with a Quantity of 2 and -4" away.

Sketch a vertical Construction line from the midpoint of the bottom edge of the previous feature. Sketch an Overall Slot, set the midpoint to the bottom point of the Construction Line, and dimension the Slot.

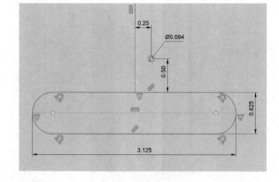

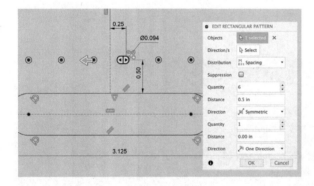

Sketch a 3/32" circle and its location, and Rectangularly Pattern it Symmetrically to a Quantity of 6 with a 0.50" Spacing.

Extrude Cut the Slot through the entire Body. Extrude Cut the 6 holes -0.625" into the Body.

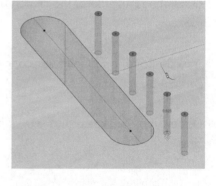

Start a new Sketch on the guitar's top and add two 0.25" equal circles joined center to center with a Construction Line.

Add a Center to Center Slot with two 5/16" circles Coincident with the slot's centerline.

Add a midpoint to the bottom horizontal line of the Extruded Cut slot.

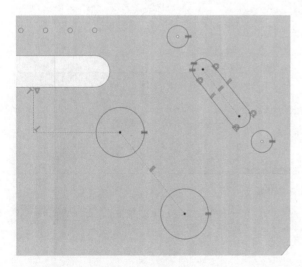

Equally constrain the 2 circles and the slot. Add a Horizontal Constraint to the topmost circle and the slot's midpoint.

Make the 2 angled Construction Lines parallel.

Add a Construction Line to one of the 0.25" circles.

Dimension the following sketch.

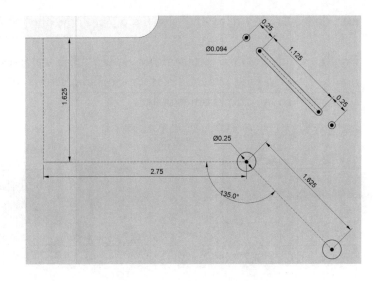

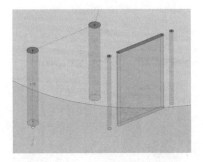

Extrude cut the 5 profiles through the part.

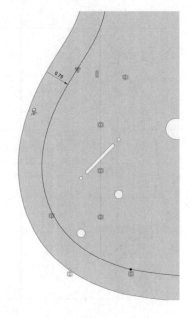

Start a sketch on the guitar's underside to make a large cavity for the electronics. Press O for Offset, select the guitar's outer profile, and add a -0.75" inward Offset.

Draw a vertical Construction Line and mirror the Offset profile about this line. Move the line until the mirrored curve encloses the extrusion cuts, and add a Fix/Unfix constraint.

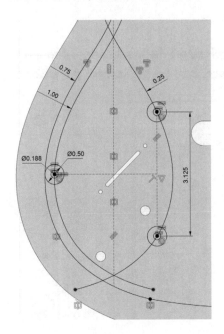

Add another inward Offset to the guitar profile of -1"; you cannot apply an Offset to an existing Offset. Add an inward 1/4" Offset to the mirrored profile.

Add 3 pairs of equal Concentric circles (3/16" and 1/2") to the left and right of the new Offset curves. Join the centers of the right 2 circles with a 3.125" vertical Construction Line. Join the left circle to the midpoint of the vertical Construction Line with a horizontal Construction Line.

Extrude the 5/16" circles -0.5" into the guitar Body, and the Offsets and the 0.5" circles -0.125".

Finally, extrude the inner profile down -1.375". This will leave you with a large internal cavity, a depressed rim to rest a Housing plate, 3 holes for mounting screws, and 3 bulged areas that prevent the wood from splitting when the screws are installed.

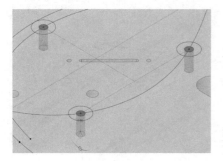
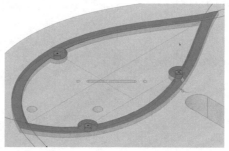
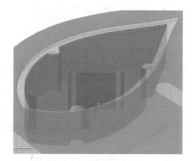

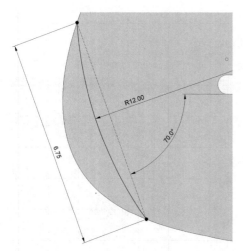

Flip the guitar over and start a new Sketch on the top surface.

Draw a 12" Radius 3-point arc with its endpoint Coincident with the left side of the profile. Draw a 6.75" Construction Line that connects the arc's endpoints and is 70 degrees to any horizontal line.

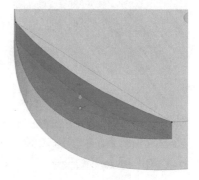

Extrude this sketch downwards -0.625".

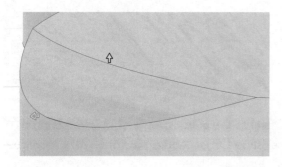

Open the Chamfer tool, select the inside edge, change the Type to Two Distance, and set the vertical dimension to 0.625".

The horizontal distance will vary based on your Original spline tracing. The value should be about 1.1", but you can increase or decrease in small increments until the sliver is negligible.

CAM

Navigate to the Manufacture workspace and change your Units to Inches.

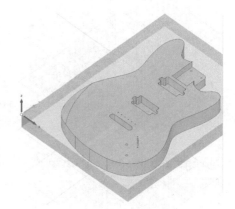

Make a new setup and place the stock point in the top left front corner. When the material is flipped over, the new stock point will be in the same place but with an underside view. Click OK. Double-click the new setup in the Browser and name it Top Operations.

Navigate to the Stock tab and set it to Relative Size Box. Add 1.5" to the Stock Side Offset and 0" to the Stock Top Offset. Click OK.

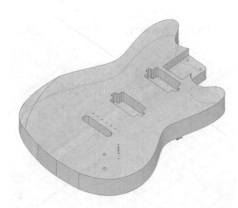

Select the 2D contour tool and use the 1/4" end mill to Cut the bottom profile. Add tabs with 4" spacing.

Navigate to the Heights tab, and then to Bottom Height and change the From the Model Bottom with an Offset to 0.875".

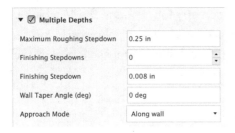

Navigate to the passes tab and Enable Multiple Depths with a Maximum Roughing Stepdown to 0.25".

Set the Safe Distance to 0.2" in the Linking tab and enable ramping. Click OK.

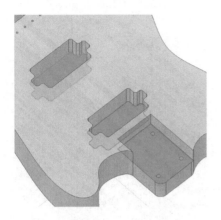

Select the 2D Pocket tool in the 2D menu. Select the 3 faces shown and use the 1/4″ end mill.

Set Multiple Depths to 0.25″ in the passes tab and uncheck Stock to Leave. Other components will cover up these surfaces, so there is no need to spend extra time on a perfect surface finish.

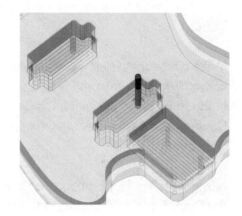

Navigate to the linking tab and set the Safe Distance to 0.2″. Click OK.

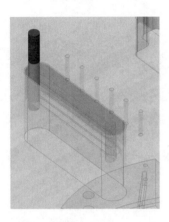

Once again, you will use the 2D pocket tool to Cut halfway through the slot.

Click the slot's bottom edge, set the Bottom Height to 0.875″, change Multiple Depths to 0.25″, uncheck Stock to Leave, and change the Safe Distance to 0.2″. Click OK.

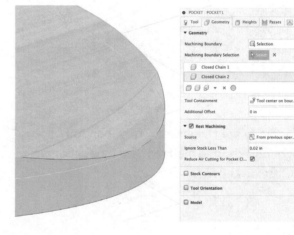

Cutting out the dual chamfered corner will require a roughing pass to remove most of the material and a finishing pass for a cleaner surface finish.

Select the 3D Pocket tool in the 3D menu and select the 1/4″ end mill as the tool.

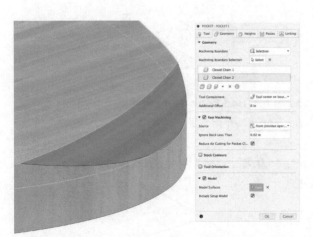

Navigate to the Geometry tab, change the Machining Boundary to Selection, and click the chamfer's top and bottom edges. Check the Model section, and click on the chamfered surface.

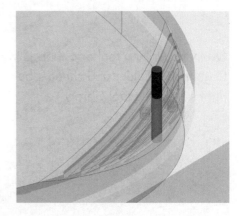

Navigate to the Passes tab, change the Stock to Leave to 0", and set Maximum Roughing Stepdown to 0.1". Click OK.

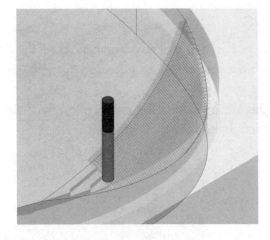

For a finishing pass, select the Parallel tool in the 3D menu. This tool makes parallel cuts that conform to the curves of the surface.

Use the same selections as the 3D pocket tool previously, and leave the stock values the same for the rest of this tool.

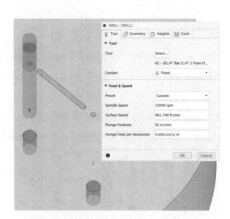

Use the Drilling tool to drill out the 2 large holes on the top surface.

Verify the plunge feed rate is 92 in/min.

Type	Flat end mill
Unit	Inches
Clockwise spindle r…	☑
Number of flutes	3
Material	HSS

Geometry

Diameter	0.09375 in
Shaft diameter	0.25 in
Overall length	3 in
Length below holder	2 in
Shoulder length	1 in
Flute length	0.75 in

Tool Assembly

Gauge length	2 in	f_x

So far, you've only used a 1/4" end mill. To mill out the 6 holes above the bridge and the slot with its coincident holes, you will make a 3/32" end mill.

To make this tool, go up to the Tool Library and open your cloud folder, and click the plus sign to add a new tool.

Name this tool 3/32" End Mill and fill in the cutter values.

Speed

Spindle speed	25000 rpm	
Surface speed	613.59232 ft/min	f_x
Ramp spindle speed	25000 rpm	f_x

Feedrates

Cutting feedrate	200 in/min	
Feed per tooth	0.00267 in	f_x
Lead-in feedrate	200 in/min	f_x
Lead-out feedrate	200 in/min	f_x
Transition feedrate	200 in/min	f_x
Ramp feedrate	13.333 in/min	

Vertical feedrates

Plunge feedrate	70 in/min	
Plunge feed per revolution	0.0028 in	f_x

Open the Drilling tool and change the tool to the 3/32" End Mill. Select your Custom tool Folder and change the selection from Hole Making to Milling on the right side of the tool Library.

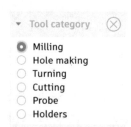

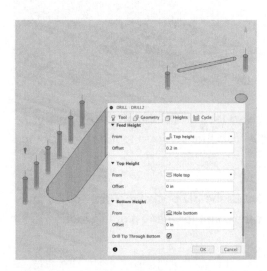

Typically end mills are not used to make plunge cuts, but if the end mill's blades go to the center, they can be used this way.

Navigate to the Heights tab and check the box to allow the drill bit to Drill Tip Through the Bottom. Click OK.

You will use the Slot tool to carve out the slot between the 2 holes. Select the same 3/32" end mill and select the bottom edge of the slot.

Check Multiple Depths. It should be set to 0.04", close to half its diameter (0.046"). Keep this value as is.

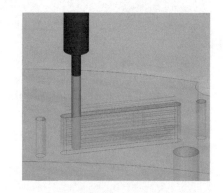

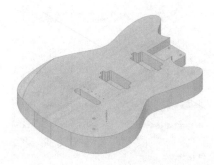

That was the last operation on the guitar's top surface. Rotate the part about the Y-axis so your view is upside down.

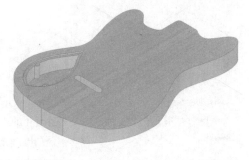

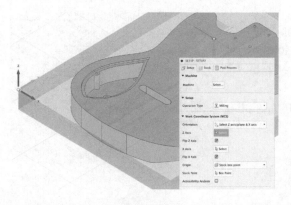

Create a new Setup. Instead of typing the same numbers, navigate to Mode >> and select the bottom entry.

Set the Stock Point in the Top, Left, Front corner. Click the X, Y, and Z arrows until they point in the same direction in the photo. X should point down the width, Y should point down the length, and Z should point up.

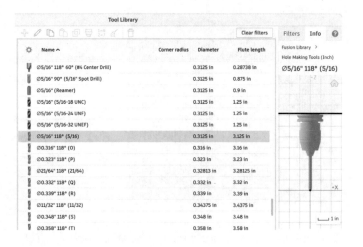

Open the Drilling tool, and click to change the tool. Expand the Autodesk Fusion library, select Hole Making tools (Inch), and activate the cloud tools.

Select the 5/32" drill bit.

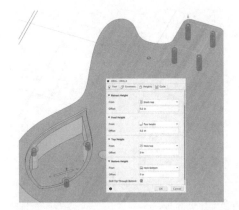

In the Geometry Tab, check Select Same Diameter, click Select next to Hole faces, and select any of the 4 holes on the neck or the 3 holes for the electronics cavity. Click OK.

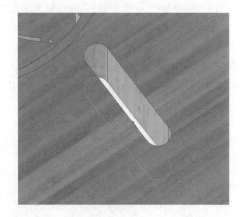

Cut out the other half of the slot by running a 2D Pocket, using the 1/4" end mill, and selecting the bottom edge.

Navigate to the Heights tab, change the Bottom Height to From Stock Bottom, which is the top of the guitar Body, and set the Offset to 0.875". Navigate to the Passes tab, enable Multiple Depths of 0.25", and uncheck Stock to Leave.

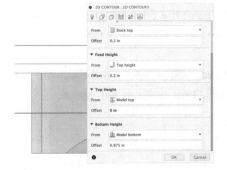

This will cut out the rest of the material, leaving a cut-through slot. You don't need to perform this Operation in 2 cuts if you have a long enough end mill. Unfortunately, you are often limited by the length of the cutter or by the maximum vertical travel the CNC allows.

Use the 2D Pocket tool to cut out the back cavity.

Set the Multiple Depths Maximum Roughing Stepdown to 0.25", Uncheck Stock to Leave, and set the Safe Distance to 0.2". Click OK.

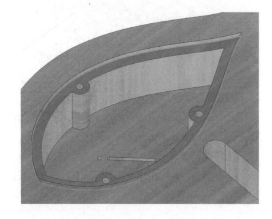

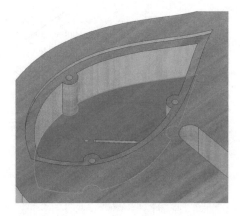

Use the 2D Pocket tool again with the same settings, but select the back cavities bottom. Click OK.

This is the largest cavity and will take the longest time to cut. Right-click the Operation in the Browser and select the machining time to see an estimate of how long it will take.

Cut out the guitar's profile from the stock with the 2D Contour tool. The tabs you created earlier will hold it in place.

Select 2D Contour and select the top outer edge as the profile.

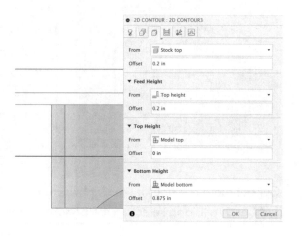

If you select the bottom edge, you will see the cut-in from the chamfer. To correct this, set the Bottom Height to From Stock Bottom with an Offset of 0.875".

Change the sideways compensation to right, enable a 0.25" roughing step-down, and a 10-degree ramp in the Linking tab.

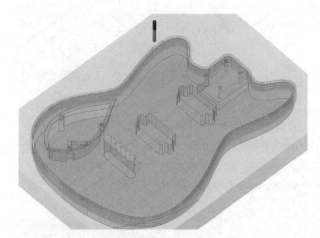

Select both the Set Ups in the Browser and click Simulate with Machine in the Actions menu.

At the end of the video, you should see the cut-out guitar profile with only tabs holding it in place.

Finally, post the files into group files that share the same tools. This project requires the following posts:

1. 2D Contour (Top half of profile), 2D Pocket (neck and pickups), 2D Pocket (Top half of bridge), 3D Pocket (Chamfer Roughing), 3D Parallel (Chamfer Finishing), and Drilling (2 holes).
2. 3/32" Drilling and 3/32" Slot.
3. 5/32" Drilling
4. 2D Pocket (Bottom half of Bridge), 2D Pocket (Cavity step), 2DPocket (Back cavity), and 2D Contour(Bottom half of profile).

Highlight the first set of Operations and click Post Process.

Set up a machine (if you can access one), enter an appropriate name, and export the file in the Unit appropriate for your machine.

Repeat this process for the other 3 sets of Operations.

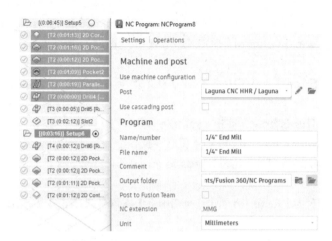

| 1.4 End Mill Bottom.nc | 1.4 End Mill Top.nc | 3.32 Drill.nc | 5.32 Drill.nc |

With all the files completed and exported, this project is done and ready to be cut!

Consult with a professional if you plan to cut it on a CNC and do so at your own risk. Many values here will need to be modified for your machine.

DISCUSSION

Feeds and Speeds

If you are serious about machining, you will inevitably come across Discussions about feeds and speeds. The spindle speed refers to how quickly the cutter head spins. The cutting federate refers to how quickly the cutter head travels along the workpiece. And the surface speed refers to how quickly the cutter head travels in one revolution. Rather than go more in-depth here, since this is primarily an Autodesk Fusion CAD workbook, we suggest you research this topic online or seek mentors in the CNC field. This topic is explored in great depth by people who use this machinery every day.

Flipping Stock

A common problem in double-sided machining is how to reference the stock when flipping it over. There are a variety of ways to do this such as dowels, registration pips, and fixed squared corners. If you'd like to know more, we suggest you research this advanced topic online.

Cutting Data

This is a broad topic and the math here is simplified. For the 1/4" End mill, you only need to know 2 values; how fast the cutter rotates (speed) and how fast it travels (Feed).

Speed = (Surface Feet/Minute) * 3.82 / (tool Diameter)

Surface feet per minute (SFM) is the speed of the blade's outer point as it moves past the material. This constant number will decrease if your material is rigid and will increase if your material is softer. Wood has a value of 1500. 3.82 is the conversion from the tool's foot circumference to its diameter in inches.

Speed = 1500 * 3.82 / 0.25" = 22,920 ~ 23,000 RPM

This is how fast the spindle will be spinning. If you used a 1/2" end mill on a machining plastic like Delrin, which has an SFM of 800, your spindle speed would be = 800 * 3.82 / 0.5" = 6112 RPM. To work out how fast the tool needs to move linearly, use this formula:

Feed Rate (in/min) = Speed (RPM) * Chipload (in/rev/flute) * # of Flutes * Depth Modifier

Use the same speed as was just calculated.

Chip load is the literal size of the sliver of material cut away and can be found on a chart as a decimal value relative to the tool's diameter. Softwood, like our project, is ranked as 0.007"-0.009". You used .008" in this project.

Flutes are the number of spiral grooves in the cutter; 2, 3, 4, 6, and 12 are the most common in that order. The more flutes you have, the more material you can take off in the same amount of time, but the more expensive the tool.
Depth Modifier is how deep your Cut is divided by the tool's diameter. If you are only cutting a 1/4" deep with a 1/4" End mill, the Depth Modifier is 1.

Feed Rate = 23,000 RPM * 0.008" * 2 * 1 = 368 in/min

These are the basics of CAM feeds and Speeds. This topic is better explored in-depth using resources dedicated to CNC machining and routing.
3/32 End mill Calculation:

Speed = 1500 SFM * 3.82 / (3/32") = 61,120 RPM

Reduce this value to 25,000, usually the standard maximum RPM for CNC routers.

Feed Rate = 25,000 RPM * 0.008" * 2 Flutes * 1/2 Depth Modifier = 200 in/min

The depth modifier is half of the tool's diameter for safety. In reality, you would run a series of tests to see how fast you can push your tools for maximum profit, but since this is a one-off, you will run this job slowly.

CHALLENGE

Most surfboards are made out of a large piece of Styrofoam and then fiberglassed to retain buoyancy and rigidity. Use the surfboard model made in Chapter 1 to make a CAM file that can be Cut on a router, flipped, and Cut a second time. Note that the cutter can Cut significantly faster in foam than in wood, so you will need to research these values.

CHAPTER 11 QUESTIONS

1. What does CAM stand for?

    a. Computer Aided Manufacturing

    b. Computer Aided Making

    c. Computer Altering Modeling

    d. Computer Altering Manufacturing

2. True or False? Stock box represents the physical material being cut.

3. Where is the best place to put the stock point for an engraving procedure?

    a. Bottom Corner

    b. Bottom Middle

    c. Top Middle

    d. Top Corner

4. True or False? Drilling speeds should be set very high because of their small diameter.

5. The Green arrow on a CAM toolpath represents what?

    a. Confirmation of a passable toolpath

    b. The entry point of the toolpath

    c. The exit point of the toolpath

    d. Location of the datum point

6. To cut out a simple circular profile, you would use which tool?

    a. Drilling

    b. 2D Pocket

    c. 2D Contour

    d. 3D Contour

7. Where can countersink bits be found?

    a. Machine Library

    b. Local Library

    c. Autodesk Fusion Library

    d. Template Library

8. What are CNC Tabs?

    a. Stopping and starting points of the toolpath

    b. Cutting Speeds list

    c. The tip of a drill bit

    d. Small pieces of material used to secure the part to the stock

9. Which tool would be the best option to clear out a large cavity?

    a. 3D Pocket

    b. 2D Pocket

    c. 2D Contour

    d. Parallel

10. True or False? Multiple CAM operations using the same tool, can be grouped into a single file.

CHAPTER 12
FULL ARC

BRING EVERYTHING YOU'VE LEARNED
TOGETHER IN A FINAL PROJECT

• SPACE PROP HILT

FULL ARC

To conclude this book and reflect on everything you've learned, you will design a space sword prop, combining many different aspects of Autodesk Fusion into one large project. You will use concepts from each of the following chapters: Assemblies, Joints, Mechanical Design, Engineering Drawings, Appearances, Rendering, and Exploded Diagrams.

We hope you enjoyed this workbook and wish you success with your new CAD skillset. We'd love to hear from you if you have any questions, comments, or feedback. You can reach us by email at **create@ CADclass.org**, through our website at **CADclass.org**, or via Discord **Discord.gg/5hbt6xDPqf**

Lastly, reflect on where you started and where you are now. Did you experience a transformation in your skillset? Are you feeling confident with digital CAD design? What do you plan to do now?

Good luck and happy modeling. It has been a pleasure working with you!

Sincerely, Jake and Josh

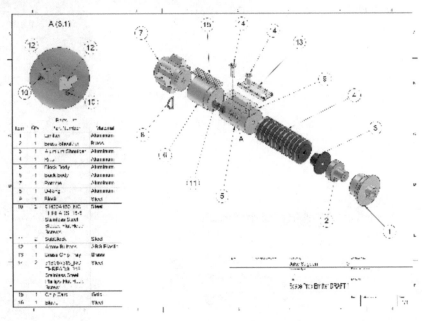

CHAPTER 12

By this point in your CAD journey, you are prepared to venture out on your own.

Before you do, you will want to make sure you are prepared for the battles that lie ahead.

This project will be your final test!

DIFFICULTY:
★★★★★

TIME ESTIMATE:
5 HOURS

KEY LEARNING:
- Combine all of your knowledge amassed over the program into one large project

DISCORD LINK:
Discord.gg/5hbt6xDPqf

INTRODUCTION

This large CAD project will combine skills from most previous chapters. Consider it as a final test of your accrued skillset. It requires knowledge of Assemblies and Joints to make the CAD model. You will take it a step further to make a film-accurate rendering, an Engineering Drawing, an Exploded Animation, and an Exploded Diagram to show off all the parts.

CAD

Emitter

Verify your Units are set to Millimeters (mm), make an Internal Component called Emitter, and Sketch this shape on the Front Plane.

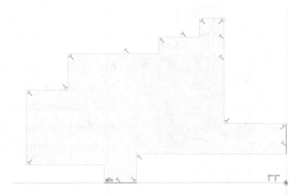

The bottom horizontal line and the right vertical line are Coincident with the Origin. Dimension the Sketch and verify it is defined in the Browser.

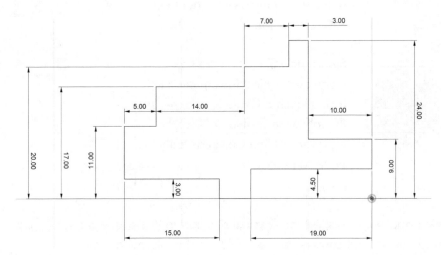

Revolve the profile about the X-axis and set the Physical Material to aluminum.

Add an M6 thread. M6 threads are the closest metric thread to a standard ¼-20 imperial thread.

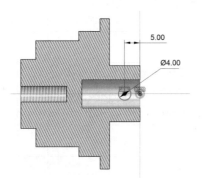

Start a Sketch on the Front Plane and check Slice on the Sketch Palette. Add a 4 mm circle 5 mm to the left of the Origin. Horizontally Constrain the Origin and the circle's center.

Extrude Cut the circle through All towards you.

Add 0.4 mm fillets to all internal edges and 0.4 mm chamfer to all external edges.

Note, the internal edges will naturally have a small radius from the round nose of the cutting tool (assuming you made this in real life). In machining, it is common to design parts with chamfered outside and filleted inside edges.

Brass Shoulder

Activate the Root Component and make a new Internal Component called Brass Shoulder.

Start a new Sketch on the Front Plane and project the Emitter's left face. Sketch a Centerline, dimension the following profile, and set the right vertical line Collinear to the projected line.

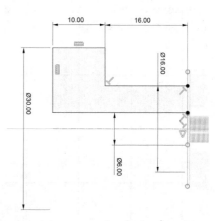

Revolve the profile about the X-axis, set the Physical Material to Brass, add an M6 thread to the hole, add 0.4 mm chamfer to the external corners, and 0.4 fillets to the internal corners.

Aluminum Shoulder

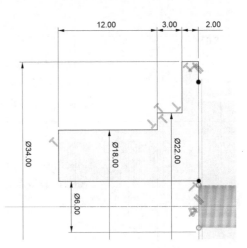

Activate the Root Component and make an Internal Component called Aluminum Shoulder and create this Sketch on the Front Plane. Add a Centerline.

Project the Brass Shoulder's left face and set the right vertical line Collinear to the projected line.

Revolve this profile about the X-axis, add an M6 thread to the central hole, add 0.4 mm internal fillets, and set the Physical Material to Aluminum.

Open the Appearance tool, search and download Powder Coat - Rough (Black).

Change the Apply To to Faces and drag the Appearance onto all the surfaces except the left and right faces.

Add a 0.4 mm chamfer to the part's 4 external edges.

Because the Aluminum was added before the Black Powder Coat, the effect is a part with worn away edges, exposing the shiny metal underneath similar to how a weathered part would look in real life.

Ribs

Activate the Root Component, make an Internal Component called Ribs, and make the following Sketch on the Front Plane.

Project the Aluminum Shoulder's leftmost face and draw 3 lines with the right endpoint Coincident with the projected line.

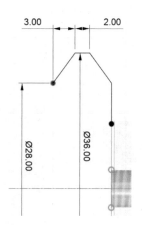

Horizontally Constrain the bottom 2 endpoints and make the 2 sloped lines equal. Dimension the Sketch to a Centerline.

Select the 3 lines, and Rectangularly Pattern 10 of them spaced 8 mm to the left.

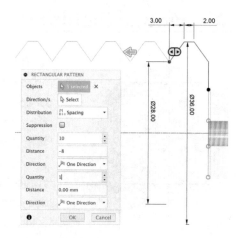

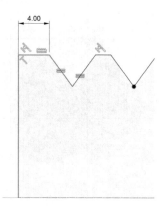

Enclose the profile with a 4 mm line, a vertical line Coincident with the Origin.

Revolve the profile about the X-axis and set the Physical Material to aluminum.

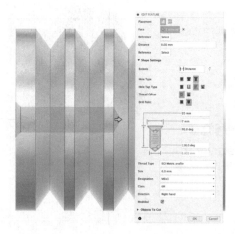

Use the hole tool to add an M6 tapped, 7 mm countersunk, 20 mm deep hole to the leftmost face's center.

Hide the other components and make a midplane between the left and right faces.

Mirror the hole feature about this midplane, add a 0.4 mm chamfer to the left outer edge, and Hide the Construction Plane.

Add the Black Powder Coat Appearance to the inside angled faces. You can click the View cube's Front face, hold down Ctrl, select all 21 faces (which highlights them in blue), and drag the Appearance onto 1 of the faces to apply it to all selected faces.

Block Body

Activate the Root Component and make an Internal Component called Block Body and Sketch on the Rib's left face.

Hide the other components. Sketch and dimension the profile shown. Vertically Constrain the rectangle's center to the Origin.

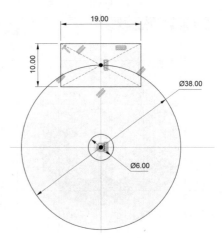

Extrude the lower profiles 54 mm away from the Ribs and set the Physical Material to Aluminum.

Add 0.4 mm chamfers to the left and right faces and an M6 thread to the central hole.

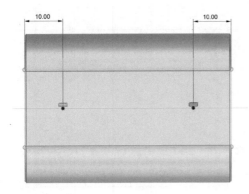

Make a new Sketch on the top rectangular face, add two points, and add Horizontal Constraints between the points and the Origin.

Dimension them 10 mm from either end of the part and Finish the Sketch.

Open the Hole tool. Change the placement from Single Hole to Multiple Holes and select the 2 points.

Make 8 mm countersunk, 9 mm deep, M6 tapped holes.

Activate the Root Component and add a Rigid Group to all components in the project.

Back Body

Activate the Root Component, make an Internal Component called Back Body, and make the following Sketch on the Front Plane.

Project the Block's leftmost face and sketch and dimension the profile shown.

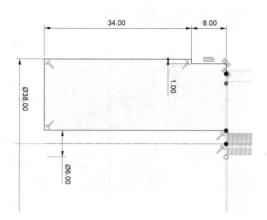

Revolve the profile about the X-axis, set the Physical Material to Aluminum, add 0.4 mm chamfers to the part's outer edges, and an M6 thread to the hole.

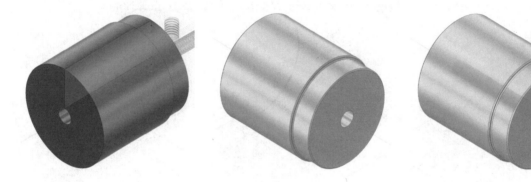

This part is short enough where 2 mirrored holes, like the Rib components, aren't necessary, and a long threaded hole is easy to manufacture.

Activate the Root Component and add an As-Built Joint to the Block Body.

Pommel

Make an Internal Component called Pommel and Sketch on the Front Plane. This is arguably the hardest component in this project. As you will see, most complex projects that seem intimidating to model are simply made up of simple individual parts.

Project the Back Body's leftmost face and draw lines from the projected points to make an enclosed profile.

Constrain the 2 angled lines to be Equal and add a Collinear constraint to the 2 horizontal highlighted lines.

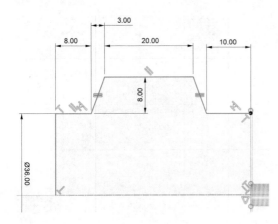

Dimension the Sketch and revolve the profile about the bottom horizontal line.

Set the Physical Material as Aluminum.

Add a 0.4 mm chamfer to the left outer edge, click the (+) symbol, and add a 2 mm chamfer to the right outer edge.

Large chamfers hide imperfections in Joints where parts are screwed together.

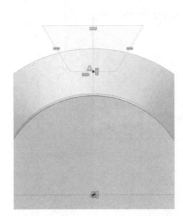

Make a new Sketch on the part's left face and draw an upside-down trapezoid. Add Equal constraints to the angled lines and a midpoint to the bottom horizontal line. Add a vertical Constraint between this midpoint and the Origin.

Project the part's angled surface, which will add 2 projected circles. Add a point to the inner circle and a vertical Constraint to the midpoint.

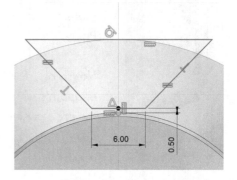

Add a Perpendicular constraint between the angled lines and a Tangent constraint to the top horizontal line and the outer projected circle. Set the distance between the 2 bottom points to 0.5 mm and the length of the bottom horizontal line to 6 mm.

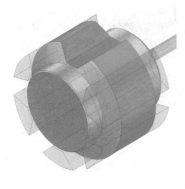

Extrude Cut this trapezoid profile through the entire Pommel and Circularly Pattern it around the X-axis 6 times.

Turn off the other components and add an 8 mm countersunk, 12 mm deep, M6 tapped hole to the right face.

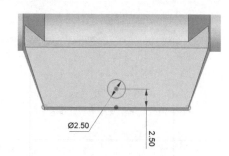

Make a new Sketch on the Top Plane, project the lower fin, and add a point at the midpoint.

Draw a 2.5 mm circle that is Vertically Constrained and 2.5 mm above the midpoint.

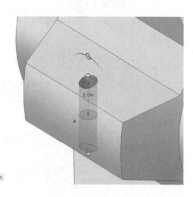

Symmetrically Extrude this profile through All to make a hole for a D ring to pass through. You may need to hide the Body to select the circle.

Add a 0.4 mm chamfer to the hole's surface.

Activate the Root Component, Show all components, and add a Rigid As-Built Joint to the Back Body.

D-Ring

Because the D-Ring hole is in a strange location, building it in place would be rather difficult. Instead, open a new blank workspace and make a new Sketch on the Right Plane.

Sketch an 18 mm vertical line from the Origin. Connect the endpoints with a 3-point arc. Add a Coincident constraint to the arc's center and the line.

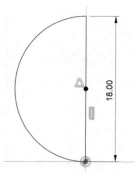

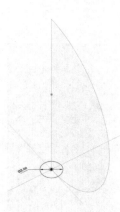

Make another Sketch on the Top Plane of a 2 mm circle at the Origin.

Use the Sweep tool, select the circle as the profile and the "D" shape as the path.

Add 1 mm fillets to the vertical section's sharp outer top and bottom corners.

Save this file, navigate back to the Space Prop Hilt file, open the Data Panel, right-click the D-Ring file, and click Insert Into Current Design.

Add a Revolute joint between the middle of the straight section on the D-Ring and the middle of the Pommel's hole.

To select the midpoint on the Pommel's hole, move your cursor to the hole, hold down Ctrl/Cmd, and click on the middle point.

Block

Turn on all the components and make a new Internal Component called Block.

Start a Sketch on the Block Body's rectangular face and sketch a 54 x 19 mm rectangle that is positioned over the rectangular face of the Block Body.

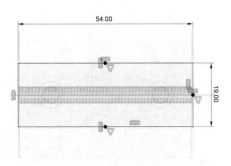

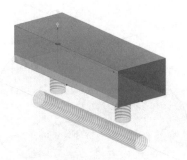

Extrude the profiles upwards 12 mm and set the Physical Material to aluminum.

You should select 3 profiles, including the 2 circular projected holes.

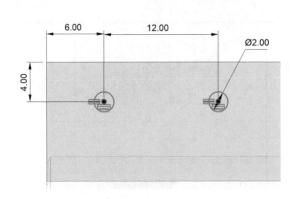

Make a new Sketch on the Block's front face.

Draw 2 equal 2 mm circles that are Horizontally Constrained and dimension the circles as shown.

Add 4 more circles to the right side.

Add Equal and Horizontal Constraints to the top and bottom pairs of circles. Add a vertical Constraint to the right 2 circles.

Dimension the Sketch as shown in the picture.

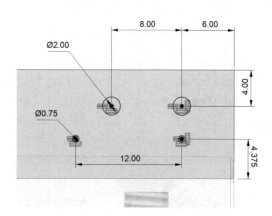

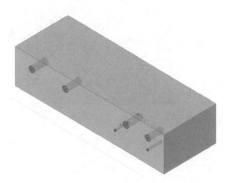

Extrude Cut all 6 circles -5 mm.

Add 0.6 mm chamfers to the Block's top, bottom, left and right faces (but not the front and back faces) and the bottom right 2 holes.

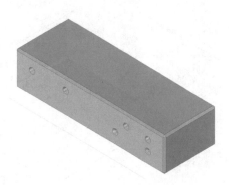

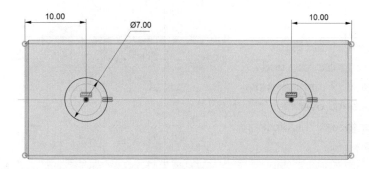

Start a new Sketch on the Block's top surface and draw two 7 mm circles Horizontally Constrained with the Origin.

Project the Block's left and right faces and dimension the circle's centers 10 mm from each edge.

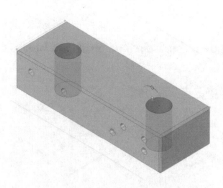

Extrude Cut these profiles through the entire component and add 0.8 mm chamfers to the holes' top edge.

Activate the Root Component and add a Rigid As-Built Joint to the Block Body.

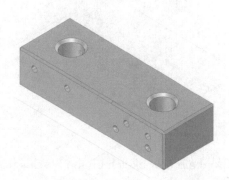

Import the small flathead screws, 91430A150, with the McMaster Carr tool and rigidly join them to the bottom right countersunk holes.

Use the Duplicate With Joints to add a 2nd screw to the lower left hole.

Sub Block

Make an Internal Component called Sub Block.

Create a Sketch on the Block's front face, project the leftmost circle, and sketch a 12 x 7 mm Center Rectangle. Extrude this circle into the Block 4 mm.

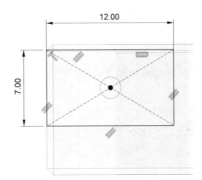
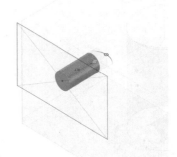

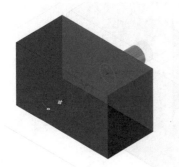

Extrude the rectangle and circle 6 mm.

Add a 1 mm chamfer to the front face, set ABS as the Physical Material, and make the appearance black.

Activate the Root Component and add an As-Built Joint to the Block Body.

Select this component in the Browser, copy and paste a duplicate 12 mm to the right, and add a Rigid As-Built Joint to the Block.

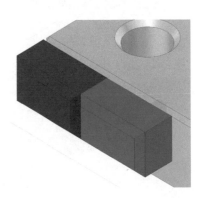

Arrow Button

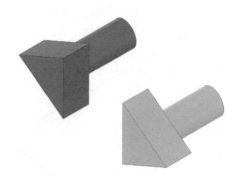

Make an Internal Component called Arrow Button.

Make a Sketch on the Block's front face and project the left circle in the top right corner.

Extrude the left circle into the Block 4 mm.

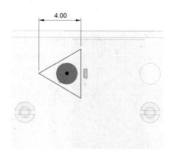

Add the Red LED appearance to the cylinder, make a new Sketch on the same face, and use the Polygon tool to draw a triangle. Vertically Constrain the right line. Dimension the triangle as shown in the picture.

Extrude the triangle and the circle outwards 2 mm.

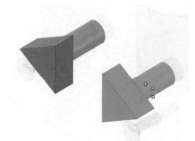

Activate the Root Component and add a Rigid As-Built Joint to the Block Body.

Select the Body, not the component, in the Browser, copy and paste it, rotate it 180 degrees about the cylinder's axis, and move it 8 mm to the right. Add an As-Built Joint to this component and the Block Body.

Add the Green LED appearance to the right arrow.

Brass Chip Tray

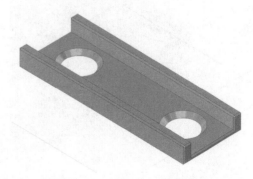

Make an Internal Component called Brass Chip Tray and make a Sketch on the Block's right face.

Project the Block's top, front, and back faces.

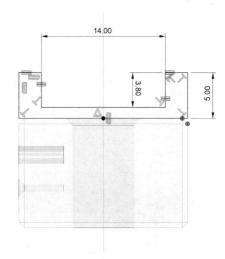

Add Collinear constraints to the left vertical line and left projected line, the right vertical line and the right projected line, and the bottom horizontal sketch line and the horizontal projected line.

Add Collinear constraints to the top 2 horizontal lines. Add the dimensions shown.

Extrude this profile to the other side of the Block and set the Physical Material to Brass.

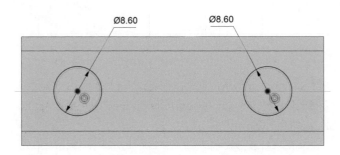

Make a new Sketch on the top inside face and add two 8.6 mm circles Horizontally Constrained with the Origin and 9.6 mm from the edges.

Extrude Cut the profiles through the entire component.

Add 0.4 mm chamfers to the top 2 rails, as shown in blue. Click the (+) symbol and add 1.2 mm chamfers to the hole's top edges.

Activate the Root Component and add a Rigid As-Built Joint to the Block Body.

Import the 2 countersunk screws, 91801A315, with the McMaster Carr tool and Rigidly join them to the countersunk holes in the Brass Chip Tray.

As you can see in the Section Analysis, these screws pass through the Brass Chip Tray, through the Block, and screw into the Block Body's threads.

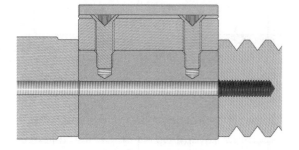

Chip Card

Make an Internal Component called Chip Card and start a Sketch on the Brass Chip Tray's top.

Project the Brass Chip Tray's inner top face and Finish the Sketch.

Turn off all other components and extrude these 3 profiles up 2.8 mm.

Make a new Sketch on the top face and draw a rectangle on the left side. The total width of the Chip Card is 53.2 mm; to get 13 equally spaced extrusion cuts, set the rectangle's width to 53.2 / 13 / 2 mm.

Extrude Cut this profile -0.5 mm and set the Physical Material to Gold.

Rectangularly pattern the extrusion 13 times along the length of the part with a Spacing of 53.2 / 13 mm.

Add the Black Metallic Paint to the 13 groove's bottom faces. Activate the Root Component and add a Rigid As-Built Joint to the Brass Chip Tray.

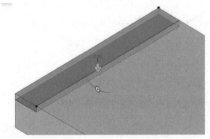

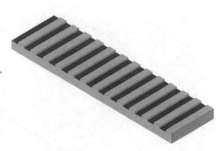

Blade

Make the final Internal Component and call it Blade.

Show all components and make a new Sketch on the Front Plane. There are several ways to draw the following Sketch.

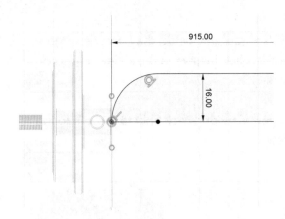

One way is to draw an Overall slot with its leftmost point Coincident with the Origin.

Draw a horizontal bisecting line from 1 endpoint to the other and Trim away the bottom half of the slot.

Dimension the total length of the slot to be 915 mm and the distance from the mid-line to the top horizontal line to be 16 mm. Add a Coincident constraint between the arc's middle and the X-axis line.

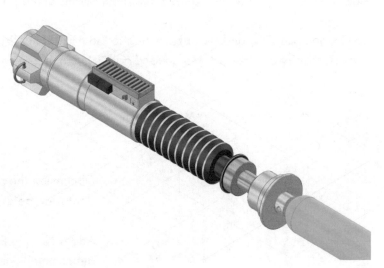

Revolve this profile about the X-axis and add a green LED Appearance to the component.

Activate the Root Component and add a Rigid As-Built Joint to the Emitter.

And the CAD portion of this project is done!

ENGINEERING DRAWING

Right-click on the Emitter component in the Browser and click Create Drawing.

Start an ASME Size B Drawing.

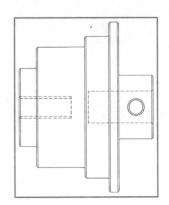

Keep the Style as Visible and Hidden Edges and change the Scale to 5:2.

Place this view on the left side of the page.

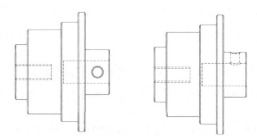

Select the Projected View tool and select the Base View. Move your cursor downwards, click below the Base View, and click the green check mark.

Click and move the new view and click Shift to move it to the right of the Base View.

Add another Projected View to the bottom left corner of the page.

Select the Base View and click above and to the right of the Base View to make an Isomeric view. Set it to Shaded and 3:2 Scale.

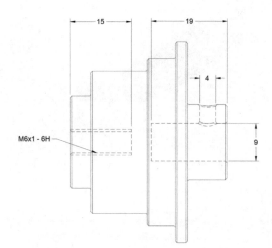

Dimension the right view and define the diameter and depths of the 2 drilled holes.

Add a Note to the threaded hole to denote it as an M6 and dimension its depth.

Dimension the diameter and depths of the features on the left view without crossing dimension lines.

Add a Center Mark to the center of the radially drilled hole and set its 5 mm distance to the right face.

Double-click on the Title Block in the bottom right corner and edit any information about this part, such as material, tolerances, sizes of drill bits needed, your name, and date of design.

Save this file to the folder and navigate back to the Assembly file.

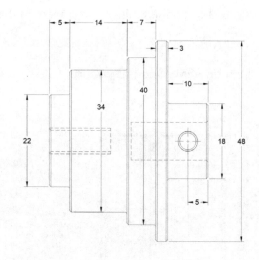

RENDERING

Navigate to the Render workspace.

Open the Appearance tool and double-click on the Red LED to change its luminance. Currently, the value is too low and doesn't shine like as brightly as an LED should.

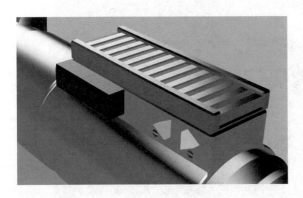

Set the value to 20,000 cd/m^2 to get enough glow to reflect off the other shiny aluminum parts but not too bright where you can't see the red color. Click on the In Canvas Render tool to get a quick preview of the amount of glow.

Add this level of luminance to the green LED and the Blade and verify with a quick In Canvas Render to see how bright they glow.

Open the s tool and open the Environment tab. Download and click and drag the Dry Lake Bed environment into the background. Make sure you change the Background to Environment.

Return to the Settings tab to adjust the scene's brightness. Adjust the brightness to 20,000 or less, and analyze the aluminum parts. You should see details like reflections of the blue sky and the sandy ground.

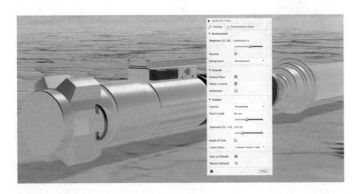

Check Ground Plane and Flatten Ground to place the Assembly on the ground. Adjust the focal length to 59 mm.

Move the camera to an angle of your choosing.

If you want a blurry background in your render, check Depth of Field, click on a point in the project in the foreground, and set it to 0.1.

Adjust these settings until the rendering preview is coming out how you want.

EXPLODED ANIMATION

It is best to break the Space Prop into 2 subassemblies: the Block and the Hilt.

Navigate to the Animation workspace and move the playhead to the Scratch zone. Get an overhead view of the entire project.

Move the play head to 5 seconds and get an isometric view of the prop.

Double-click the View Block and set the start to 1 second.

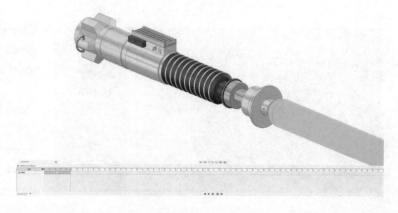

To make the Blade disappear while zooming in, keep the playhead at 5 seconds and expand the components list in the Browser. Select the Blade and click the Show Hide tool in the Transform menu; this will add a yellow bar to the Timeline.

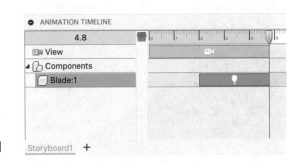

Move the playhead out of the way and move your cursor to the left side of the lightbulb icon until you see a left and right arrow. Click and drag it to the 2-second mark.

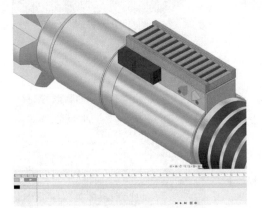

Play the video to see the Blade for 2 seconds and then slowly disappear for 3 seconds.

Make another View Block from 5.50 to 7.50 seconds to zoom into the Block subassembly.

Move the playhead to 11 seconds to Transform the Brass Chip Card 70 mm to the left; start this Move block at 8 seconds.

With the playhead at 11 seconds, Hide the component and start the transition at 10 seconds so it disappears while moving.

Move the playhead to 14.5 seconds and Transform both bolts up 50 mm with trail lines enabled to start at 11.5 seconds.

Stagger the Transform blocks by half a second to make the animation more compelling. Hide these bolts from 12.5 to 14.5 seconds.

Transform the Brass Card Tray away 30 mm from 15 to 18 seconds.

Set it to be hidden from 16 to 18 seconds.

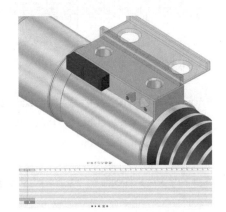

Zoom in slightly from 18 to 20 seconds to show a closer inspection of the Subblocks, arrows, and small bolts exploding sequentially.

Move the playhead to 22.5 seconds, select all 6 components attached to the Block, and Transform them -20 mm. Select all 6 Move blocks in the Timeline and set their starting time to 20.5 seconds.

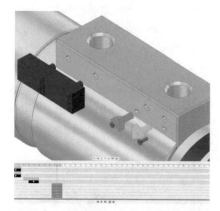

Stagger Move blocks by 0.25 seconds to make the parts eject sequentially.

This should set the last Move block to end at 23.75 seconds.
Move the playhead to this value and change the camera's view to another isometric corner view.
Set this View block to start at 20.5 seconds.

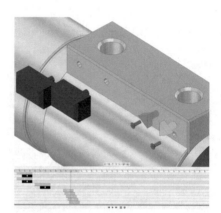

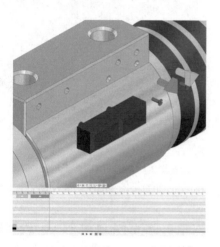

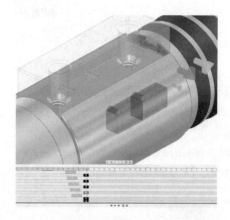

Move the playhead to 25 seconds, select the 6 most recent exploded components and the Block, and set this to Hide with a fade from 24 to 25 seconds.

Now, you can work on the hilt subassembly.

Move the playhead to 29.5 seconds and select the Top/Front Edge of the View cube to get a diagonal downward view of the bottom of the hilt.

Set this View block to 25.5 to 29.5 seconds.

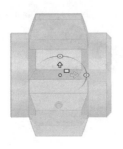

Transform the Pommel – 50 mm to the left, away from the hilt, from 27 to 29.5 seconds.

Over the same time interval, manually explode (not Transform) the D ring towards you.

You can't Transform the D Ring since it is at an angle and will not move in the same X Y Z directions as the other components.

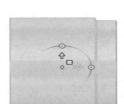

Finally, Transform the Back Body -25 mm over the same timespan as the Pommel and the D Ring.

Move the playhead to 34 seconds and move the view to the top right isometric view on the View Cube with the end of the Ribs in the top left of your screen.

Start this View block at 30 seconds.

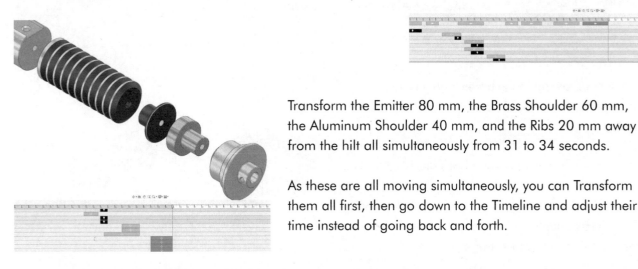

Transform the Emitter 80 mm, the Brass Shoulder 60 mm, the Aluminum Shoulder 40 mm, and the Ribs 20 mm away from the hilt all simultaneously from 31 to 34 seconds.

As these are all moving simultaneously, you can Transform them all first, then go down to the Timeline and adjust their time instead of going back and forth.

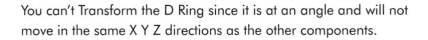
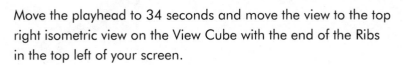

Move the playhead to 37 seconds and zoom out to show the entire exploded project. Start this View block at 34.5 seconds.

Move the playhead to 41 seconds and get a view of the project from the other front top isometric view to start at 37.5 seconds.

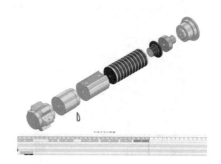

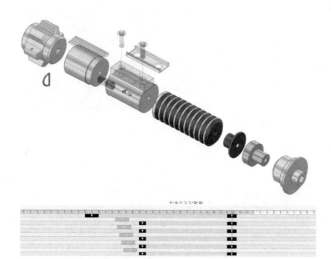

Finally, move the playhead back to 37 seconds and expand the Browser. Select 11 Hidden components but not the blade and click the Show/Hide tool. Expand the fade period to the right from 37 to 38.5 seconds.

Publish the video to your desired resolution, and the Animation is done!

To conclude the project and the program, you will make an Exploded Diagram showing all the components and their unique dimensions and materials.

Navigate to the Drawing workspace >> and select From Animation. Make an ASME Size B drawing.

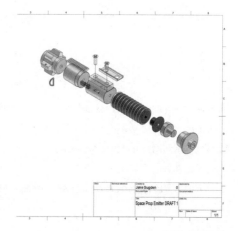

Place the drawing in the upper right corner, change the Scale to 2:3, and change the Style to Visible Edges.

The Arrows and countersunk bolts are hard to see.

Open the Detail tool to draw a small circle around the 4 components and place a 3:1 Detail view in the top left corner of the page.

A (3:1)

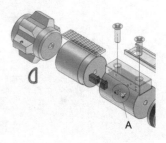

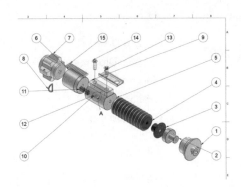

Add a Parts List from the Tables menu and place it in the bottom left corner of the page.

You may need to move the Detail view and its text to avoid overlapping.

Delete the Balloons pointing to the Arrows and the flathead bolts on the exploded model, and add new balloons to the 4 components in the Detail view.

Parts List			
Item	Qty	Part Number	Material
1	1	Emitter	Aluminum
2	1	Brass Shoulder	Brass
3	1	Alumium Shoulder	Aluminum
4	1	Ribs	Aluminum
5	1	Block Body	Aluminum
6	1	Back Body	Aluminum
7	1	Pommel	Aluminum
8	1	D-Ring	Aluminum
9	1	Block	Steel
10	2	91430A150_NO THREADS_18-8 Stainless Steel Slotted Flat Head Screws	Steel
11	2	SubBlock	Steel
12	1	Arrow Buttons	ABS Plastic
13	1	Brass Chip Tray	Brass
14	2	91801A315_NO THREADS_316 Stainless Steel Phillips Flat Head Screw	Steel
15	1	Chip Card	Gold
16	1	Blade	Steel

Move the Balloons around the model so they are all evenly spaced and don't overlap. Add extra Balloons to the second Phillips bolt and the second Sub Block.

Once this is done, save the file as a reference image, and this project is done!

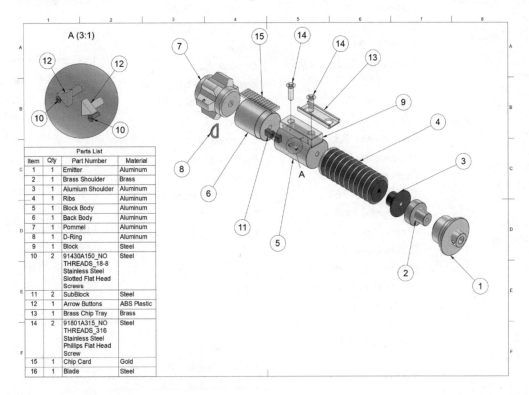

Congratulations on finishing this textbook; we hope you learned enough to bring your creativity to life. When you started, you likely had little familiarity with Autodesk Fusion or CAD modeling. Now, after working through 27 projects, you're on the path to becoming a master. We wish you success if you decide to start a company, continue as a student, or move on to new endeavors.

If you've enjoyed this workbook, please leave us a positive review. If you have ideas or projects you'd like us to consider in our next book or feedback about what we can improve, email **Create@CADclass.org** or leave a comment on Discord. You rock!

Cheers, Jake and Josh

Symbols

2D Pocket 324
2D Sketch 18
3D Body 18
3D Mirror 79
3D Pocket 320
3D Printing 37
3-Point Arc 145
10 Editable Files 29

A

Activate 115
Add-Ins 189
Add to Favorites 32
Anchor Icon 98
Animate Joint 187
Animate Joint Relationship 187
Animation workspace 279
Annotation/Create Callout 284
Anodization 93
Appearance 26
Apply To 37
Area 63
As-Built Joint 121
Aspect Ratio 236
Assemble 98
Augmented Reality 37
Auto Explode 284
Axes 16
Axis of Revolution 25

B

Balloon 296
Base View 258
Body 25
Boundary to Selection 320
Bounding Box 304
Box 69
Break View 258
Browser 16
Bump Map 213

C

Calibrate 211
Canvas 43
Centerline 90

Center Mark 346
Center Point Arc Slot 193
Center Rectangle 61
Center Slot 59
Center to Center Slot 59
Chain-Link Icon 219
Chamfer 54
Change Active Units 16
Change Dimension Units 259
Change Parameters 89
Circle 24
Circular Pattern 34
Cloud Credit 237
Cloud Libraries 304
Coil 79
Coincident constraint 36
Collinear 148
Color 136
Combine 212
Component Color Swatch 127
Concentric 71
Constraints 24
Construction 33
Construction Line 50
Copy and Paste 138
Counterbore 162
Countersink 120
Create 18
Create Copy 277
Create Group 80
Create Sketch 23
Cutter tab 305
Cylinder 77
Cylindrical 154

D

Data Panel 15
Decal 222
Decal Appearance 43
Decal Thread 116
Delete All Unused 216
Density 103
Depth of Field 236
Designation 151
Design workspace 17
Detail View 259
Dialog Box 43

Diameter Dimension 260
Dimension 24
Dimension Break 260
Direction 36
Display Settings 129
Distribution 70
Document Settings 16
Draft 69
Drawing workspace 258
Drill 306
Duplicate 213
Duplicated with Joints 168
DXF 176

E

Edit Canvas 211
Edit Feature 17
Edit Motion Limits 121
Edit Start/End 280
Ellipse 41
Emboss 82
Environment Library 213
Equal constraint 71
Export 38
Exposure 236
Expression 89
Extent Type 64, 93
External Component 219
Extrude 28
Eye Icons 16

F

Face 34
Feature 17
Fillet 46
Finish Sketch 25
Fit Point Spline 26
Fixed Size Box 304
Fix/Unfix 27
Flag Revolve Icon 203
Flatten Ground 235
Flip 46
Focal Length 236
Folder 16
From Preceding Setup 322
Full Length 81
fx 90

G

Google Drive 43
Graphic Diagnostics 235
Grid and Snaps 18
Grid Settings 18
Grounded 98

H

Half Length 36
HDRI 237
Hide 42
Highlight 167
History Marker 17
Hole 54
Horizontal/Vertical constraint 24
House Icon 32

I

In-Canvas Render 236
Include 44
Insert 83
Insert into Current Design 219
Insert SVG 83
Interference 221
Internal Component 145
Intersect 44
In This Design 26
Isolate 119
Isometric View 18
ISO Pipe Thread 160

J

Join 35
Joints 117

K

Keep Tools 279
Knurls 92

L

Laser Cutter 176
Line 57
Linear Precision 259
Linetype 90
Linking tab 319
Local render 237

Loft 43
Luminance 233

M

Manual Explode 284
Manufacture workspace 319
Maximum 121
Maximum Roughing Step-down 309
McMaster Carr 117
Measurement 36
Midplane 147
Midpoint 59
Minimum 121
Mirror 72
Mirror Line 51
Model Bottom 319
Modeled 114
Model Parameters 89
Modify 18
Motion 154
Motion Link 155
Motion Study 204
Move 71
Move block 280
Multiple Passes 309

N

Navigation Bar 18
New Body 45
New Component 98
New Named View 251
New Setup 304
Notes 261
No Units 89
NPT 166

O

Object Type 115
Object Visibility 129
Offset 62
Offset Faces 78
Offset Plane 33
Origin 118
Opacity Control 122
Operation 31
Orbit 18

Origin 15
Orthographic 236
Overall Slot 316

P

Pan 18
Parallel 321
Parallel constraint 50
Parts List 353
Passes Tab 307
Path Direction 215
Pattern Along Arc 215
Perpendicular constraints 53
Perspective 236
Physical Material 103
Planes 16
Plunge Speed 305
PNG 43
Point 53
Point to Point 75
Polygon 49
Post Library 310
Post Process 310
Preferences 19
Preview Limits 121
Profile 32
Project 32
Projected View 258
Projection Type 223
Properties 107
Publish 284
Pull Direction 69

Q

Quadrant 260
Quantity 37

R

Rails 198
Ramp 309
Rectangle 16
Rectangular Pattern 70
Red Padlock 62
Reflection 235
Reflectiveness 216
Relative Size Box 319
Rename 77
Render workspace 235

Rest 121
Restore Home 284
Reverse 283
Revolute 154
Revolve 25
RGB 233
Rigid Group 106
Rigid joint 120
Ring Icon 32
Root Component 98
Rotate block 281
Roughness 213

S

Save 29
Save as Mesh 55
Scale 26
Scene Settings 213
Scratch Zone 280
Search 91
Section Analysis 83
Section View 266
Select Same Diameter 307
Send to 3D Print Utility 55
Set as Default 16
Shaded 213
Shortcuts 182
Show 42
Sideways Compensation 309
Simulate 309
Sketch Palette 23
Slider Joints 121
Slot 59
Spacing 133
Spindle Speed 305
Spline 26
Split Body 26
Split Face 33
Spur Gear 189
STEP 104
Steps 204
STL 46
Stock Points 304
Stock to Leave 320
Subassembly 157
Suppression 60
Sweep 61
Symbols 268

Symmetric 36
Symmetry Constraint 99

T

Tables 353
Tabs 308
Tangent 58
Tangent Arc 57
Taper 35
Tapered Coil 233
Target Body 221
Text 70
Texture Map Controls 223
Thread 78
Timeline 17
Title Block 268
To Object 93
Tool Body 221
Tool Library 321
Trail Lines Enabled 281
Transform 281
Two Distance 318

U

Undefined 24
Undo 117
Unground From Parent 148
Unisolate 193
Upload 104
USDZ 38
User Parameters 89
Utilities 189

V

View block 280
View Cube 18
Visible Edges 266
Visual Style 213

W

Whole Length 36
Wireframe View 295
Workspace 17

Z

Zoom 18

Chapter 1
1. A
2. C
3. C
4. B
5. B
6. D
7. A
8. C
9. A
10. C

Chapter 2
1. C
2. False
3. A
4. B
5. D
6. B
7. A
8. D
9. C
10. A

Chapter 3
1. C
2. A
3. False
4. B
5. False
6. True
7. A
8. True
9. D
10. D

Chapter 4
1. B
2. D
3. B
4. A
5. C
6. C
7. A
8. C
9. C
10. B

Chapter 5
1. D
2. A
3. D
4. False
5. True
6. True
7. A
8. C
9. A
10. B

Chapter 6
1. B
2. A
3. D
4. B
5. True
6. A
7. D
8. E
9. B
10. D

Chapter 7
1. A
2. False
3. C
4. B
5. B
6. False
7. D
8. B
9. True
10. A

Chapter 8
1. True
2. B
3. C
4. False
5. D
6. C
7. D
8. A
9. A
10. B

Chapter 9
1. B
2. C
3. C
4. True
5. A
6. False
7. C
8. B
9. False
10. A

Chapter 10
1. A
2. D
3. D
4. True
5. B
6. B
7. A
8. False
9. C
10. D

Chapter 11
1. A
2. True
3. D
4. False
5. B
6. C
7. C
8. D
9. B
10. True

ADDITIONAL CADCLASS TITLES

Here at CADclass, we provide comprehensive resources for all levels of expertise and interests. Alongside this Autodesk Fusion 360 Textbook, we offer an exceptional Tinkercad workbook designed for students, beginners, and educators. Tinkercad is an excellent entry point into 3D modeling, with an intuitive and user-friendly interface that simplifies the design process. Our Tinkercad workbook guides you through the basics, helping you build a strong foundation in 3D modeling and design principles.

The CADclass Tinkercad Workbook includes engaging projects and exercises that gradually increase in complexity, developing your skills step by step. Each section offers detailed instructions, helpful tips, and practical examples that make learning enjoyable and effective. Whether you are a student, teacher, or hobbyist, our Tinkercad workbook is an invaluable resource that sparks creativity and sets you on the path to becoming a proficient 3D designer.

Explore the world of Tinkercad with CADclass and discover how easy and fun 3D modeling can be. Visit CADclass.org to learn more about our Tinkercad workbook and other educational materials to help you achieve your design goals.

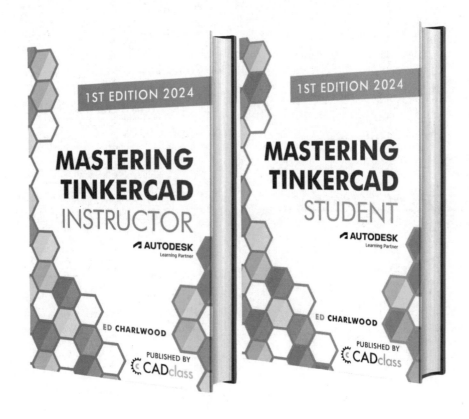

FUSION
SHORTCUTS

DESIGN WORKSPACE

Appearance	A	
As-built Joint	Shift+J	
Compute All	CTRL + B	CMD + B
Extrude	E	
Freeform Selection	2	
Hole	H	
Joint	J	
Measure	I	
Model Fillet	F	
Design Shortcuts	S	
Move	M	
Paint Selection	3	
Press Pull	Q	
Show/Hide	V	
Component Color	Shift+N	
Window Selection	1	

SKETCH WORKSPACE

2-point Rectangle	R
Center Diameter Circle	C
Line	L
Construction	X
Offset	O
Project	P
Sketch Dimension	D
Trim	T

DRAWING WORKSPACE

Balloon	B
Center Mark	C
Dimension	D
Move	M
Projected View	P
Text	T

ANIMATION WORKSPACE

Auto Explode All Level	U
Manual Explode	E
Publish Video	P
Transform Components	M
View	C

CAM WORKSPACE

Duplicate	CTRL + D CMD + D
Generate Toolpath	CTRL + G CMD + G
Scripts and Add-Ins	Shift + S
Show Log	CTRL + L CMD + L

RENDER WORKSPACE

Appearance	A

SYSTEM COMMANDS

Recovery Save	CTRL+Shift+S	CMD+Shift+S
Save Version	CTRL+S	CMD+S

CANVAS SELECTION

Copy	CTRL + C CMD + C
Cut	CTRL + X CMD + X
Orbit	Shift+Click+Hold Middle Mouse
Pan	Hold Middle Mouse
Paste	CTRL + V CMD + V
Redo	CTRL + Y CMD + Y
Undo	CTRL + Z CMD + Z
Zoom	Roll Middle Mouse